# Voice Processing
## Second Edition

For a complete listing of the Artech House Telecommunciations Library,
turn to the back of this book

# Voice Processing
## Second Edition

Walt Tetschner

Artech House
Boston • London

**Library of Congress Cataloging-in-Publication Data**

Tetschner, Walt.
   Voice processing / Walt Tetschner. — 2nd ed.

     p.   cm.
   Includes bibliographical references and index.
   ISBN 0-89006-637-X
    1. Speech processing systems industry. 2. Speech processing systems.
3. Market surveys. I. Title.

HD9696.S642T48   1993                92-21881
338.4'7621399—dc20                     CIP

**© 1993 ARTECH HOUSE, INC.**
**685 Canton Street**
**Norwood, MA 02062**

**International Standard Book Number: 0-89006-637-X**
**Library of Congress Catalog Card Number: 92-21881**

**10  9  8  7  6  5  4  3  2**

# Contents

# *Preface*

Voice processing uses speech technology to facilitate the dissemination and retrieval of information. Voice processing is a group of technologies combined in different ways to perform specific functions. It frequently interacts with other environments such as host databases, telephone systems, and facsimile machines as part of a larger communications and information management system. Voice processing has undergone great changes during the 1980s and has become a familiar and useful vehicle for enhancing communications and providing information. The market growth has been dramatic and is likely to continue in the future.

This book presents the basic technologies, products, and applications of voice processing. In Chapter 1, we discuss the historical development of the voice-processing area. We cover milestones that influenced the development of the industry and identify early products in each of the voice-processing segments. We also cover key technology and regulatory developments. Chapter 2 covers the basic technologies that compose voice processing. Digitized speech, speech and voice recognition, and text-to-speech are discussed. The various techniques are presented in terms of their advantages and disadvantages. For each technology, we present the present status and project its future direction. In Chapter 3, the architecture of a voice-processing system is addressed. We also discuss the components that make up a voice-processing system.

Basic voice-processing functions are presented in Chapter 4. Voice mail, automated attendant, information providing, interactive voice response, and outbound call processing are defined, and their functions are described. Chapter 5 describes the types of generic voice-processing applications that exist. The caller obtaining public or private information, the caller providing information, calling someone to provide or obtain information, automatic call routing, automatic messaging, and hands- or eyes-busy environments are generic voice-processing applications.

Specific applications of voice processing are discussed in Chapter 6. We identify and discuss voice-processing applications in each of the major market areas—finance, telephone services, education, transportation, medical, retail, utilities, government, publishing and communications, insurance, wholesale, and manufacturing. The past, present, and future roles of the telephone company in the voice-processing area is analyzed in Chapter 7.

In Chapter 8, we highlight each of the products in the various voice-processing segments. Voice mail, automated attendant, transaction processing, information provider, passive intercept, and outbound are the functional areas in which the products are discussed. We also present the features and capabilities of specific products in each of the functional segments. Multiple-function products and subsystem components and tools that are used to implement a voice-processing system are also covered in Chapter 8.

In Chapter 9, we introduce the computer-telephone integration area. The basic functions, the applications, and the components that make up a computer-telephony integrated system are discussed. The status of standards activities and architectural issues are presented.

We show how to economically justify a voice-processing system in Chapter 10 by using specific examples. We discuss the services portion of the voice-processing area in Chapter 11. These services include voice mail, transaction processing, telemarketing, information provider service bureaus, and information providers. Chapter 11 also includes a discussion of 900 and 976 dial-it services. In Chapter 12, we discuss the parameters that must be considered when sizing a voice-processing system. We describe techniques for determining the number of telephone ports and the amount of speech storage required. We cover the voice-processing market, revenue and unit shipment profiles during the late 1980s, and projections into the 1990s in Chapter 13. Voice-processing technology can be used as a communications tool by individuals with disabilities, which we describe in Chapter 14.

# Chapter 1
# Historical Background

## 1.1 VOICE PROCESSING—HISTORICAL DEVELOPMENT

The basis for much of the voice-processing industry is the ubiquity of the telephone. The telephone was invented by Alexander Graham Bell, a Scottish immigrant who came to Boston in 1870. Bell was a teacher of the deaf and an amateur inventor with no formal scientific training. The two basic principles of the telephone had been discovered many years before the invention of the telephone by Bell. The first was *electromagnetism*: the fact that an electrical current generates a magnetic field about itself that is proportional to the amount of current that is flowing. The second was *induction*: the fact that a changing magnetic field generates a current in a circuit. Bell's genius lay in the application of these principles to the transmission of human speech over wire. In early 1876, Bell was issued patent 174,465 for the basic telephone. This patent would turn out to be one of the most valuable patents ever issued. It withstood twenty years of intensive litigation and permitted the Bell Telephone Company to establish its dominant position in the telephone industry. One of the major legal contests was with the Western Union Company, which had initially viewed the telephone as an unimportant development [1].

The telephone is the underlying capability that is the cornerstone of the voice-processing industry, but the widespread application of voice-processing technology required that touch-tone telephones be readily available. The first *touch-tone (dual-tone multifrequency* (DTMF)) telephone was demonstrated at Bell Laboratories in 1958, and deployment in the business and consumer world started in the early 1960s. Since DTMF service was introduced to the commercial and consumer world less than thirty years ago, voice processing has had a relatively short history. In the early 1970s, DTMF services had become available in a large-enough area that voice processing services requiring interaction with the caller could be implemented.

Voice-processing applications that do not require interaction with the caller have existed for some time. In 1931, John Leonard Franklin formed the Audichron Company and developed a product that would provide the current time and temperature to a caller. These systems were usually purchased by the telephone companies, and they were housed in the *central offices* (COs). A local organization, such as a bank or major retailer, would often sponsor this service. During the time-and-temperature announcement, the sponsor would be given credit. The first time-and-temperature system was installed in Atlanta and was sponsored by the Coca-Cola Company. The time announcement was followed by "Time for the pause that refreshes." The service is, to this day, provided by the Coca-Cola Company.

The original device was quite a contraption. Two 78-rpm records played in sequence a recording of the time and temperature and an advertising message. When a call was received, the bell rang into a microphone, which in turn carried the impulse to relays that activated a motor to lift the receiver of a "gooseneck" telephone. The record player started after the telephone earpiece was taken off the hook. (See Figure 1.1.)

More than 12,000 Audichron systems are now in place. At least ten of them have been in continuous operation for fifty years and have had more than six billion calls. An estimated 5% of all local calls in the United States each day are answered by Audichron systems. Through the years, Audichron has emphasized the quality of the speech recorded. For many years, Audichron has had the same people recording the announcements. The voices of these people have become very familiar, and they are known as the *time lady* and the *time man*.

The telephone answering machine is another voice-processing device that does not require caller interaction. In 1949, George Danner and Joseph Zimmermann invented the first answering machine. The rights to it were subsequently sold to GTE in 1957, which marketed the device as the *Electronic Secretary*.

The original Electronic Secretary weighed 80 pounds and could not attach directly to the telephone system. To take the phone off the hook, the ringing was sensed acoustically, which started a motor inside the box. The motor would raise a metal lever that in turn raises the receiver off the hook. A 78-rpm record player was used to play a prerecorded message to the caller. The playing of the record would be activated after the phone was taken off the hook. The message complete, a wire recorder would be switched in to record the caller's message. The item that made the Electronic Secretary practical was the invention of the wire recorder, which occurred during World War II. Without it, you would have to make a platter recording of each telephone call.

Bell Telephone Company opposed the Electronic Secretary and was against any outside device that came close to its sets or lines—it even objected to wrappers on the telephone book. Furthermore, it contested that there simply was not a market for an automatic answering machine. Until the late 1960s, Bell Telephone

**Figure 1.1(a)** Early time and temperature system. (Photograph courtesy of ETC Corporation.)

Company placed severe restrictions on the attachment of foreign devices to the telephone network. The Carterfone decision in 1967 was instrumental in eliminating many of these restrictions. Foreign devices could be attached, although a device for attaching to the network had to be obtained from the telephone company. Within ten years, the requirement for this isolating device was eliminated and was replaced by an FCC certification process.

**Figure 1.1(b)** Inventor of time-and-temperature system and "time lady." (Photograph courtesy of ETC Corporation.)

## 1.2 VOICE PROCESSING—RECENT TECHNICAL PROGRESS

In 1970 George Danner formed another company called *Electronic Telecommunications Corporation* (ETC), which was a provider of passive and interactive voice-response systems. In 1989 ETC acquired Audichron. The availability of DTMF service and the ability to attach non-Bell devices to the telephone network made possible a variety of voice-processing applications that required caller interaction. In 1970, Periphonics introduced the first voice-transaction processing system, which was installed at Emery Air Freight. In 1975, Sudbury Systems installed the first voice-processing system for centralized dictation and transcription of radiology results at Framingham Union Hospital in Massachusetts. This product used a general-purpose computer, the Digital Equipment Corporation PDP/11, and magnetic tape for audio storage. (See Figure 1.2.)

**Figure 1.2** Early voice storage and retrieval system. (Photograph courtesy of Sudbury Systems Inc.)

In 1979, Gordon Matthews formed ECS (later renamed VMX), obtained a patent on voice mail, and installed the first stand-alone voice mail system at 3M. In 1982, Rolm introduced PhoneMail, which was the first voice mail system to be integrated with a *private branch exchange* (PBX). In 1983, the Bell System was broken up by federal mandate, and the individual Bell companies were restricted from providing information services. This essentially created the audiotex industry. In 1984, Dytel Corporation introduced the first automated attendant system.

In the early 1980s, IBM introduced the *audio distribution system* (ADS) and Wang Laboratories introduced the *digital voice exchange* (DVX), which helped to legitimize the market. In 1983, GTE TeleMessager introduced one of the first nationwide voice mail services. The early interactive voice-processing systems were large and expensive, compared with today's standard. Voice processing tends to be memory intensive. The decrease in the cost and size of memory storage space has been the most important technology advancement to date, which has led to a significant reduction in system size, weight, and price. Products based on *personal computers* (PCs) first became commercially available in 1983, and within a few years became a major factor in the voice processsing area. At first, they were used primarily for low-end configurations in which the number of ports and memory requirements were relatively small. However, advances in networking and switching capabilities have recently allowed application to large-system configurations.

See Table 1.1 for a summary of voice-processing technical progress. A number of voice-processing patents have been issued that have affected voice processing. The best known are given in Table 1.2.

**Table 1.1**

Voice Processing Technical Progress

| Year | Event |
|------|-------|
| 1931 | Audichron Company introduces time and temperature system. |
| 1949 | Zimmermann and Danner invent the telephone answering machine. |
| 1962 | Touch-tone service is made available by AT&T. |
| 1970 | Periphonics introduces the first voice transaction-processing system. |
| 1974 | Sudbury Systems introduces a centralized dictation and transcription system. |
| 1979 | Gordon Matthews invents voice-mail, starts ECS, and installs the first stand-alone voice mail system at 3M. |
| 1984 | Dytel introduces the first automated attendant. |

**Table 1.2**
Voice processing patent summary

| Number | Issue Date | Patent Title | Assignee | Inventors |
|--------|-----------|--------------|----------|-----------|
| 4,124,773 | Nov. 7, 1978 | Audio storage and distribution | Rob Elkins | Elkins |
| 4,260,854 | April 7, 1981 | Rapid simultaneous multiple access information storage and retrieval system | Sudbury Systems, Inc. | Kolodny, Hughes |
| 4,328,396 | May 4, 1982 | Total service telephone answering system | Peter F. Theis | Theis |
| 4,338,494 | July 6, 1982 | Telephone call inventorying and sequencing system and method | Peter F. Theis | Theis |
| 4,371,752 | Feb. 1, 1983 | Electronic audio communication system | ECS Telecommunications | Matthews, et al |
| 4,439,635 | March 27, 1984 | Message delivery system | Peter F. Theis | Theis, et al |
| 4,540,855 | Sept. 10, 1985 | Detecting signals within pass-band on a telephone line | Melita Electronic Labs | Szlam, Quinn |
| 4,539,436 | Sept. 3, 1985 | Programmed conversation recording system | Peter F. Theis | Theis |
| 4,696,028 | May 25, 1987 | PBX interactive and bypass system | Dytel | Morganstern, et al |
| 4,692,817 | Sept. 8, 1987 | Programmed conversation recording system | Morgan Industries | Theis |

**Table 1.2 (continued)**

| Number | Issue Date | Patent Title | Assignee | Inventors |
|--------|-----------|--------------|----------|-----------|
| 4,338,494 | July 6, 1982 | Telephone call inventorying and sequencing system and method | Peter F. Theis | Theis |
| 4,766,604 | Aug. 23, 1988 | Method for receiving and delivering voice messages | MessagePhone, Inc. | Axberg |
| 4,719,647 | Jan. 12, 1988 | Telephone message retrieval system with improved processor and retrieval console | Morgan Electronics | Theis, et al |
| 4,783,796 | Sept. 6, 1988 | PBX telephone call control system | VMX | Ladd |
| 4,825,460 | April 25, 1989 | Line interface unit for caller-controlled receipt and delivery of voice messages | MessagePhone, Inc | Carter, et al |
| 4,901,341 | Feb. 13, 1990 | Method and apparatus for call-controlled receipt and delivery of voice messages | Messager Partners | Carter, et al |
| 4,918,722 | April 17, 1990 | Method of retrieving electronic information | Brooktrout Technology | Giler, et al |
| 5,121,421 | June 9, 1992 | Interactive Telephone System for hearing-impaired person | DiRAD Technologies | Alheim |

## REFERENCE

1. Bruce, R. V., *Bell*, Ithaca, New York, Cornell University Press, 1973.

# Chapter 2

# Speech-Processing Technologies

The basis of voice processing is a set of technologies that manipulate speech. The technology of the telephone system is also a crucial component of voice processing. It is the information input, information output, and transport mechanism for the reception and delivery of most of the voice-processing information.

## 2.1 SUMMARY OF SPEECH-PROCESSING TECHNOLOGIES

The four basic speech-processing technologies are

1. Speech digitization;
2. Speech recognition;— *identify words*
3. Voice recognition; — *identify speakers*
4. Text-to-speech.

For a computer to manipulate speech, speech must be converted from analog to digital form. Speech digitization is the basic technology underlying voice mail and is used by most voice-processing systems for generation of speech prompts and information. Speech recognition compares spoken words to stored templates and attempts to match them to recognize the particular word being spoken. Voice recognition compares a person's speech to the speech templates to identify a particular speaker uniquely. Text-to-speech is the process of converting computer text into continuous speech, from a visual into an audible form. Of these four, speech digitization is by far the dominant technology in of commercial deployment. Speech recognition and text-to-speech conversion are quite suitable for a variety of niche applications. Both technologies possess implementation imperfections, which tend to restrict severely their widespread application.

## 2.2 HUMAN SPEECH PRODUCTION AND PERCEPTION

The study of the human vocal tract and the human ear provides a number of clues in creating the technology to understand human speech. It might be assumed that a detailed study of human speech production and perception would lead directly to the design of excellent automatic speech generation and speech recognition devices. Ironically this has not been the case. Early attempts at automatic speech generation and speech recognition depended on simple models of human speaking and hearing mechanisms. During the last 25 years, researchers have moved away from primarily considerations of human anatomy and focused their efforts on sophisticated mathematical signal processing and computational methods for decoding speech. However, all speech generators and recognizers today are to some extent based on an understanding and knowledge of human speech and human speech perception. A review of these topics is important for understanding speech generation and recognition [1].

The human vocal tract shown in Figure 2.1 extends from the vocal cords to the lips and includes the nasal cavity. Schematically the human vocal tract may be modeled as shown in the figure by two connected tubes of varying cross section. The sound in the vocal tract is created by air forced through the vocal folds (cords) or *glottis*. This airflow causes the vocal folds to open and close rapidly, a vibration that provides a driving acoustic energy wave for the vocal tract much like a trumpet player's lips do for the trumpet. Human beings create different speech sounds by changing the shape of their vocal tracts. The shape of the vocal tract is changed by moving the position of the tongue, opening and closing the nasal cavity, moving the velum, or closing or opening the lips. In addition, speech sounds are created simply by forcing air through the lips or teeth as in *f* or *s* sounds.

The character of speech sounds is due to the overtones or harmonics that are excited in the vocal tract by the fundamental frequency of the glottis vibration. Harmonics in acoustic systems vocal tracts, or musical instruments, occur at whole multiples of the fundamental frequency. The particular combination of harmonic frequencies that are emphasized depends on those that find resonances in the vocal tract. In the case of a musical instrument, it is the particular combination of overtones that determines the characteristic sound of the instrument. The overtones a violin makes sound very different from those of a trumpet, even if both instruments are playing the same fundamental note. Likewise, even though the glottis may be vibrating at the same frequency, an *ah* sound is very different from an *ee* sound because the position of the tongue has changed and emphasized different overtones of the two vowels.

The shape of the vocal tract determines the different sounds to create speech. The shape of the vocal tract also determines the particular character of a speaker's voice. Like fingerprints, no two vocal tracts are exactly alike, so every individual's voice has certain acoustic peculiarities that are characteristic of that individual's vocal tract. This fact is the basis for speaker recognition.

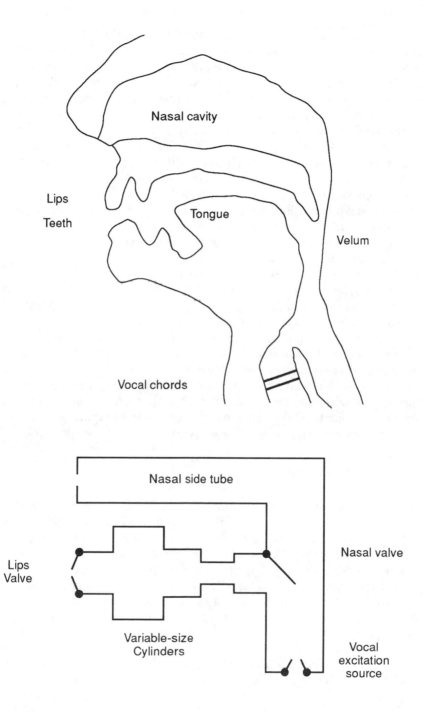

**Figure 2.1** Human vocal tract.

The human ear is shown schematically in Figure 2.2. Like the other human sensory organs, it is a very sophisticated and sensitive detection device, detecting a wide range of loudnesses and frequencies. This dynamic range allows humans to detect sounds that vary by 10 trillion times in intensity and frequencies that range from approximately 20 to 20,000 hertz. The ear's complex design serves as a transducer to effectively make the gentle pressure differences of an acoustic wave in the air that impinge on the ear selectively excite the array of nerve endings in the cochlea. Depending on their position along the spiral of the cochlea, these nerve endings are sensitive to sounds of different frequencies. In addition to this capability to distinguish sounds by frequency and loudness, the ear can determine the direction and the phase of individual sound waves. These four perceptual abilities make it possible for human beings to understand speech even in noisy environments. Individual conversations can be picked out and understood on the basis of direction even when simultaneous conversations are going on close by. By contrast, automatic speech recognition systems today can only distinguish sound by frequency and loudness within significantly more limited dynamic ranges, making these systems very susceptible to interference from extraneous sound. The ear's ability to analyze sound, based on frequency and loudness, is the basis for the acoustic analysis in automatic speech recognition systems.

Evolution has matched human speech production and perception. An interesting example of this match lies in the fact that energy in human speech tends to be reduced by approximately a factor of 4 (6 dB) per octave. But the sensitivity of the human ear over a good portion of the frequency range for speech tends to increase in sensitivity by roughly 5 decibels per octave, neatly offsetting the reduction in speech energy. This makes the human ear quite sensitive to the range of frequencies present in speech sounds from a variety of speakers.

## 2.2 SPEECH SOUNDS

Speech sounds may be divided into three different categories, depending on the glottis action. Sounds are *voiced* if the glottis is closed and air is forced through it. This causes the glottis to open and close rapidly, producing glottal pulses or vibrations that excite the vocal tract. If the glottis is open, air passes through it without exciting glottal pulses and the result is *whispered* sounds. If the glottis is closed and no air passes through it, but air is forced through the lips or teeth, the result is a *fricative*, as in the sound of *f* or *s*. Voiced sounds are vowels and most other consonants. If the nasal passage is open, then the nasalized consonants *m* and *n* are pronounced. The position and shape of the tongue are critical in creating different vowel sounds.

A detailed analysis of sounds that can be produced in the human vocal tract goes beyond what can be presented here. The range and character of these sounds depend on the particular human language or dialect being spoken. The human

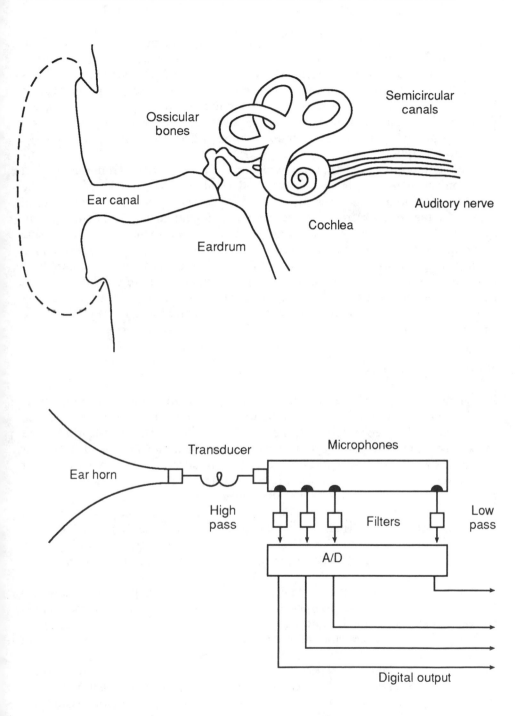

**Figure 2.2** The human ear.

vocal tract can produce and the ear can distinguish a great variety of individual sounds. In English we recognize approximately 40 individual phonetic sounds (phonemes). However, spoken English uses thousands of *allophones* or variations on those basic 40 sounds. The reason for these variations in phoneme pronunciation is that, in English, the pronunciation of a phoneme depends on the adjacent phonemes, on adjacent words, and on the stress placed on the phoneme. This coarticulation effect in normal, continuous spoken English results in a very large number of allophones.

In addition to these variations, variations in pronunciation from the physical or emotional condition of the speaker and from the rate and loudness of the utterance also occur. These variations in speech sounds by a single speaker are in addition to the large variation in speech sounds in individual vocal tracts of different speakers. Particularly striking is the difference between men and women whose vocal tracts differ significantly in size. The result is that the 40 basically identifiable phonemes in English, spoken by any given population, multiply into hundreds of thousands sounds—many of which sound quite similar and are difficult for automatic speech recognition systems to distinguish as different or recognize as equivalent. This variability is what makes the generation and recognition of speech so very challenging.

## 2.4 SPEECH ANALYSIS

For analysis, speech must be converted into a spectrum that shows the energy level of all frequencies that are present plotted against time. The process involves the conversion of the speech signal into a digital form, a Fourier transformation of the speech signal, and the plotting of the transformed signals versus time. The Fourier transformation is a mathematical process that provides a frequency spectrum or energy versus frequency curve for a given sample of speech. Such a process is a good analogy with the loudness and frequency discrimination of the human ear. The cochlea might be thought of as an array of microphones, each sensitive only to a particular frequency and able to detect the energy changes in time of that part of the frequency spectrum. The Fourier transformation analysis typically determines the energy for the frequencies present in a 10-millisecond timeframe of the speech waveform.

The information in these 10-millisecond timeframes is plotted as shown in Figure 2.3 in a speech spectrogram. In this figure, the frequency is plotted along the vertical axis and time is plotted along the horizontal axis. The darkness of the spectrogram plot indicates the intensity of the frequency present. The waveform for the phrase "Joe took father's shoe bench out" is shown below the spectrogram. The arrow at the right of the spectrogram indicates the position at which the curve shown in the lower right has been taken. In that plot the horizontal axis represents the frequency, and the vertical axis represents the energy present in that frequency.

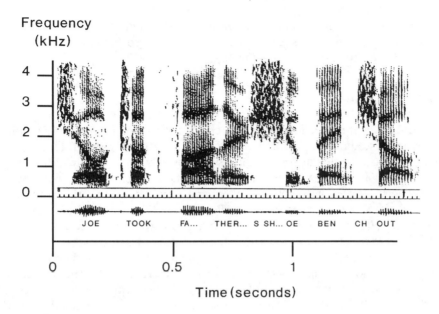

**Figure 2.3** Speech spectrogram.

Looking at the spectrogram, it is clear that there are phonemic sounds that have distinguishable patterns. The dark, broad bands in the spectrum are called *formants* and represent the major overtones in human speech. The relative intensity, position, and change in time of these formants are major features in distinguishing among phonemes. From the spectrogram it is also possible to see that there are differences in these formants for different phonemes, but, at least to the unpracticed eye, not as great a difference as one could perhaps hope. Note that the formant patterns for the vowels are affected significantly by the consonants preceding and following those vowels. Further, the spectrogram reflects the difficulty in determining or establishing beginning and end points for phonemes, syllables, and even words.

## 2.5 SPEECH DIGITIZATION

Speech digitization is the conversion of analog speech into a digital bit stream suitable for storage on a disk or in RAM. Devices that perform both conversion from analog to digital and from digital to analog are called *codecs* (a contraction for coder-decoder). A variety of techniques to convert speech into digital form have been commercialized. Because digitized speech tends to require significant amounts of memory, most techniques have focused on ways to reduce the number of bits required to digitize speech. In addition to reducing the amount of physical memory required to store speech, a lower bit rate also proportionately reduces the transmission time of a speech message.

### 2.5.1 Speech Digitization Techniques

A speech digitization technique can be characterized by speech digitization rate (usually expressed in kb/s), speech quality, and robustness (noise tolerance). Converting speech into digital form requires a relatively large bandwidth. For good intelligibility and speaker recognition, the frequency range must encompass 300 to 4,000 hertz. Based on the Nyquist theorem, which states that the sampling rate for a periodic signal must be twice the highest rate to recover the signal, speech digitization requires an information sampling rate of 8,000 hertz. At 8 bits per sample, this translates into a sample rate of 64 kb/s, which creates large memory storage and high-performance transmission system requirements. The goal of most speech digitization techniques has been to reduce significantly the speech digitization rate, while maintaining good speech quality and robustness. This goal frequently becomes a tradeoff of these characteristics. The techniques that yield the lowest bit rates often reduce the speech quality and tend to be sensitive to noise. Development of techniques with algorithms that are simpler to implement has been a goal of past development. With the advent of *digital signal processors* (DSPs), this has become a much less important goal, because very complex computations can be accomplished with DSPs without a significant increase in the hardware and software requirements. Speech digitization techniques can be categorized into distinct families as follows:

*Waveform reconstruction.* In this category, hardware samples the input speech signal and generates an output signal identical to the input signal. A bandwidth reduction is obtained by taking advantage of the fact that a speech signal changes relatively slowly; therefore, the sample being taken does not differ dramatically from the previous sample of the same speech signal.

*Frequency domain transform coding.* In this category, the bandwidth requirement is reduced by eliminating certain frequency components in the speech signal because they have been found to be unimportant. This technique simply discards the samples with a low information content and retains those samples determined to be important.

*Analysis-synthesis (vocoding).* In this technique, the hardware transmits a description of the speech rather than the actual signal. Devices that perform speech digitization by synthesis are known as Vocoders. A Vocoder analyzes the speech signal, then extracts and transmits the information necessary for synthetic reconstruction. Models of the human speech production mechanism are made by a

Vocoder. Although these techniques can achieve very low bit rates, they can be quite sensitive to noise.

The main digitization techniques are summarized in Table 2.1.

**Table 2.1**
Speech digitization techniques

| Digitization technique | Digitization rate | Digitization family |
|:---:|:---:|:---:|
| PCM | 64 kb/s | Waveform |
| CVSD | 16 - 32 kb/s | Waveform |
| ADPCM | 16 - 32 kb/s | Waveform |
| Sub-band | 9.6 - 24 kb/s | Transform |
| LPC | 2.4 - 12 kb/s | Vocoder |
| Formant | 0.6 - 2.4 kb/s | Vocoder |

### 2.5.2 Pulse Code Modulation

*Pulse code modulation* (PCM) is the most common type of digital coding system used for speech. PCM is used by telephone companies both in the United States and abroad. In the United States, more speech circuits use PCM than analog carrier systems. PCM was invented in 1938 and was put into service in the early 1960s when the first T-1 carrier systems were installed. With PCM, the speech signal is sampled at 8 kHz, and each sample value is encoded into an 8-bit word, resulting in a 64-kb/s bit stream. PCM is not a bit-rate compression system, but the standard bit rate and the resulting high quality speech obtained have become the standard with which all bit-rate compression systems are compared. PCM is extremely robust; unlike most other bit-compression techniques, it can handle nonspeech analog signals such as those from a modem. PCM codecs are readily available at low cost. PCM is illustrated in Figure 2.4.

### 2.5.3 Continuous Variable Slope Detection

Also known as adaptive delta modulation, *continuous variable slope detection* (CVSD) is by far the simplest digital encoding technique. CVSD uses a single bit to record the direction of change in the speech signal and can detect a rapidly

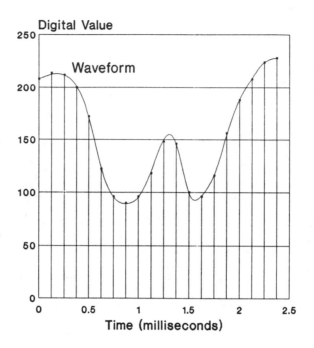

**Figure 2.4** Pulse code modulation.

changing signal and adjust the step size of the encoder. CVSD has been used extensively in voice mail systems because it can be implemented quite economically, and a 2-to-1 bit-rate reduction (from PCM) can be obtained with only a slight degradation in speech quality. Reduction to 4 to 1 is possible, but the speech quality, although still intelligible, is severely reduced. CVSD is also quite robust; most voice mail systems using CVSD run between 24 and 32 kb/s.

CVSD codecs are readily available on the commercial market. Although CVSD has been used extensively in commercial systems, it is becoming less important. The cost of the hardware and software for implementing more complex algorithms has decreased to the point at which the primary advantage of CVSD has disappeared [2]. The *Consultative Committee for International Telegraph and Telephone* (CCITT) has established *adaptive differential pulse code modulation* (ADPCM) as the standard coding scheme, which means that CVSD will no longer be acceptable for the exchange of voice information among systems from different suppliers.

### 2.5.4 Adaptive Differential Pulse Code Modulation

ADPCM takes advantage of the fact that each speech sample value can be accurately predicted by the previous value. Because only the difference between adjacent sample values is encoded, the process requires fewer bits. This is the *differential* portion of ADPCM. The quantizing levels, or step sizes, in an ADPCM system adjust or adapt to the input signal level. This is the *adaptive* portion of ADPCM. At 32 kb/s, ADPCM is virtually indistinguishable from PCM. ADPCM is quite robust, but it has one limitation: it will not handle voice-band data well. The fact that the CCITT has standardized on ADPCM as a low-bit-rate digitizing technique indicates that ADPCM use will increase during the next few years.

### 2.5.5 Sub-Band Coding

In *sub-band coding* (SBC), the speech frequency band is divided into either four or eight sub-bands. Each is then sampled at its Nyquist rate (i.e., twice the bandwidth) and digitally encoded by using PCM or ADPCM. Each sub-band is encoded according to specific perceptual criteria. Bit-rate compression is obtained by eliminating certain frequency bands, depending on the type of speech that is occurring. SBC is used to achieve speech digitization rates that are lower than CVSD and ADPCM, with only a slight degradation in speech quality.

### 2.5.6 Linear Predictive Coding

*Linear predictive coding* (LPC) is a vocal tract model based on the principle that speech can be reasonably predicted by weighing the sum of previous speech samples. This process involves solving a set of linear equations to obtain *predictor coefficients*. Bit rates below 9.6 kb/s can be achieved with LPC, although the speech often has a synthetic quality. Female and children's voices tend to sound more synthetic than a mature male voice. LPC is not a robust coding technique, and the results are quite poor in a noisy environment. LPC is used primarily in environments where a low bit rate is essential and a degradation of the speech quality is acceptable.

Figure 2.5 compares the LPC, SBC, CVSD, ADPCM, and PCM coding schemes.

### 2.5.7 Formant Synthesis

Formant synthesis uses a vocal tract model that is a series of cascaded resonators for voiced sounds and parallel resonators for unvoiced sounds. Formant frequencies and bandwidths are the parameters that are extracted and coded. With formant synthesis, we can achieve bit rates below 2.4 kb/s, but the speech will have a synthetic quality. Formant synthesis is not a robust coding technique, so it will not produce good results in a noisy environment. The application areas of formant synthesis are similar to the ones that we previously identified for LPC.

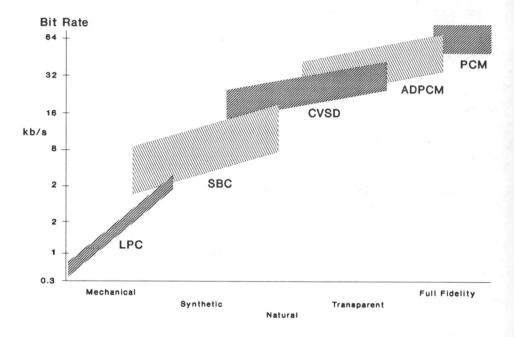

**Figure 2.5** Speech quality versus bit rate—various coding schemes.

### 2.5.8 Speech Digitization Direction

The dramatic decrease in the cost of digital storage since the mid 1980s has changed some of the motivation for obtaining low-bit-rate coding. Although some sets of applications require extremely low bit rates and are able to tolerate a degradation in the speech reproduction quality, most applications require good-quality speech. Only a slight degradation from so-called "PCM toll quality" is commercially acceptable. The requirement for transmitting speech from one system to another makes incompatible coding schemes intolerable. As digital telephone services such as T-1 and *integrated services digital network* (ISDN) services become universally available, a system will be required to possess a coding scheme compatible with a T-1 or ISDN service. Techniques to convert PCM to another coding scheme and vice versa will be the focus of considerable development. The CCITT has established standards for speech coding. We anticipate that these standards will become dominant in the voice-processing area.

### 2.6 TEXT-TO-SPEECH TECHNOLOGY

Text-to-speech technology is the conversion of continuous text into speech. The quality of the speech produced (how human it sounds) is the dominant characteristic of this technology [3]. The conversion of text into speech typically requires the following three steps: (1) converting letters to sound, (2) calculating acoustic parameters, and (3) synthesizing the speech output.

The text-to-speech process is shown in Figure 2.6.

### 2.6.1 Letter-to-Sound Conversion

The output of the letter-to-sound conversion process is a phonemic string, comprising phonemes, stress identifiers, and clause boundaries. Letter-to-sound processing consists of a set of rules that are applied to the input string and an exception dictionary. The letter-to-sound rules are the phonemic rules of a language. For the English language, many exceptions to the rules exist. For example, seven different pronunciations of words that end in -*ough* exist (e.g., cough, bough, rough, through, hiccough, though). The rules would handle only one of the words; the others should be handled by the exception dictionary. The exception dictionary would also handle abbreviations (Jan., St., Dr.), commonly used words from other languages (detente, lasagna), and money pronunciation ($12.58). The different pronunciation of *Dr.* as the abbreviation for *doctor* versus the pronunciation when it is used to abbreviate *drive* is handled by many of the letter-to-sound techniques.

Number handling is another area in which the pronunciation rules are not rigid. The number string *1234* could be pronounced one-two-three-four, one thousand two hundred and thirty-four, or twelve thirty four, depending on the environment. The approach that is used with most letter-to-sound processes is to have a default method of pronunciation, with other cases handled by modifying the text sent. For example, placing a space between each of the digits would cause them to be pronounced as individual digits. Techniques for obtaining the proper pronunciation must be addressed when dealing with a text-to-speech converter. For example, the word *present* is pronounced one way in the phrase "I gave him a birthday *present*," and differently in the phrase "We *present* it to him." Many text-to-speech converters let the user specify which pronunciation is desired. The pronunciation most commonly used is the default, and the user must explicitly indicate that an alternative pronunciation is desired. To implement variations in contextual pronunciation, the system must perform an analysis of the word's pronunciation within a phrase. Approximately one hundred common words exist in the English language that have pronunciations that vary with context. Pairs of words that are spelled exactly the same but are pronounced differently, depending on how they are used, are called *homographs*. They are usually noun-verb pairs like *insert* (noun: stress on first syllable) and *insert* (verb: stress on second syllable), although adjective-verb and verb-verb pairs also occur. Table 2.2 lists English-language words with alternative pronunciations.

The techniques for letter-to-sound conversion are well understood. They vary primarily in their suitability for real-time computer processing (speed of execution and memory size). With an adequately large dictionary, the techniques can be

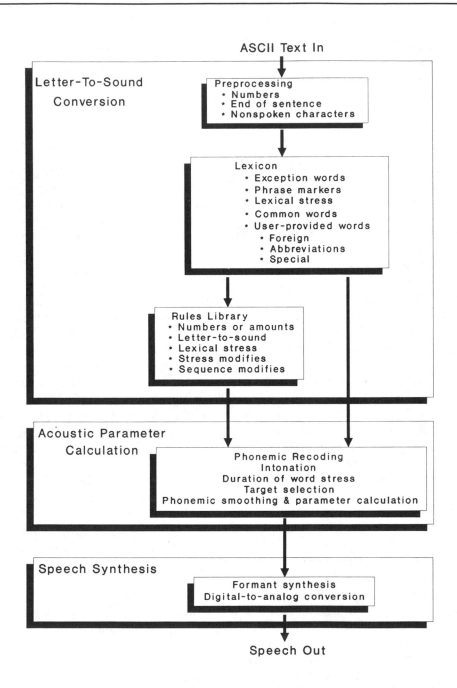

**Figure 2.6** Text-to-speech process.

## Table 2.2
### Words with alternative pronunciations

| | | | |
|---|---|---|---|
| abstract | contest | insert | recount |
| abuse | contract | insult | refill |
| addict | contrast | interchange | refresh |
| advocate | converse | intimate | refund |
| affix | convert | invalid | refuse |
| alternate | convict | lead | reject |
| ally | coordinate | live | relapse |
| animate | defect | minute | relay |
| annex | delegate | misconduct | remake |
| appropriate | deliberate | misuse | rerun |
| arithmetic | desert | moderate | research |
| associate | desolate | object | resume |
| attribute | digest | overrun | retake |
| august | discharge | perfect | rewrite |
| bass | dove | permit | segment |
| baton | duplicate | pervert | separate |
| close | elaborate | polish | sow |
| combat | estimate | predicate | subject |
| combine | excuse | predominate | sublet |
| compact | exploit | present | subordinate |
| compound | export | proceed | suspect |
| compress | extract | produce | syndicate |
| conduct | germinate | progress | tear |
| conglomerate | graduate | project | torment |
| console | implant | protest | transform |
| consort | import | read | transplant |
| content | imprint | rebel | transport |
| conflict | incense | recall | upset |
| console | incline | recap | use |
| construct | increase | recess | wind |
| | | record | wound |

made to generate phonemic sequences that are comparable to those generated by a person [4].

The proper pronunciation of surnames is difficult in the United States because of the heterogeneous ethnic makeup of the population [5]. There are approximately 1.5 million different surnames in the United States, with about one-third of these being unique. Generally, the better a text-to-speech device is for its native language, the worse it is at pronouncing words from other languages. In addition, the anglicization that has occured in many cases yields names with alternative pronunciations. Using dictionaries for the most commonly found names is of value, but the sheer number of names makes a pure dictionary approach for all names impractical. If the application is one in which the text to be pronounced is restricted to names and addresses, many of the problems dissappear. For example, parsing discrepancies such as *Carbone* versus *bygone* and *Schultz* versus *school* are eliminated. The basic technique that is used is to properly pronounce non-native names is to categorize the name into a particular language group and then use the pronunciation algorithm that is appropriate for that language group. A variety of techniques exists for performing this classification: the letter $L$ does not occur in Japanese, $X$ does not occur in Polish, $J$ and $K$ do not occur in Italian, and so on; sequences such as CZ, PF, SH, EE (or longer ones) unambiguously define certain language groups. This identification process is made more complex by a name such as *O'Shinski*, which contains positive identifiers for two language groups.

### 2.6.2 Calculation of Acoustic Parameters

In this step of the text-to-speech process, the prosaics are addressed: phonemic recoding, word-stress duration and intonation, and phonemic smoothing. Whereas the letter-to-sound conversion deals largely with only individual words as the basis for selection of phonemes that determine pronunciation, this step concerns the effects of the surrounding phrase and sentence. The pronunciation selected by the letter-to-sound conversion may need to be recoded phonemically because of words that follow and precede it. For instance, the word *the* is usually pronounced one way when followed by a word beginning with a vowel phoneme (the apple; *thee*) and another way when followed by a consonant phoneme (the book; *thuh*). Rules for intonation, duration, and word stress (which word in the sentence should be stressed) are then applied to modify the phonemic representation. One intonation rule, for instance, deals with the fact that a word generally has a higher pitch at the beginning of a phrase but drops at the end of the phrase. The duration of a sequence of phonemes that constitutes a word may change with its position in the sentence. Phoneme smoothing is performed to ensure that transitions from one phoneme to the next contain no discontinuities. In synthesizing the human voice, there must be smooth transitions between phonemes at each formant frequency rather than discontinuities that produce audible clicks in the output speech [6].

### 2.6.3 Synthesizing Speech Output

Formant synthesis is the technique that has achieved the most commercial success in text-to-speech. The text-to-speech technique we have described, *parametric* text-to-speech, has been successfully commercialized. Another technique, *concatenative* text-to-speech, exists and has its proponents, although, until recently, it has generated very little interest outside the laboratory. The concatenative technique generates speech by linking prerecorded speech segments to build words and phrases. Basic sound elements known as *diphones* and *demisyllables* are the basic components used. Although this technique has some attractive aspects, the most fundamental disadvantage is that the prosody of speech is extremely difficult to achieve because the diphones and demisyllables are almost impossible to manipulate. Another drawback with the concatenative technique is that large amounts of memory are required to store all of the speech elements. Creating a different-sounding voice or a foreign language with the concatenative technique is not a accomplished readily; this really requires that the entire development process be replicated.

### 2.6.4 Performance Characteristics of Text-to-Speech

The primary item that determines the characteristics of a text-to-speech device is the speech quality. The factors that determine the speech quality include proper word pronunciation, word stress, and intonation. The quality of speech obtained from text-to-speech device varies from devices that sound robotic and are barely intelligible to devices that are clear and understandable with only a slight accent detectable. No concise metric exists for specifying speech quality, and the best way to make a judgment is to listen to it. Most text-to-speech devices are able to accept text from a computer and speak it in real time.

### 2.6.5 Present Status of Text-to-Speech

The best quality commercial text-to-speech products are quite intelligible and sound human. They sound like a person with an accent. Female and children's voices tend not to have the same level of human-like quality and sound more like a computer. The speaking rate can be readily changed and different voices can be selected. Prices vary from less than $100 to $3,000 for a single text-to-speech device. Better speech quality is generally obtained with the higher priced models. Specialized text-to-speech implementations exist, such as the ORATOR technology that Bellcore has developed. This technology has been designed specifically to pronounce names and addresses well.

### 2.6.6 Future Directions of Text-to-Speech

Text-to-speech algorithms attempt to replicate a human person speaking. Both the English language and the human speech process are immensely complex—thousands of rules exist. Many details of what the human voice does when speaking are not well understood. Creation of a high-quality text-to-speech device requires that each of the human speaking processes be precisely replicated and included as part of the text-to-speech model. Implementing these processes is a tedious and drawn-out effort. Text-to-speech techniques are unique to a particular language. For each language, both the letter-to-sound conversion and the acoustic parameter calculations are different. This means that a text-to-speech converter for a non-English language requires an entirely new set of algorithms. Fortunately, most foreign languages are not as complex as English. The quality of the speech generated by text-to-speech products will improve very gradually during the 1990s, so the speech will continue to sound not quite human and will have only a limited set of voices [7].

### 2.6.7 Applications for Text-to-Speech Technology Products

The basic application of text-to-speech is for the direct conversion of computer text into speech. Although a broad range of applications exists for text-to-speech technology products, the ones that will be most successful are those in which the vocabulary to be spoken is extremely large and changes frequently. The speech output from a text-to-speech device is extremely easy to modify; the user simply retypes or edits the computer text. The storage of voice in text form is much more efficient than the storage of digitized speech. Digitized speech typically requires 300 times more memory. The only real drawback to the widespread use of text-to-speech technology is the quality of the speech. For many applications, either digitized speech or text-to-speech could do the job, but digitized speech will be the technology of choice simply because the speech quality is superior.

### 2.7 SPEECH AND VOICE RECOGNITION TECHNOLOGY

Speech and voice recognition is the identification of speech into specific words. Two distinct forms of the technology have been developed: speech-to-text (speech recognition) and speaker verification (voice recognition).

### 2.7.1 Speech Recognition

A specific vocabulary is defined, and a speech-recognition device will identify an utterance (or string of utterances) as being part of this vocabulary. The techniques associated with speech recognition typically require four distinct steps:

1. Speech capture;
2. Spectral feature extraction;
3. Pattern matching;
4. Decision strategy.

(See Figure 2.7.)

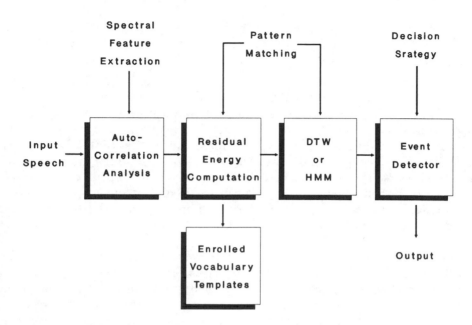

**Figure 2.7** Speech-recognition process.

## 2.7.1.1 Speech Capture

This is the basic mechanism for conditioning the speech signal for processing. It usually consists of a microphone and an analog-to-digital converter that digitally encodes the raw speech waveform.

## 2.7.1.2 Spectral Feature Extraction

Feature extraction transforms speech signals into time-varying parameters called features. These features are derived from obtaining the frequency energy profile, which is then used to calculate the coefficients of a vocal tract model such as LPC. This technique reduces the amount of data that must be processed.

## 2.7.1.3 Pattern Matching

Acoustic speech recognition may be thought of as a pattern-recognition problem using the data shown in the spectrogram. In fact, some crude automatic speech recognition has been done by applying image pattern recognition to speech spectrograms. But this is not a pattern recognition technique used commercially for speech recognition [8].

There are several pattern-recognition techniques employed in automatic speech recognizers. These include template matching, Hidden Markov Modeling, and neural nets.

*Template matching.* Template matching is typically used for the recognition of isolated words. The speech spectrogram in the earlier section may be envisioned as a three-dimensional plot. This plot would show a surface with mountains and valleys, where the mountain ranges represent the formants. A speech template for a given word could be considered to be a three-dimensional contour map. This three-dimensional contour map or word pattern could be stored in the memory of the speech recognizer and compared with the three-dimensional contour maps produced by test utterances. If the match between the contour maps was good, the utterance could be considered to be recognized. If it was poor the utterance would not be matched and another template tested to see if a match could be found.

Template matching illustrates two of the essential elements of automatic speech recognition. The first is the acoustic spectral analysis and the generation of stored template or speech model to which the test utterance will be compared. The second element of automatic speech recognition relates to the comparison of the stored model and the new utterance. Because of the great variability in speech, no two utterances are ever identical, so that any comparison of the two contour maps described above representing the template and the new utterance must include a tolerance for variation and an automated basis for deciding whether a match exists or the variance between the template and utterance is too great. The spectral analysis of automatic speech recognition is a fairly straightforward process. It is the second part of the problem, the matching of the templates and the determination of the effective discrepancy between them, that represents the real heart of automatic speech recognition.

In template matching, the effective discrepancy between a test utterance and a set of stored utterances is carried out as follows:

Based on the overall energy level of the sound, beginning and end points are determined for the test word. Next, each speech frame in the word in sequence is compared with each speech frame of the stored word template. In the contour map analogy, this is like taking the test contour map, placing it over the stored map, and then measuring the total space between the two. If this comparison is done for every stored word template, a best match to the test word can be found. Based on experience for the expected variations in successive articulations of a given word, a decision can be made as to whether the best match is good enough. Alternatively, several candidate matches might be determined and other information used to determine the right choice.

A major source of variation between the stored model and the new utterance is in the timing. Words may be spoken slowly in training but faster in actual ASR system use. In addition, certain syllables may be shortened or drawn out. A major advance in ASR was the development of *dynamic time warping* (DTW) methods. These methods permit two speech samples like those shown in Figure 2.8 to be compared after removing time variation. DTW methods allow the comparison of two templates using an elastic time scale determined to minimize the differences in the patterns of the two utterances.

*Hidden Markov Model.* Template matching of words will work well for only a limited number of words in a vocabulary because the storage of word templates requires many bytes of data. Further, the time to compare a word to a potential template will increase with the number of words in the vocabulary. To overcome these problems, particularly for recognition of words in large vocabulary systems,

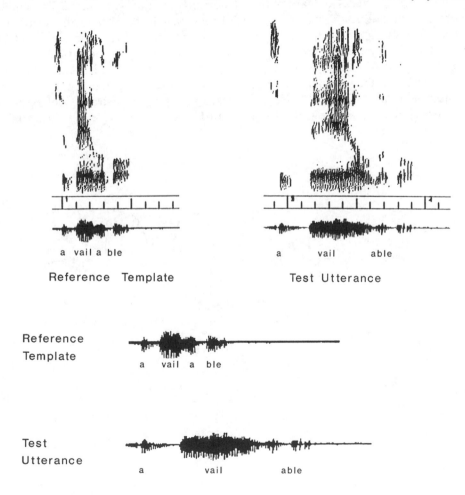

**Figure 2.8** Dynamic time warping.

the *Hidden Markov Method* (HMM) for speech recognition has been developed. In the HMM, the frequency spectrum of each timeframe is assigned a probability of belonging to a particular phoneme pattern. Each successive timeframe that is analyzed by the system is considered to have some probability of belonging to a particular phoneme. In addition, the probability that a sequence of such a time-frames could occur depends on the phoneme model of the word. In this way it is possible to assign a probability that a sequence of speech timeframes represents a given word model. This method takes into account both the variability of the individual spectra in the timeframes and the frame-to-frame variations that may occur because of timing variations in pronunciation.

Figure 2.9 shows a Markov model network for the word *bass*. The circles represent states through which the model may pass in describing the word: (1) /b/closure; (2) /b/burst; (3) /pae/aspiration; (4) /ae/vowel; (5) /s/fricative; and (6) final state. The model shown here allows the word "bass" to be articulated in a variety of ways with different probabilities. For example, if the phoneme *ae* is very short, then the model recognizes a transition from state (3) to state (5); conversely, if the vowel *ae* is long, the model recognizes a looping-back transition. Because the probability of each transition in the word model is known from the training

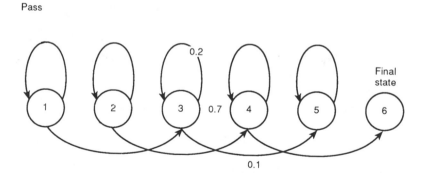

1. /P/closure

2. /P/burst

3. /Pae/aspiration

4. /ae/vowel

5. /s/fricative

**Figure 2.9** Hidden Markov model.

data, the total probability of a given test utterance can be calculated for the model. This probability is combined with the individual probabilities that speech frames from the test utterance were part of the phoneme states. To determine the total probability that a given utterance was the word modeled, the combined transition probabilities and state probabilities are calculated. The total information storage requirements for the HMM method are much less for large vocabulary ASR systems because the models for all possible phonemes and phoneme parts that make up the states in the word models only have to be stored once. The information storage requirements for the word model then includes the transition probabilities (in this case 13 numbers and the identification numbers of the six phonemic states). This may be compared with the information per word required to be stored for template matching. Each word in template matching must store all the numbers describing each possible, distinguishable speech frame in the utterance. The storage requirements for HMM systems for all possible phonemes are not insignificant, so it is only for very large vocabularies that HMM becomes economical. This example is clearly oversimplified compared with the HMM in actual systems, but it illustrates the difference in the information storage requirements.

The HMM is also more flexible than a word template model and requires less computation in the determination of word matches.

Hidden Markov models derive their name from the great Russian mathematician Markov, who developed the formalism for a method of calculating the probabilities of different sequences of letters in Russian texts knowing the last letter in the sequence. In his case, the last letter was known with certainty. As they are used in ASR, Markov methods can only assign a probability that the last phoneme (letter) in the sequence is a given one. The actual phoneme or state is said to be *hidden*.

HMM is a powerful technique because it allows coded speech input to be used to train the statistical model off line and the amount of data, or parameters, characterizing the model is relatively small compared to those that need to be stored in the case of template matching.

*Neural nets.* Neural net technology employs quite a different method of pattern recognition from template matching or HHM. Neural nets simulate the functioning of the human nervous system in imitating the interconnection of layers of neurons. These interconnected neuron-like layers can effect a transformation from a complex pattern to be recognized to simple output pattern. A simple neural net classifier for automatic speech recognition might take as its input a simplified two-dimensional speech spectrogram pattern as shown in Figure 2.10. The output pattern would be a grid, each point of which represents a member of the phonetic alphabet. In order for neural nets to recognize complex patterns, they must include one or more hidden layers where the weightings of the interlayer connections can be trained. In the very simple model shown in Figure 2.10, weighting can change between layers 1 and 2 and between layers 2 and 3.

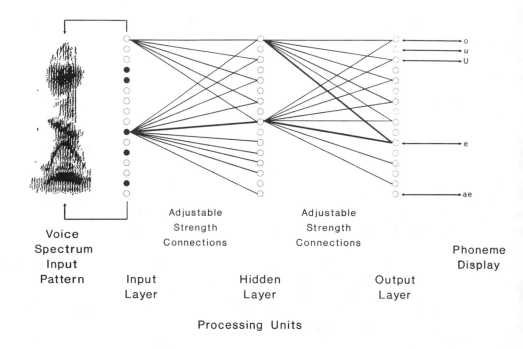

Voice
Spectrum
Input
Pattern

Adjustable
Strength
Connections

Adjustable
Strength
Connections

Phoneme
Display

Input
Layer

Hidden
Layer

Output
Layer

Processing Units

**Figure 2.10** Neural net model for speech recognition.

Each node or neuron in a neural net layer is connected to some or all of the nodes in the preceding layer and, in turn, is connected to some or all of the nodes in the succeeding layer. Each neuron as shown in Figure 2.11 sums the inputs from the preceding layer that it receives; this sum, through the threshold function, determines the neural output to each node in the succeeding layer. The weights w(in) are individually determined in the training of the neural net. The neural net is typically trained by presenting the net with a known input pattern and working backward from the desired pattern on the output layer adjusting the weightings of the interconnections. This is an iterative process but can be carried out automatically in an appropriately designed network.

To address real recognition problems, neural networks must be massively parallel, containing millions of neurons or processors with billions of interconnections. Real hardware with these specifications and powerful software to simulate networks easily on regular computers are just now emerging. Neural nets have shown considerable promise in principle for speech-recognition problems but are still in the experimental stage.

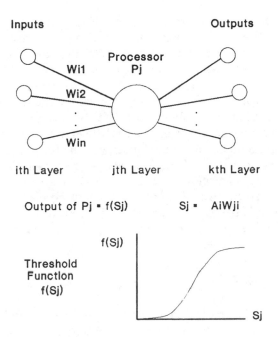

**Figure 2.11** Neural net processor.

## 2.7.1.4 *Linguistic Speech Recognition*

Up to this point we have considered only the acoustic aspects of automatic speech recognition. Human beings use the knowledge of the grammar of their language and information about the content of the speech to understand spoken language. ASR systems can also use some linguistic tools in automatic speech recognition. The simplest way in which linguistic processing can be used is by imposing a grammar; that is, at any given time only certain words will be recognized by the speech recognizer. Even in relatively small vocabularies systems it may be advantageous to divide the vocabulary of perhaps 64 words into subvocabularies of 8 words each so that the recognizer will only have to distinguish among 8 words and not among 64 words in determining the choice of the utterance. A measure of the average number of words that a speech recognizer must be able to recognize at any given time is called the *perplexity*. Grammatical constraints to reduce the perplexity in a given speech recognizer, not surprisingly, results in higher accuracy. In the case of large vocabulary systems for free dictation, artificial grammars are not feasible. In this case, true natural language processing must be used to parse the utterance to determine the probable parts of speech in a given sentence and help the system to make choices between words. In the phrase "in a sad/t state," a linguistic processor could help the system to determine that the third word would was *sad* rather than *sat* based on grammatical constraints.

A second type of linguistic processing involves semantics or the meaning of the words. An automatic speech recognizer that uses semantic processing requires the system to have a high-level ability to relate the meanings of different words and decide at least on a probabalistic basis which word of two, if both were grammatically correct and linguistically similar, was the correct choice. A simplified nonsemantic processor that simply determines the best choice of words based on a statistical model of language is used in some ASR systems. In this case, the phrase "computer screen" would simply be judged more likely than "computer scream." As automatic speech recognizers evolve toward larger vocabulary, continuous-speech machines, considerably more linguistic processing will be required to resolve acoustic ambiguities.

### 2.7.1.5 Decision Strategy

The speech signal being measured is, at best, somewhat similar to the stored templates. The basic task of the decision strategy is to decide that the word should be recognized as a member of the stored vocabulary or rejected as not being a member of the vocabulary. The word being analyzed will not typically be an exact match with any of the templates; it will simply be closest to a particular word in the template library. The recognizer will identify the word and indicate the probability of its being the word it is most similar to in the template library.

### 2.7.1.6 Performance Characteristics

The items that determine the characteristics of a speech recognizer are

Speaking rate—Discrete, connected, or continuous
Speaker dependency—Dependent or independent
Vocabulary size—The number of different words that can be recognized
Accuracy
Bandwidth—Telephone or local microphone
Noise immunity
Robustness
Response time

The speaking rate can be either discrete, where 200- to 500-ms pauses are required between each word; connected, where each word needs to be articulated clearly and distinctly without being slurred; or continuous, where the speech can be natural without any constraints.

Speaker-dependent recognition requires that the recognizer be trained to the voice and words of a particular user. Speaker-independent recognition will recognize any speaker that uses a word in the vocabulary of the recognizer. Speaker-independent recognizers have much smaller vocabularies than speaker-dependent recognizers.

The accuracy of a recognizer is a measure of how often a recognized word is the correct one. The patterns being matched are always different from the pattern of the actual word being uttered. The recognizer's ability to reject noise is essential in most applications. Recognizers have been developed that can perform satisfactorily in environments in which the ambient noise level is more than 85 decibels.

Speech recognizers that work over the telephone network have a lower bandwidth (less than 4,000 Hz) than recognizers that work with a local microphone. The telephone network does not pass signals that have a frequency greater than 4,000 Hz. This makes recognition more difficult because the information contained in the higher end of the audio spectrum is not available.

The response time of a recognizer is the duration between the completion of an utterance and the recognition of the word. A response time less than 0.5 seconds is typically required to avoid user problems in an application.

### 2.7.2 Speaker Verification Technology

Conceptually, speaker verification is similar to speech recognition. In implementation however, the two are quite different. For example, dynamic time warping would not be effective in voice verification, because the length of a particular person's utterance is often a key identification parameter. The mean frequency and frequency variance associated with the pitch of a person's voice have little significance for speech recognition but are powerful classifiers of voice types. Similarly, means and standard deviations of parameters relating to the resonances of the vocal tract can provide statistics that help characterize a person's voice.

### 2.7.3 Speech Recognition Technology and Product Status

Speech recognizers with vocabularies of more than 5,000 words have been implemented and commercialized. These products are mostly speaker-dependent, discrete-utterance devices and require that the speech input be highly controlled. A few products that work over the telephone network are small-vocabulary devices.

### 2.7.4 Speech-Voice Recognition—Future Directions

Vocabulary size and recognition accuracy will continue to improve in a very gradual fashion. The availability of high-performance DSPs has helped to reduce costs.

The basic difference between what can be achieved versus what is desired will continue to be a significant disadvantage. Many improvements that can be made in this area are linked to improvements in computing power. As low-cost DSPs increase the available computing power, speech-recognition improvements will follow directly.

### 2.7.5 Speech-Voice Recognition Applications

A variety of niche applications exists for speech-voice recognition equipment, and several have been implemented. These are invariably applications in which the user's hands or eyes (or both) are busy. The use of speech recognition in the telephone network as an alternative to DTMF signaling has been applied with some success outside of the United States. In the United States, however, the DTMF penetration is high enough that there has been little application of speech recognition technology for this application. The fact that an "overstrike" capability has not been available is a very serious practical limitation to widespread use of this application. Overstrike is the ability of a voice-processing system to detect that the caller has entered a DTMF digit and to stop speaking immediately. This lets experienced callers enter a system much more quickly because they need not listen to all of the speech prompts. Commercial speech-recognition products have begun to be manufactured with this capability. The use of speech recognition to provide a more natural modality for a caller to use is an attractive application and one that will come into broad use in the future. The main application for voice verification has been security, where personnel entry and exit is controlled by voice recognition.

### 2.8 TELEPHONICS

The existence of the *public switched telephone network* (PSTN) is an essential requirement for the vast majority of voice-processing applications. The United States PSTN handles over 500 billion telephone calls per year, with approximately 85% of the traffic being voice communication and the balance being data and video communication. [9]

### 2.8.1 Public Switched Telephone Network

The public telephone network (see Figure 2.12) consists of three basic components:
1. Customer premises equipment (CPE);
2. Switching facilities;
3. Transmission facilities.

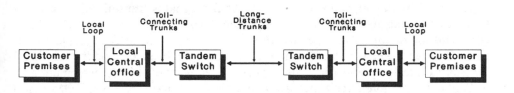

**Figure 2.12** PSTN.

CPE is equipment that is located at the customer's location. This includes telephone instruments, answering machines, PBXs, keysystems, ACDs, and other equipment that allows the user to interface with the telephone network [10].

Transmission facilities are the communication paths that carry telephone traffic between physical points in the network. The local loop connects CPE with the local telephone company's central office. Trunk lines are used to connect one telephone company switch with another. Trunks are high-capacity lines that carry traffic generated by many local loop lines. Copper wire pairs have traditionally been used for transmission, but satellite, terrestrial microwave, and fiber-optic cables have begun to supplant copper wire. The early trunk lines were copper wire connections between telephone company offices, each carrying a single circuit. Within a few decades of the commercialization of telephone service, the amount of wiring that existed for connecting telephone company switching offices was beginning to reach a point of saturation. The skies above cities were filled with poles, cross arms, and countless wires. The availability of the vacuum tube saved the situation. Using amplifiers and oscillators, *frequency-division multiplexing* (FDM) was invented.

FDM is a technique in which multiple channels are combined by assigning each channel to a different frequency band. For the telephone network, each voice channel was assigned a 4-kHz frequency band. In all, 24 voice channels were combined into a single 96-kHz channel, which was well within the transmission capacity of a single twisted wire pair. FDM reduced the number of trunks that were required by a factor of 24. Figure 2.13 is a simplified diagram of an FDM

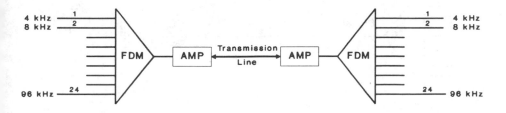

**Figure 2.13** FDM system.

system used by the telephone companies. As the signal is transmitted it becomes weaker and needs to be regenerated by an amplifier known as a repeater. In large cities, manholes for splicing cables were located at 1-mile intervals, and this is where the repeaters were located. FDM has generally been superseded by digital transmission techniques, such as *time-division multiplexing* (TDM), which are able to handle many more circuits per trunk and are much more reliable. FDM is still used for long-haul transmission over microwave transmission links [11].

Line noise causes analog transmission to be relatively unreliable. Every wire is an antenna that is able to receive signals from electrical radiation sources of all sorts. Sources include electrical motors, fluorescent lights, switches, and other telephone circuits. In a transmission circuit, noise will usually exist uniformly along it. The signal that is being sent is strong at the sending end and is attenuated at the receiving end. The repeater amplifier is unable to distinguish between the signal and noise and consequently the noise is amplified as the signal travels through the network. This is the reason that, years ago, calls to distant locations yielded much poorer voice quality. Figure 2.14 illustrates the effect of noise on a signal transmitted using an FDM transmission link.

TDM is an electronic switching system in which each voice channel is separated in time. A TDM switch has a finite number of timeslots, and each voice channel is assigned to a specific slot. The TDM output is known as a *frame*. The number of timeslots in a frame is a design option. One of the primary advantages of digital transmission is that it essentially eliminates analog noise problems inherent in FDM transmission systems. A digital signal can have only one of two states. A digital amplifier is readily able to distinguish between the signal and noise. Figure 2.15 illustrates what happens to a signal that is transmitted using a digital transmission link. Practical TDMs were made possible by the availability semiconductor technology. Figure 2.16 is a simplified diagram of a TDM link. The TDM, in combination with codecs for conversion between analog and digital domains, is known as a *channel bank*.

Telephone switches connect the transmission facilities to provide the maximum number of connections with the minimum amount of wiring. The switches that serve a specific local exchange are known as *central office* (CO) switches. The

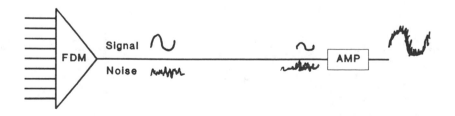

**Figure 2.14** Noise impact on FDM system.

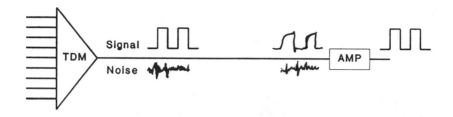

**Figure 2.15** TDM signal regeneration with noise rejection.

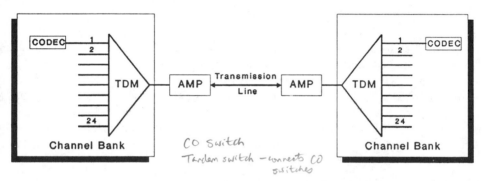

CO switch

Tandem switch — connects CO switches

**Figure 2.16** TDM transmission system. Toll switch — connects to long-distance network

basic services provided by a CO switch are dial tone, ring-back signals, local call switching, and switching of nonlocal calls to an external switch. Tandem switches connect one CO switch with another CO switch. Toll switches connect with the long-distance network. The switches were primarily electromechanical until the late 1960s and early 1970s when they were replaced by electronic analog switches. Since the mid 1980s, the electronic analog switches have been undergoing a gradual replacement by digital switches. The conversion to digital switches is essential for achieving full implementation of ISDN.

The PSTN has historically transmitted both voice and signaling over the same transmission facility. This is known as *inband signaling*. Inband signaling has many disadvantages: it has long call setup and teardown times, which is an inefficient use of the telephone network; it is susceptible to fraud; it is relatively unreliable; and it makes it difficult to offer enhanced services. Since the late 1980s, the telephone network has been undergoing a conversion to an out-of-band signaling system called *common channel signaling system number 7* (CCSS7). CCSS7 promises to eliminate the limitations of inband signaling.

Attachment of voice processing equipment to the telephone network requires a variety of specialized technologies. A telephone network interface needs to perform the functions of ring detection, phone off- or on-hook placement, DTMF detection, hangup detection, and call-progress detection.

### 2.8.2 Central Office Connections

A variety of central office connections is available from the telephone companies. The main ones are loop start, ground start, and *direct inward dialing* (DID). Each of these connections offers a unique set of capabilities that may be useful in a specific voice processing environment.

#### 2.8.2.1 Loop Start

Loop start is the most common station-side interface. Battery and ground are supplied at the CO, and current flows when the tip-ring connection is made at the station. This connection operates a line sensor to inform the system that a call is being originated. The primary disadvantage of this interface is that, depending upon the particular CO switch or PBX, it cannot detect a far-end caller hangup. In some cases, the system must detect a dial tone to determine that a caller has hung up, adding many seconds to the call.

#### 2.8.2.2 Ground Start

In the ground start interface, an origination is accomplished by the station grounding the ring lead. Ground start interfaces provide the following advantages: glare minimization, use of the tip lead for other supervisory functions (i.e., payphone coin-collection signaling), and quick and positive hangup detection, which improves system use.

#### 2.8.2.3 Direct Inward Dialing

DID allows outpulsing the last $n$ digits of the called party's number to the station. The receiving system is able to decode these digits and direct the call to a specific location. In voice mail systems, the DID number could be a subscriber box number, thus eliminating the need for the caller to enter that number. The outpulsed digits can be provided as either DTMF or pulse. Supervision is also available whereby the digits are not outpulsed until the station has signaled that it is ready to accept them. With DID, line use is improved because the system can detect a hangup.

#### 2.8.2.4 DTMF Detection

Reliable detection of DTMF signals is a nontrivial function. The requirement is to detect a signal that may be significantly attenuated by loop losses in a noisy environment. The detector must also be able to reject normal speech as a DTMF signal. If the detector is too sensitive, the system will be susceptible to "falsing" and will only work in a noise-free environment. If the detector is not sensitive enough, it will not detect real DTMF signals that are attenuated.

### 2.8.2.5 Call Progress Monitoring

The telephone interface of a voice-processing system must be able to detect the following conditions:

Dial tone
Busy
Phone has been answered
Hangup
Ring, no answer
Reorder

The ability to detect reliably each of these telephone call states is particularly essential in systems that perform outdialing.

### 2.8.2.6 Automatic Number Identification

*Automatic number identification* (ANI) automatically identifies the directory number of the calling subscriber. It was developed primarily to permit the telephone companies to automate their billing systems, but it has also been used in other applications. The 911 emergency service is one of the more visible examples. Other applications include *cable television* (CATV) pay-per-view automatic subscriber identification, telemarketing, and *automatic customer name and address* (ACNA) services. The interface often uses inband multifrequency (MF) signaling, but it has also used DTMF. The number of the calling subscriber is outpulsed along with supervisory signals. One of the major applications of ANI has been for emergency 911 service, where ANI has typically been provided inband as part of the call setup. Out-of-band services are also provided (e.g., ANI service provided by AT&T).

ANI has run into opposition from groups that are concerned about invasion of the caller's privacy. These groups claim that ANI discourages calls to anonymous help hotlines, passes unlisted numbers along with listed numbers, and generally discourages the belief that the caller is anonymous. Proponents of ANI say it enhances privacy for the called party, reduces obscene or harassing calls, and increases business efficiency up to 20%. In many states, the PUC has sided with the anti-ANI faction and requires that the telephone company provide comprehensive ANI-blocking capabilities. Per-call blocking (the caller decides on each call whether to block the ANI) is one type of capability. The other type is per line (it is done once per line). The latter is the more contentious—if it became the standard, services that were based on ANI would be emasculated. In cases in which the state PUC has required both per-line blocking, the telephone companies have withdrawn their tariff application and decided not to offer ANI services. Clearly, if a large percentage of the telephones is blocked, ANI will not have the commercial potential the telephone companies imagined [12].

### 2.8.2.7 T-1 and E-1 Transmission

*T-1* refers to a transmission system used in the United States, Canada, and some other parts of the world (Japan and Australia) to transfer digital signals at a rate of 1.544 Mbyte/s. T-1 uses TDM and PCM and is a TDM switching system with a 24-timeslot frame length, composing 24 separate voice channels. T-1 is used extensively within the telephone network to provide economical, low-loss, noise-

**Table 2.3**
Digital transmission link hierarchy

| Signal level | Bit rate | Equivalent voice circuits | Carrier system | Typical transmission medium |
|---|---|---|---|---|
| • | North America | | | |
| DS0 | 64 kb/s | 1 | | Copper wire |
| DS1 | 1,544 kb/s | 24 | T-1 | |
| DS1C | 3,152 kb/s | 48 | T-1C | |
| DS2 | 6,312 kb/s | 96 | T-2 | Microwave or optical fiber |
| DS3 | 44,736 kp/s | 672 | T-3 | |
| DS4 | 274,176 kb/s | 4,032 | T-4 | |
| | CEPT | | | |
| DS0 | 64 kb/s | 1 | | Copper wire |
| DS1 | 2,048 kb/s | 30 | E-1 | |
| DS2 | 8,448 kb/s | 120 | E-2 | |
| DS3 | 34,368 kb/s | 480 | E-3 | Microwave or optical fiber |
| DS4 | 139,264 kb/s | 1,920 | E-4 | |
| DS5 | 565,148 kb/s | 4,032 | E-5 | |

free voice signal transmission. A T-1 link is made up of twenty-four 64,000-bps channels, with an additional 8,000 bps used to keep the TDMs at each end of the link synchronized.

E-1 refers to the transmission system that is used in Europe, Latin America, and the Far East. It transfers digital signals at a 2,048-Mbyte/s rate. It also uses TDM and PCM and is composed of 30 separate voice channels. E-1 actually has 32 channels, but two are used for control purposes. Both T-1 and E-1 are called *data-signal level one* (DS1). The term T-1 originated with the telephone company and initially meant a very specific type of physical equipment: selected cable pairs and digital regenerators at 6,000-foot intervals. Over the years the common usage of the term has corrupted its original meaning and now T-1 is used to refer to the DS1 rate.

T-1 has been used extensively within the telephone network since the early 1970s. It was first tariffed in 1983. T-1 has significant advantages over analog circuits:

Much lower cost
Improved reliability
Reconfiguration flexibility

T-1 uses less wiring, simpler circuits, less power and is easier to monitor and maintain, translating into lower costs. The initial tariffs for T-1 did not reflect this since the earlier FCC tariff pricing guidelines were oriented toward bandwidth-based pricing. By the mid 1980s, the FCC and the telephone companies adapted the concept of cost-based pricing, which made it possible to offer T-1 for less than the cost of separate analog lines.

T-1 is a digital service, and all of the problems inherent to analog transmission of voice signals, such as susceptibility to noise and crosstalk, are eliminated. In general, a T-1 circuit either works perfectly or not at all. This makes maintenance and troubleshooting much easier.

### 2.8.2.8 Integrated Services Digital Network

The PSTN has the following limitations:

- Narrow bandwidth of each voice line (4 kHz);
- Primarily inband signaling (inefficient, expensive, and susceptible to fraud);
- Separate voice and data networks for users (inefficient, expensive, and limiting);
- Separate administrations of CPE and telephone network;
- Many different incompatible voice, data, and digital interface standards;
- Expensive and inefficient workstation access to computer, environments via remote sites.

The ISDN intent addresses these limitations: it is the ultimate telephone service, providing voice services to subscribers in an all-digital form. ISDN systems have four main capabilities:

1. An internationally accepted standard for the transmission of voice, data, and signaling over the public telephone network;
2. Completely end-to-end digital transmission circuits;
3. Standard out-of-band signaling system;
4. Significantly more bandwidth to the individual subscriber.

ISDN standards have been developed by the CCITT, and some of the access interfaces have been defined. The first configuration is the basic rate interface (BRI) access configuration, which consists of a multichannel structure of two B- (bearer) channels that operate at 64 kb/s and one D- (delta) channel that operates at 16 kb/s. *Primary rate interface* (PRI) access operates at the T-1 DS1 1.544-Mbyte/s rate. This structure also provides multichannel access, which is broken down into twenty-three B-channels and one D-channel (23B + D), with each channel operating at the 64-kb/s rate. The B-channels are used to transmit voice or data, while the D-channel is used for supervision and control. A 24-B-channel configuration is also available. A single D-channel can support up to 20 groups of 24 B-channels, which is where the 24-B configuration is appropriate.

A group 4 fax would use ISDN and would be able to transmit a full page in approximately three seconds, with quality comparable to that of an office copier.

A user with a BRI line would be able to able to use a single telephone for data transmission and simultaneously be able to use the line to place and accept voice calls.

Despite all of the potential benefits of ISDN, its deployment has been relatively slow. In early 1992, the number of ISDN lines installed was approximately 200,000—with the vast majority being used by carriers, CPE ISDN suppliers, and a few trial services. The result is that ISDN presently consists of "islands" that limit the usefulness of the service. A variety of reasons exists for the slow deployment. The availability of CCSS7 throughout the network is a key requirement for widespread deployment of ISDN. The out-of-band signaling associated with ISDN requires CCSS7. Although telephone companies are aggressively deploying CCSS7, the sheer magnitude of the telephone network requires a significant amount of time for this to occur. Tariffs for ISDN had not been filed in many parts of the country, and the ones that have been have varied dramatically from one telephone company to the next. This makes it difficult for an end user to make an economic assessment of ISDN.

Another problem has been the incompatibility of different ISDN equipment vendors. Proprietary implementations of ISDN features were causing interoperability problems with ISDN equipment from different vendors. In early 1991,

Bellcore issued a standard called National ISDN-1, which has been embraced by the entire industry. The principle components of National ISDN-1 are:

- A standard BRI interface protocol;
- Support of PRI and vendor-specific implementations;
- Access to PSTN and Centrex features;
- Selected BRI supplementary services;
- Standard recording to support billing;
- Support of initial operations features.

National ISDN-2 is the follow-on to National ISDN-1, issued by Bellcore in 1992. It aims at strengthening National ISDN-1 in five areas:

1. Uniform customer interfaces and services;
2. Uniform PRI services;
3. Improved data capabilities;
4. Uniform recording capabilities to support billing;
5. Generic operations capabilities.

### 2.8.2.9 Dialed Number Identification Service

*Dialed number identification service* (DNIS) is an ISDN-like service that provides the number being called. One of the primary applications for DNIS is for inbound telemarketing applications in which multiple campaigns may be running simultaneously, and the number being called identifies a particular campaign. The number that is being sent can be captured and either provided to a telephone service representative (TSR) taking the call or to a host computer. DNIS is available from the major *interexchange carriers* (IXCs) and *local exchange carriers* (LECs) with non-ISDN lines as inband signaling. The exception is AT&T, which only provides DNIS with ISDN services.

### 2.8.2.10 Rotary Telephone Pulse Detection

Although DTMF telephones have become commonplace is the United States, major rural areas of the country still have rotary telephones. The central offices serving these areas have not yet been upgraded with newer switches that support DTMF service. With a few exceptions, most countries outside of the United States have mostly rotary telephones. Their use for entry of information has a number of severe limitations; many of the switches totally block the dial pulses once the call is set up. They are either ignored, or, with some switches, the caller will be disconnected if an attempt to dial occurs. When they pass through the telephone network, the dial pulses are usually severely attenuated and distorted. Therefore, reliable detection of dial pulses is not a trivial effort. The time necessary to transmit rotary signals is much longer than the time for DTMF. DTMF transmittal is generally limited by the entry time of the caller, while the time to transmit rotary digits depends on the particular digit. The digit nine takes 0.9 seconds, the digit eight takes 0.8 seconds, and so forth. Despite all of these limitations, devices that detect rotary pulses are commercially available and have been used in a limited fashion. The most successful devices are ones that are attached in series to the telephone interface. For DTMF signaling, they are transparent. For pulse signaling, they convert the dial pulse string to a DTMF equivalent. A calibration input is required on each call to accommodate the variation in pulse duration that is common with mechanical devices of this sort. This is really a situation in which we are dealing with the best of poor alternatives. Although many calls cannot be handled with rotary detection, rotary is successful with calls that would not be completed otherwise.

### 2.8.2.11 DTMF

Eight frequencies in the 700- to 1700-hertz range compose the four-by-four code designed for DTMF dialing. The eight frequencies, which were selected to avoid harmonically related interference from speech signals, are divided into four low-band and four high-band tones as illustrated in Figure 2.17. Pressing a pushbutton results in the generation of two tones: a high-band and a low-band frequency. Pressing 7 (PRS), for instance, causes the generation and transmission of 852- and

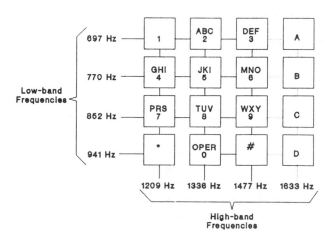

**Figure 2.17** DTMF frequency layout.

1,209-hertz frequencies. For the ten pushbuttons on a conventional telephone, only ten frequency combinations are required and the 1,633-hertz frequency is not used. The four keys associated with the 1,633-hertz frequency are known as the A-, B-, C-, and D-keys and have been used in some military applications.

*DTMF input schemes.* The DTMF keyboard is suitable for the entry of numeric information and limited control. The keyboard layout is shown in Figure 2.18. Note that the alphabetic characters (with the exception of the Q and the Z) are included on the keyboard. The letter Q is usually assumed to be part of the PRS group, and the letter Z is assumed to be part of the WXY group. This suggests that the DTMF keyboard could possibly be used for the entry of alphanumeric information.

Many voice-processing applications require the input of alphabetic information in addition to numeric information. Catalog item numbers may include alphabetic characters, and converting all the numbers to eliminate the alphabetic characters would be difficult. Despite the universal existence of numeric identifiers, such as Social Security numbers, the primary identification of a person is still by name. Alphanumeric pagers require that brief messages be obtained from the paging party.

A variety of schemes has been developed and implemented for the entry of alphabetic information with the DTMF telephone. The simplest scheme is to enter each letter directly. If the letter A is required, the caller would press the 2 key. Note that this could also represent the B or the C characters. This scheme takes advantage of the fact that within a particular environment the number of meaningful alphabetic combinations is finite and often very small. For example, the vast majority of surnames are uniquely identified by the first four alphabetic characters. This means that a caller could dial into an organization that has ten thousand employees and uniquely locate a particular employee by spelling the first four digits of the person's name. When more than one employee's name has a particular four-

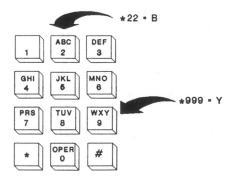

**Figure 2.18** DTMF keyboard layout.

character sequence, the system can either ask the caller to enter additional characters or provide a menu of choices. For example, if the caller entered 2,3,2,6,7, the system might respond with, "Press one for Michael Adams or two for Susan Becor." The number of conflicting names is quite small, and this scheme has been used very effectively. The entry of messages is conceptually quite similar. The only real difference is that a termination of the character string is required. The # is usually used for this purpose. The caller would enter a character string and then press the # key. The system would then look in a dictionary to find the words that correspond to this input string and would first speak the most common word to the caller. If the word were not the one desired by the caller, the word would immediately be discarded by pressing the # key. The system then would speak the next word that was found. If there were no word found in the system dictionary that corresponded to what the caller desired, the system would start to spell the word. Again, the caller discards a particular letter immediately after hearing it by pressing the # key. Spelling is typically required when dealing with proper nouns. An asterisk (*) embedded in a string signifies both a decimal point and that the string is numeric. An asterisk at the beginning of a string is used as an escape code. This permits a virtually unlimited number of commands to be implemented. For example, *Bn# would mean backward *n* words, and *Fn# would mean forward *n* words, providing the basis for an editing capability. Three additional commands would be *P# for *playback*, *T# for *transmit*, and *O# to *obtain help*. The scheme described above was developed by fon-ex of New Hope, Pennsylvania, and the firm claims to have patents pending. A scheme of this sort takes a bit of effort to learn and use effectively, but it appears to be useful for the entry of short alphabetic messages using a DTMF telephone.

Other schemes for entry of alphanumeric characters identify them precisely by locating their position on the key. An input sequence such as *22 would identify the character B. The first numeric digit would indicate that it is either the character A, B, or C. The second digit would specify that the character is the second character on the key, which in this case is the letter B. This works except for the letters Q and Z. A similar approach would identify the particular character by pressing the key a number of times, corresponding to the location of the character gon the key. With this scheme, an input sequence such as *999 would identify the letter Y, because this letter is the third on the 9 key. Another approach would assign a numeric to each of the letters (A = 01, B = 02, C = 03, and so forth). Therefore, the input sequence *030102, would correspond to the word CAB.

### 2.8.3 Telephone Connection Specifications

In the United States, AT&T maintained an effective monopoly on connection of devices to the public telephone network until 1956. Only AT&T equipment could be connected, and only AT&T could provide local and long-distance service. In the 1956 "Hushaphone" case and later in the 1968 "Carterfone" case, the interconnect monopoly of AT&T was terminated. Other companies were allowed to interconnect with the telephone network, provided that the interconnection did not cause harm. To prevent that harm, the telephone company supplied an interface device known as the *protective connecting arrangement* (PCA). The interfaces provided for telephone connections were known as *voice connecting arrangements* (VCAs) and the *data connecting arrangements* (DCAs) were used for the attachment of modems to the telephone network. The company that was connecting with the telephone network was required to purchase the DCA from the telephone company. The expense of the DCA and the inconvenience of dealing with an often-unfriendly telephone company caused enough of a problem that the FCC developed regulations that would permit direct interconnection of equipment with the telephone network without the use of a DCA. In 1976, the FCC promulgated the regulations that are now contained in *part 68* (title 47 of the United States Code of Federal Regulations, parts 20–69). The purpose of the regulations is "to provide for uniform standards for the protection of the telephone network from harms caused by connections of terminal equipment thereto." Note that the purpose of these FCC rules is to protect the telephone network from harm, not to protect the consumer. Devices designed to meet the requirements of part 68 do not necessarily work properly. The "harms" to the network that concern the FCC fall into four major categories. (1) Hazardous voltages and currents placed on the telephone lines by customer equipment could damage central office equipment or injure persons. (2) Signal levels must be maintained within certain maximum limits to prevent the overloading of amplifiers within the network, prevent crosstalk, and to permit proper multiplexer operation. (3) On-hook impedances are specified, because the central office uses these to evaluate the condition of its lines and because it must drive the telephone ringer. (4) Balance of the line is also specified. The telephone network consists of a balanced, largely open-line transmission arrangement. An imbalance of the line will cause hum and crosstalk. Finally, the telephone company is concerned about billing protection. Certain time delays and the absence of signals on certain prescribed signaling frequencies are required.

### 2.8.4 Telephonics—Future Direction

As ISDN becomes a reality, it will have a significant effect on the voice-processing area. Cost and reliability will improve dramatically. Networking of systems will be performed without the degradation of speech quality that is intrinsic to the analog transmission schemes now employed. Without the noise-signal degradation problems of an analog telephone network with which to contend, speech recognition performance will improve significantly. Services such as ANI and DNIS will be commonly available with ISDN.

# REFERENCES

1. Oberteuffer, J. A., *Automatic Speech Recognition 1991, A Study of the U.S. Market*, Lexington, Massachusetts, 1991.
2. Sabine, E. A., Digital Signal Processors Make Speech Products a Reality, *International Speech Tech 87 conference*, London, May 1987, pp. 105–110.
3. Klatt, D. H., Text-to-Speech: Present and Future, *Speech Tech 86 conference*, New York, April 1986, pp. 221–226.
4. Vitale, A., Recent Improvements in Speech Synthesis, *American Voice Input-Output Society conference*, Alexandria, Virginia, September 1986, pp. 227–234.
5. Vitale, T., An Algorithm for High-Accuracy Name Pronunciation by Parametric Speech Synthesizer, *American Journal of Computational Linguistics*, Vol. 17, No. 3, 1991, pp. 257–276.
6. Pickett, J. M., *The Sounds of Speech Communications*, Baltimore, Maryland, The University Press, 1980; Ch. 5, Prosodic Features, pp. 79–102.
7. Moody, T. S., and M. G. Joost, Synthesized Speech, Digitized Speech, and Recorded Speech: A Comparison of Listener Comprehension Rates, *American Voice Input-Output Society conference*, Alexandria, Virginia, September 1986, pp. 263–280.
8. Higgins, A. L., Speaker Recognition by Template Matching, *Speech Tech 86 conference*, New York, April 1986, pp. 273–276.
9. Talley, D., Basic Telephone Switching Systems, Hasbrook Heights, New Jersey, Hayden Book Company, pp. 33–36.
10. Nelson, E., S. Ryba, S. Silverman, and M. Bradshaw, *Introduction to the History, Structure, and Technology of the Telecommunications Industry*, Washington, D.C., NATA, 1991, pp. 19–29.
11. Flanagan, W. A., *The Guide to T-1 Networking*, New York, Telecom Library, 1988.
12. Newton, H., *Newton's Telecom Dictionary*, New York, Telecom Library, 1989.

# *Chapter 3*

# *Voice-Processing System Architecture*

## 3.1 BASIC CAPABILITIES

The architecture of a voice-processing system consists of hardware and software components configured to perform the voice-processing function. The vast majority of voice-processing systems uses a general-purpose computing environment with specialized hardware and software components. The basic capabilities included in a voice-processing system are:

- Perform the telephone call management;
- Process speech;
- Capture caller information;
- Provide information to the caller;
- Provide system monitoring and control.

Performing the telephone call management includes listening for ringing and answering the phone; detecting caller hangup or disconnect; transferring calls; routing calls based on ANI, DID, or DNIS; and dialing out.

Processing speech includes recording the caller's speech; compressing the signal being recorded; and playing a voice message to the caller.

Capturing caller information includes recognition of DTMF, rotary pulse, or speech input as commands and recording speech messages left by the caller.

Providing information to the caller could be a voice message left by another caller, or it could be a voice message that is translating information from a database.

The monitoring and control capability includes telephone traffic and caller usage reports as well as facilities for administering system startup, operation, maintenance, and shutdown.

Figure 3.1 shows the major elements of a voice-processing system. Each of these elements contains both a hardware and a software component.

**Figure 3.1** Major elements of a voice-processing system.

## 3.2 HARDWARE ARCHITECTURE

The hardware components of a voice-processing architecture typically include:

- General-purpose computer;
- Mass storage;
- Telephonics interface;
- Communications processor.

### 3.2.1 General-Purpose Computer System

The heart of a voice-processing system is a computer—the hardware portion of the controller identified in Figure 3.2. In most voice-processing systems that have been implemented, this has been either a small minicomputer or a PC. The IBM PC/AT has become the dominant controller in the voice-processing area. More than 90% of all voice-processing systems currently manufactured use the IBM PC/ AT architecture or the IBM PS/2. *Random access memory* (RAM) is more than 512K and is typically 1024K. A hard disk is used to store the system software and applications programs. This is the hardware portion of the system storage element in Figure 3.2. In many systems the digitized speech obtained from a caller and the application database is also stored on this same hard disk. A few of the systems use Motorola 680XX as the computer. Voice-processing systems have also been implemented with general-purpose minicomputers and workstations such as the DEC VAX and MicroVAX, IBM System 88 and RS/6000, Stratus machines, and Tandem machines.

The general-purpose computer's basic function is to run the system and applications software, provide the flow of information between the different system

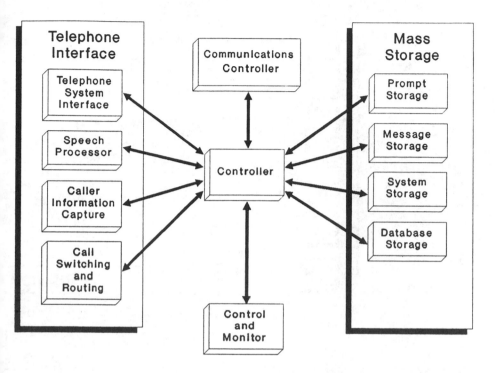

**Figure 3.2** Hardware components of a voice-processing system.

elements, and provide an interface that permits the operation of the system to be monitored and controlled.

Most of the PC configurations will handle 24 ports, but some will support 48 ports. The number of ports that can actually be supported depends on the particular application. To achieve higher port counts than a single computing environment can accommodate, *local area networks* (LANs) are used. The primary purpose of networking is to provide a central management and control capability. Centralized statistics reporting, prompt updates, and program updates typically are highly desirable. Without a centralized management mechanism, the alternative is an approach that is derisively referred to as sneakerNet. With sneakerNet, the system manager needs to go from system to system, loading floppies and pulling individual reports. A typical voice-processing system using multiple nodes and a LAN to connect them is shown in Figure 3.3.

The LANs that have been implemented include industry-standard LANs such as Ethernet and Token-Ring as well as proprietary ones. Voice-mail systems, in addition, require that the messages be networked. Proprietary networking interfaces have also come into existence. A voice-mail standard is being developed by

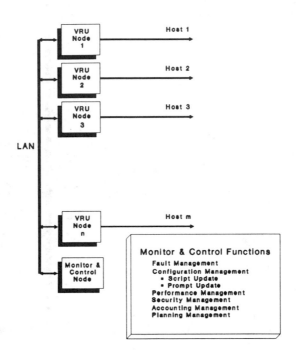

**Figure 3.3** Networked voice-processing nodes.

the *audio messaging interchange specification* (AMIS) project group, made of a cross-section of vendors and users. This activity is sponsored by the *Information Industry Association* (IIA). At present, the AMIS project group has decided on a digital networking scheme, based on the CCITT X.400-series message-handling recommendations. An analog networking scheme has also been defined, which is intended to serve as an interim scheme and for smaller networks until the digital standard becomes widespread.

### 3.2.2 Mass Storage

Mass storage is used for the system's programs, the applications programs, or the digitized speech. In many cases, the same storage system is used for storage of all three. In some systems, the digitized speech is stored on a separate speech storage subsystem. The storage that is used is a hard disk based on winchester technology. The size of the hard disks currently used ranges from 60 Mb to more 1,000 Mb. Storage of digitized speech takes a great deal of memory. A rough estimate of speech storage requirement is that each hour of digitized speech equals 11-Mb disk storage at a 24-kHz digitization rate, which is commonly used. By contrast, an hour's worth of speech in text form requires approximately 33 kb. Of course, disk access time and transfer rate are critical performance parameters. Not being able to retrieve speech rapidly enough from the hard disk delays response to the callers and, when phrases are made of multiple speech segments, results in halting and stilted speech. Providing RAM for storing the most frequently used speech phrases is a technique that is used to significantly improve the performance of a voice-processing system. The hard disks that are used in high-performance voice-processing systems have approximately 12-ms access times. This is an important parameter since, assuming that the processor and the operating software do not limit performance, it provides a hard boundary of system port capacity. With a 12-ms hard disk, a single VRU node is able to handle approximately 100 ports. This is a worst case situation in which all of the callers require disk access simultaneously. It can be assumed that a more typical environment would have many callers entering digits or performing other functions that do no require disk access. This means that a practical limit for a single VRU node is approximately 150 ports. The availability of *redundant array of independent disks* (RAID) will improve this by a factor of 3 to 4.

### 3.2.3 Telephonic Interface

The telephone interface consists of special-purpose hardware that performs the telephony and speech processing functions. It consists of the following elements:

- Telephone system interface;
- Speech processor;
- Caller information capture;
- Call switching and routing.

### 3.2.3.1 Telephone System Interface

The telephone system interface is a separate special-purpose processing device that attaches to the computer system and receives commands from and provides information to it. The functions performed include:

- Loop-start interface;
- Ring detection;
- Taking phone off hook after $n$ rings;
- Placing phone on hook;
- Call-progress tones detection;
- Dial tone;
- Busy reorder;
- Answer detection;
- Hook-flash performance;

- Out-dial DTMF or pulse string;
- Call switching to other destinations;
- Silence detection.

The PBX interface is part of the voice-processing telephonics interface. One of the basic PBX integration capabilities is to accept the dialed number identification (the extension that was previously dialed by the caller). Without this capability, the caller would be required to reenter the extension when entering the voice-mail system. The other important PBX integration capability is the ability of the voice-processing system to indicate to the PBX that a message was left, and that the message waiting indicator should be turned on. Although a few of the PBX interfaces are accomplished using separate RS232C data interfaces from the PBX, the majority have been inband (analog signaling over the telephone line).

These are the basic telephonic functions. Other functions performed by some of the telephonics controllers include "wink" and answer detection, DID interface, ground start interface, electrical and mechanical interface, far-end hangup detection, trunk side interface, DNIS, and ANI interface.

### 3.2.3.2 Speech Processor

The speech processor converts the analog speech signal of the caller into digitized speech for subsequent storage on the mass storage device. Bit compression is typically used to reduce the disk storage that is needed. In the reverse direction, it also converts digitized speech into an analog voice form that the caller can hear. For digital systems that are attached to digital telephone services (T-1 or ISDN) the conversion of the signal into digital form is not needed since the signal is already in digital form. Compression to a lower bit rate is usually provided to reduce the disk storage requirement.

Detection of silence is an important requirement for voice-processing systems that are recording speech from callers. Typically, a silence duration threshold is specified. When this threshold is exceeded, the system will cease recording until speech is again detected. Without a silence compression capability, a large portion of the hard disk storage will be used to store silence.

### 3.2.3.3 Caller-Provided Information Capture

The caller is able to command the voice-processing system using DTMF input. In some cases, rotary pulse or speech commands are also used to command the voice-processing system. The caller information capture detects the caller inputs and decodes them. The caller information capture function is also able to record speech messages that are left by the caller.

### 3.2.3.4 Switching and Routing of Calls

The ability to switch a call to another destination is an important capability in most voice processing. The most common way to transfer a call is to use the transfer capability of the telephone system. With telephone systems that have inband signaling, this is usually a hook-flash followed by outdialing the number to which the caller should be transferred. The timing and duration of the hook-flash signal does vary from one telephone system to the next, and most voice-processing systems provide the ability to readily change the hook-flash timing parameters. When the call transfer is completed, the port on the voice-processing system is freed and available for caller traffic.

Analog switches have also been used to bridge a call to another line. Another telephone port is seized by the voice-processing system, and an outbound call is made. The caller is then bridged to that port. One disadvantage to this approach is that two ports are now tied up for the duration of the call. Another disadvantage is the quite severe attenuation through the bridging loop (6 dB or more). With an analog switch, it is not necessary that the call be switched back to the telephone system, because it is possible to switch the call directly to a local operator. Switching the call to a shared system resource is also available with most voice-processing systems. Shared resources are devices such as speech recognizers or text-to-speech devices that are relatively expensive but also not typically required for use during most of the call.

Digital switches are available and integrated with many voice-processing systems. A drop-and-insert capability permits a voice-processing system to receive a call on an inbound T-1 span, perform a voice-processing function on the call, and when complete, pass the call to an outbound T-1 span. Each DS0 on the input T-1 span is connected with the corresponding DS0 on the outbound T-1 span. This tends to restrict the switching flexibility but is appropriate for some applications. A TDM provides a general-purpose switching capability and is available with many voice-processing systems. Typically, any DS0 slot can be connected with any other DS0 slot as well as with other voice-processing system ports or resources. For example, relatively expensive options such as live operators, speech recognizers, and text-to-speech converters can be connected with a call when they are needed and then released when they are no longer needed. The TDM switches that are available with voice-processing systems range in size from 192 to over 1,000 timeslots.

### 3.2.3.5 Outbound Calling

Reliable outbound calling systems must be able to detect dial tone, ringing, busy signals, intercepts, answering machines, people answering the phone, and ring-no-answer. This seems straightforward enough, but what makes detection difficult is the variability of telephone systems throughout the world. The electrical signals that are encountered vary considerably from one telephone system to the next. A comprehensive outbound calling system may be readily configured to accommodate these variations. The system must be able to vary the actual digits, their duration, and interdigit duration to accommodate the variation in telephone systems. The most difficult part is often determining the characteristics of a particular telephone system. This is frequently only accomplished by trial and error. Detection of an answering machine answering the call is an important capability in predictive and preview dialing systems since it is desirable to screen these calls. A comparison of the signals that are obtained when a live voice and a recorded voice are encountered is shown in Figure 3.4. Note that for an answering machine, the initial time period is longer, the amplitude of the speech is lower, and the speech time period is longer. By developing reference models, answering machines are able to be detected with a 90% certainty.

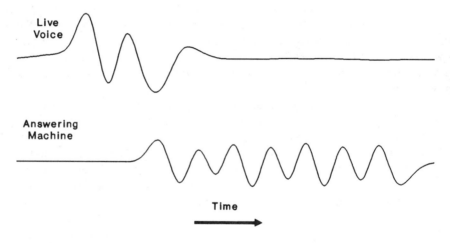

**Figure 3.4** Answering machine detection.

### 3.2.4 Communications Controller

In many voice-processing system implementations, the database is located on a remote host computer. In some system implementations, the monitor and control and the voice-processing application, in addition to the database, are located on a remote host computer. In these cases a communications controller is required. For asynchronous communications, conventional RS232C interfaces such as the com1 or com2 ports of the IBM PC/AT are used. For synchronous communications, controllers that perform the physical communication functions to support either *binary synchronous communication* (BSC) or *synchronous datalink control* (SDLC) are used. Packet transmission (X.25) links are also available.

A host computer interface requirement exists only for certain types of voice-processing applications. *Interactive voice response* (IVR) and predictive dialing usually require an interface to a host computer. Voice mail, auto attendant, and passive interception applications typically do not need a host interface.

## 3.3 VOICE-PROCESSING SOFTWARE

The heart of each voice-processing system is a multitasking executive program. This is a real-time executive that can support the running of multiple real-time processes in a concurrent fashion. It is typically port-event driven, which means that activities occurring at the telephone are the highest priority and receive the resources of the system before other lower priority processes receive service. A separate partition exists for each telephone port. This environment provides access to all of the voice and telephony functions and handles the routing of keyboard, display, serial port, disk file, and other input and output devices to the port partitions.

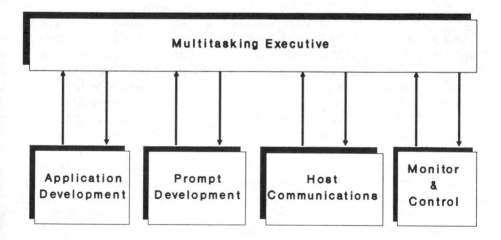

**Figure 3.5** Voice-processing software.

### 3.3.1 Application Software

Application software falls into one of two categories: specific application packages or application generation toolkits. Please note that the term "tree," used in the following sections, is defined as a specific voice response application that consists of predefined speech instructions or information (prompts) and responses to caller DTMF input.

### 3.3.1.1 Specific Application Packages

Specific application packages are designed to execute a set of functions that are defined and useful to a broad range of customers. Auto attendant and voice-mail programs are examples of specific application packages. Packages such as this can be configured to satisfy a range of user requirements.

### 3.3.1.2 Application Generation Toolkits

*Application generation toolkits* (AGTKs) are packages that permit a developer to create a custom system [1]. They fall into one of three categories:

- Menu-driven AGTKs;
- Procedural language AGTKs;
- Library of function calls.

*Menu-driven AGTKs.* These are menu-driven software packages that allow a developer to create a tree specific to a desired application without the requirement that the user possess any significant programming skills. A Lotus 1-2-3 or DBASE III user would possess the basic skill set necessary to successfully implement a specific voice-response application. These packages are so easy to use that within a few hours, a developer can become quite proficient in their use. Trees can be created and made to run in time periods measured in minutes or hours. Most important, these packages provide significant protection against mistakes the developer might make in tree creation. The code is standardized and has been used extensively, making it significantly freer of "bugs" that would exist in custom packages. The support effort for the trees created is minimized, and changes can be made quite readily. A new user can pick up a previously created tree and quickly be able to work with it. Although the developer does not have to be a C-programmer to implement a voice-processing system with a menu-driven AGTK, system architecture and design skills are still required to implement a voice-processing system of any significant complexity.

The basic functions that an AGTK performs are:

1. Define the individual steps of the script.
2. Define the logic flow between the steps.
3. Define the action to take at each step.
4. Define the parameters associated with each step.
5. Provide a display of the call status.

6. Interface with external databases.

7. Capture statistics and generate reports.

The steps are assigned numbers. The ability to give them meaningful names is a useful capability that is available in many of the packages. The logic flow between the steps is defined at each step. Each possible response from the caller is identified, and an appropriate branch to a particular step is specified.

The possible responses from the caller are to input a single digit or digit string, or enter nothing at all. There are 12 possible digits that could be input, representing the numbers 0-9, *, and #, but not all of these are valid for the application. For inputs that are specified as invalid, a branch to a step that would play a prompt saying the input was not valid will occur. If the caller fails to make an entry within the timeout interval, a branch to a step that would tell the caller that an entry is required would be made.

The action taken at each step could be:

- Play a prompt or string of prompts. This could be a menu, information that was requested, instructions, or warnings.
- Transfer call to another line. This would occur when a caller was transferred to an operator, to another station, or connected with a shared resource such as a speech recognizer.
- Hang up the line. This would occur when the caller has indicated that he or she is done, has hung up, has timed out, or has made too many erroneous inputs.
- Capture input from the caller. This could be a menu selection, password, poll response, or other input from the caller.
- Compare captured input with values in a table. The table may be local or resident in a database at a remote host computer.
- Call number. This could be to connect a caller to a remote site, or a basic function in an outbound voice-processing application.
- Detect caller hangup. This is required to free the port and make it available to handle the next call.
- Record speech from caller. Callers are able to leave messages and the user can transcribe these messages.
- Transcribe speech left by a caller. A capability for the user to listen to the messages that were left by callers is required.

For each step, the prompt or prompts to be played when that step is entered need to be defined. They also need to exist, which implies that a prompt creation capability exists. The parameters that are typically user defined for each step include the timeout interval, the number of timeouts that are permitted, the number of invalid inputs that are permitted before a caller is hung up, the number of digits that are required, repeat digits, cancel digit, and string terminator digit.

Data field information can be specified as being either character, number, date, or time. Number information can further be defined as being money or a number. Depending on this specification, the information will be handled appropriately. The ability to perform arithmetic and logical operations on the data field information is provided with most AGTKs, as is the ability to specify business hours for each day, holidays, and holiday seasons. The application program can be structured to treat a call differently depending upon the time and day.

Local database support is provided with many AGTKs. The AGTK functions that are provided to support a local database include the ability to create a database, add and delete records, edit, and read records from it. The interface to a remote database implies that an access to a remote host computer is achieved. This requires functions within the AGTK for performing data communications, logging onto a host database, recognizing screens sent by the host, and sending screens to the host. The AGTK must be able to set up the data communication parameters, capture snapshots of the host screens, and map information from and to the screen fields.

With the AGTK, it is possible to create reports that provide information about the voice-processing system. See Tables 3.1, 3.2, and 3.3 for typical available reports. The system summary report provides information about the total calls received, rotary telephone calls, all lines busy, and total calltime. The reporting period comprises the last 24 hours, or for a specified time interval. It could be set to be printed at a specified time each day, or be printed on demand. Table 3.1 is an example of a system summary report.

The usage summary report provides information about caller activity once in the system, including the number of times that each step was accessed. Table 3.2 is an example of a usage summary report.

The line-activity report provides detailed information on each line. The number of calls on each line, the number of rotary calls, and the number of early hangups are reported for each line. Table 3.3 is an example of a line-activity report.

*Procedural language AGTKs.* These are AGTKs designed for programmer use. The programming skill that the developer requires is relatively modest. The programmer is generally able to deal with the application, is not required to deal with

**Table 3.1**

System Summary Report

| April 1, 1992 at 8:00 a.m. | | |
|---|---|---|
| Total Calls Received | : | 6,578 calls |
| Rotary Calls | : | 1,300 calls |
| Total Call Time | : | 105 minutes |

**Table 3.2**

Usage summary report

| Cumulative daily usage summary at 8:00 a.m. on April 1, 1992 | | |
|---|---|---|
| Message | Step | Number of times accessed |
| | 15 | 1,778 |
| | 16 | 876 |
| | 17 | 563 |
| 500 | 8 | 1,281 |
| 603 | 22 | 236 |
| 645 | 22 | 169 |
| 655 | 22 | 476 |
| 658 | 22 | 400 |
| | | Total: 4,498 accesses |

**Table 3.3**

Line-by-line summary report

| Cumulative daily line-by-line summary at 8:00 a.m. on April 1, 1992 | | | |
|---|---|---|---|
| Line | Total | Rotary | Early Hangup |
| 1 | 987 | 209 | 136 |
| 2 | 943 | 198 | 110 |
| 3 | 915 | 186 | 104 |
| 4 | 854 | 168 | 93 |
| 5 | 810 | 155 | 88 |
| 6 | 796 | 141 | 75 |
| 7 | 663 | 128 | 70 |
| 8 | 610 | 115 | 66 |

system architecture, and can deal with complex functions at a high level. The AGTK provides a high-level programming environment for implementing voice applications. The heart of the AGTK is the language processor.

The high-level language processor is a compiler that can process a high-level procedural language. The programmer is able to specify the application in a plain-

English, fixed format without the need for strong programming skills. The low-level programming, which is the usual cause of most software development problems, is built into the language processor and has been tested extensively. Difficulties in developing an application are limited to errors in the application logic rather than the operation of the voice-processing system. The language processor source commands can be grouped as follows: program flow and control; voice and telephony manipulation; data manipulation; and file operations. Many of the existing menu-driven AGTKs use a procedural language processor as a basis and simply have a front end that converts the menu entries into commands that can be understood by the language processor. With this sort of configuration, the procedural language processor can be used by programmers to develop the script, and the menu-driven package can be used for modifications.

The compatibility between the menu-driven package and the procedural language processor is often an issue. For example, with many of the packages, scripts that are developed with the procedural language processor are not able to be edited with the menu-driven application generator.

*Library of function calls.* A library of function calls that can be readily accessed by a language processor such as C are provided with some of the systems. Many development environments are C-oriented, and the programmers are comfortable programming in C. Learning and supporting another programming environment (no matter how easy it is) is not attractive to them.

## 3.4 STANDALONE VERSUS NETWORK CONTROLLER-BASED VOICE-PROCESSING ARCHITECTURE

The open architecture climate that has come into being during the last five years is just starting to ripple into the voice-processing area. Voice-processing systems have generally been of a closed architecture. It is anticipated that this will change and that voice processing will become a layered software architecture on an open architecture platform.

Two basic types of architectures have been typically deployed in the voice-processing area. These are shown in Figure 3.6. For the standalone voice-processing architecture, a communications processor is frequently not used and the voice processor attaches directly to the host computer. In this case, the database access function is performed by the voice processor.

The standalone voice-processing architecture is attractive to many vendors since they have much stronger control of the market environment. It is also quite easy to create products that are readily differentiated from those of competitive vendors. The engineering-driven aspect of most of the initial voice-processing systems has tended to influence the implementation of proprietary architectures. The downside of these architectures typically lies in the areas of performance and extendibility. From the perspective of the customer, the fact that these systems

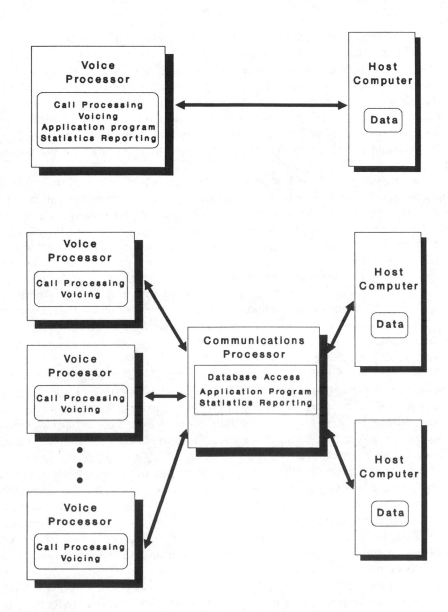

**Figure 3.6** Standalone versus network controller voice-processing architecture.

are an alien development and operating environment is a major shortcoming. As the voice-processing area becomes more of a market-driven environment, the needs of the customer will have a major influence on the decline of standalone voice-processing architectures.

Many of the initial standalone systems that were installed are being replaced by second-generation voice-processing systems. A system's ability to grow in a graceful fashion is a key requirement and one that was lacking in most of the standalone voice-processing systems. These systems had limited capacities and were not designed to function effectively in a centralized, fault-tolerant environment. As the requirement for additional capacity and capability became a reality, many of these systems proved to be a dead end. They had done a job quite well, but customer requirements had grown and outstripped the capabilities of these initial systems.

The vast majority of the first-generation products were specially programmed peripheral devices that were implemented for a set of specific applications. The programming environment was unique to each vendor and required highly specialized technical skills for the implementation of a voice-processing application. Often, the customer was totally dependent upon the vendor of the voice-processing hardware and software. Any modifications to the original system required customer contract with the vendor. The terms were typically not attractive to the customer. Exorbitant prices and extended delivery times were common. These systems had management and control schemes that were suitable for small, standalone systems. An attempt to expand them typically yielded multiple systems that each had separate management and control schemes. A centralized management and control architecture did not exist.

During the last few years, a second generation of IVR product has come into prominent deployment. Most of the IVR product suppliers have developed a networking capability that permits multiple-VRU nodes to be connected and provides a central management and control capability for the entire IVR system. Although this has improved the situation, the integration into the overall telecommunications network management and control is still lacking.

To manage it properly, the voice-processing function needs to be integrated into the customer's total network, telecommunications, and transaction processing environment. Customers want and need a unified network management architecture. This would include a command center with unified and consolidated reporting and statistics. Clearly, the most effective way for this to occur is for the voice-processing function to be an integral element of the on-line transaction processing (OLTP) system.

In these second-generation systems, programming environments are available that permit organizations other than the vendor or highly skilled VARs to implement applications. Voice application generators and tools for creating and editing prompts are available with all of the systems. Although most are very easy to use, very few end users have actually utilized them to develop their own application. No matter how easy they are to use, development of anything other than a very simple voice-response application requires a significant effort. The developer still needs to learn how to work with a new programming environment. This is particularly significant since the user may learn the environment, implement an IVR application, and then never use the development environment again.

The programming environment in many of the organizations in which voice processing is appropriate is a UNIX/C one in a Tandem or Stratus-like environment. The programmers are capable and comfortable with writing code and implementing systems within this environment. They are not particularly attracted to having to become familiar with an entirely new development environment.

The host communications capability of standalone IVR products is the weakest technical area. The products all have many weaknesses and limitations and lack the comprehensive connectivity that is generally readily available in a general-purpose telecommunications network controller.

A network-controller-based voice-processing architecture is an example of an architecture that eliminates most of the problems associated with the first- and second-generation IVR architectures. It also offers some distinct advantages:

- Ease of upgrades, expansion, and maintenance;
- Centralized management, control, and reporting;
- A single programming environment for all call processing applications.

Systems of this sort are architecturally compatible with the OLTP environment of the typical customer. The application program as well as the management and control functions reside on the communications controller, which is typically a fault-tolerant computer.

The programming staff is working in an environment that is familiar and already understood by the programming staff. The first- and second-generation voice-processing systems required that the programmers learn how to implement an application in a new programming environment. Application support that was developed was also often a problem since a limited number of people were familiar with the application development environment.

Standalone voice-processing systems typically had limited expansion and processing capabilities. Growing beyond a relatively small number of ports was often impossible or awkward. Support of multiple or different hosts was often quite limited. The number of different applications that could be run simultaneously was severely limited. The design target was for a finite (and typically quite limited) capacity, and extending beyond this capacity was accomplished with ad hoc schemes that typically yielded less-than-satisfactory results.

Network-controller-based voice-processing architecture systems are typically more powerful, easier to expand, and easier to support and maintain. The programming environment is one that the customer is already using for a variety of other applications and does not require a massive training effort on the customer's part. Comprehensive networking support software exists and is available for integration with the IVR application.

The RS232C interface has been used in many of the network-controller-based voice-processing architectures. The primary reason is that it has been the most commonly available and is a relatively low-cost interface. Vendors that have used this include Perception Technology Corporation, Missing Link Corporation, Votrax, IOCS, and Voicetek Corporation.

The voice-processing engine is a relatively dumb device that performs the base-level voice-processing/telephonics functions. The computer sends commands to it to play a prompt, answer the phone, or get a string of digits, and the voice-processing unit responds appropriately. The disadvantage of these units is that they are relatively expensive, and the relatively slow speed of the RS232-C link is a limiting factor. Sending voice recordings, for example, over this link is impractical. The fact that the applications program is decoupled from the base-level voice-processing/telephonic functions also makes it difficult to accomplish certain functions readily. Although the RS232-C interface is not a terribly attractive approach, it has been the most popular because of the widespread availability of this interface. In the future, it is anticipated that high-speed LANs will be the dominant interface.

The trend in the voice-processing area is the customer's requirement for an open architecture approach. Customers will demand that voice-processing applications be compatible with the same platforms that are used for other business applications. A variety of powerful industry-standard computing platforms exists (SPARC, RS/6000, VAX/VMS), and others, such as the ACE initiative, are being developed. These are the computing environments with which most customers are familiar. These customers want to develop, manage, and support an IVR application in the same fashion that they support other applications in their existing computing environments. Fixed function and proprietary voice-processing boxes do not fit into this trend.

## REFERENCE

1. Roeder, S., "Tools for Voice Application Development," *American Voice Input-Output Society conference*, October 1988.

# Chapter 4

# Voice-Processing Functions

Voice-processing functions provide a specific set of capabilities that use voice as the dominant communications modality. Each function provides a different type of capability. In many cases, more than one function may be performed in a single application. The voice-processing functions are call routing, voice mail, transaction processing, information providing, and outbound call processing.

## 4.1 CALL-ROUTING FUNCTION

Routing of incoming telephone calls is a basic function of most voice-processing capabilities. The routing capability that is provided varies depending on the requirement of the particular application. Types of call routing that are available include automated attendant, *automatic call sequencing* (ACS), *automatic call distribution* (ACD), and *uniform call distribution* (UCD).

### 4.1.1 Automated Attendant

The automated attendant function automates the switchboard capability. All tasks typically performed by a switchboard receptionist can be accomplished with this function. An automated attendant answers the telephone and greets the caller, then tells the caller how to reach a particular group or individual. An option to switch to a voice-mail system is frequently provided, which allows the caller to enter the extension of the called party. If the caller does not know the extension number of the called party, most systems provide a department directory or even a name directory. The caller is then given the option of being transferred to a live operator. If the caller does not make an entry from a DTMF telephone within a

---

brief time period, the call is switched to a live operator. This accommodates callers calling from a rotary telephone. Automated attendant systems came into existence in 1982, when Dytel Corporation introduced its first product. These systems were designed to satisfy a market need that was not being addressed well by existing products. Voice-mail systems and automatic call distribution systems were designed primarily for the convenience of the called party; the convenience of the caller was a secondary consideration. A caller to an early voice-mail system was not able to dial another extension or obtain live assistance but was put into a mode that was referred to as "voice-mail jail." In this mode, the caller essentially does not have any options other than to leave a voice-mail message or to hang up. An automated attendant, however, focuses on providing convenience to the caller, who is offered a complete set of options at all times. Most voice-mail products now include an automated attendant capability as either an option or as part of the basic voice-mail product.

### 4.1.2 Automatic Call Sequencer

An ACS is a system that answers the telephone, plays a greeting to the caller, and places the caller on hold. It provides information to the *telephone service representative* (TSR) about which calls have been held the longest. An ACS does not perform any call switching; it is one of the most rudimentary mechanisms for distribution of a large number of calls to TSRs.

### 4.1.3 Uniform Call Distributor

A UCD distributes large numbers of calls in a predetermined fashion among a group of TSRs. The distribution algorithm is fixed and independent of the real-time traffic load or which TSRs have been busiest or idle the longest. Again, the reports available with a UCD tend to be rather rudimentary, consisting of simple peg counts.

### 4.1.4 Automatic Call Distributor

ACDs distribute large numbers of calls in a logical fashion. The basic functions of an ACD are to answer calls automatically as they arrive; place the call in a queue if TSRs are not available; switch the calls based on a predetermined algorithm to a specific TSR group or other functional response unit; and gather and make available for presentation information that characterizes the performing status of the system. The routing algorithm typically is designed to route the call based on conditional routing that is tied to real-time traffic and TSR availability; network-directed routing related to the number that was called or the number of the calling party; caller-directed routing in which a caller identifies the service required over an IVR; or data-directed call routing in which the caller enters identification information that is looked up in a database and used to route the caller to the most appropriate place.

## 4.2 VOICE-MAIL FUNCTION

The voice-mail function allows a caller to record a voice message and leave it for an individual or group of individuals to retrieve. The earliest voice-mail systems were designed to perform very specialized messaging functions. The Sudbury Systems, Inc. RTAS system was designed specifically to provide a centralized facility for a radiologist to dictate the results of an X-ray, and for a transcriptionist to transcribe this message into a written report. This system was first demonstrated in 1974.

Many features exist in a voice-mail system. The subscriber can send voice-mail messages to distribution lists, be notified of a new message receipt by either a telephone call or a page, and reply to a received message. Subscribers are able to have messages delivered at specific times, and can find out if the recipient has picked up a particular message. Voice-mail systems have found their largest and most effective use in operations that are highly customer oriented, such as sales or field service organizations, and organizations that have a large proportion of incoming calls. The subscribers are often mobile and difficult to reach directly with a telephone call; the timing of the communication is often critical. Prompt recipient notification of a new message is an important capability of most voice-mail systems. Automatic paging and direct calling of the recipient of the voice message are two of the more common ways that are used. Messaging-waiting indicators are used effectively for recipients who are less mobile and frequently in a home office. Facsimile messaging is another capability being integrated with voice mail.

## 4.3 INTERACTIVE VOICE RESPONSE FUNCTION

The IVR function provides real-time voice access to dynamic databases and permits the caller to order something, leave information, or obtain specific account information. The information that is delivered to or obtained from the caller is private and unique to that caller. IVR systems are either transaction processing systems or inquiry systems. Transaction processing systems are IVR systems that permit the caller to order something or leave information. Inquiry systems are IVR systems that permit a caller to access specific account information that is private. An example of an inquiry application is the delivery of a caller's current bank account balance. A system of this sort automates the function of a clerk that answers the telephone, uses a computer display terminal to access the caller's information, and speaks the information to the caller. However, inquiry or transaction processing systems do not necessarily function only over the telephone system. Speech-recognition systems used for the entry of quality assurance information are examples of transaction processing systems that do not use the telephone network for access. Telephone-based IVR systems that do not require DTMF input also exist. The semiautomatic telephone company information service (411 or NPA-555-1212) is an example of a transaction processing system that does not require the caller to enter DTMF digits. Security systems that are used to control entry and exit for a facility and facsimile response are two other examples of IVR. In facsimile response, the function is virtually identical to a pure voice-response one. The primary difference is that the information requested is sent to a caller-specified facsimile machine. These applications are ones in which the information being provided is too difficult to provide in voice form. For example, a map is information most appropriately provided over facsimile.

## 4.4 INFORMATION PROVIDER FUNCTION

The information provider function provides or obtains public information in voice form. Horoscopes, weather reports, ATM locators, and soap opera updates are examples of public information provided to callers. Examples of callers providing public information are surveys in which they are asked to give their opinion on a topic. Information provider systems are frequently noninteractive if the voice message is played to the caller, but no input of any sort is expected from the caller. Telephone company intercepts ("that number has been changed. The new number is . . .") are examples of noninteractive information-provider systems. The information provided is either sponsored by someone or the caller pays for the information directly (either through a subscription to a service, or by paying for a particular call).

## 4.5 OUTBOUND VOICE-PROCESSING FUNCTION

The outbound call processing function performs automatic and semiautomatic outdialing of calls and, in some cases, obtains responses from the called person. *Automatic dialer recorded message player* (ADRMP) systems dial numbers, detect that the telephone has been answered, play a message to the caller, and obtain a response. These systems are used to provide notification, check on the availability of the person being called, or to solicit information from the called party. Semiautomatic systems (known as predictive or progressive dialers) perform the dialing and answer detection and then signal to an operator that a person has answered the telephone. These systems also provide information about the individual being called to the operator through a video display terminal. The primary advantage of a predictive dialer is that it makes the operator much more productive. Outbound call processing systems are used for operations such as collections, polling, telemarketing, and market research.

## 4.6 COMPUTER-TELEPHONE INTEGRATION FUNCTION

*Computer-telephone integration* (C-TI) is a linkage of a computer application environment such that the computer is playing a significant role in the call processing. Data from a computer database is used to determine call routing and support call processing. The computer obtains data about the call such as the number called, the calling party's telephone number, the trunk over which it came, or the identification of the caller (often obtained by an IVR function in which the caller enters an account number).

## 4.7 MULTIPLE FUNCTIONS

Multiple function systems are quite common. Automated attendant and voice-mail functions frequently go together. Many of the IVR systems use both an automated attendant and a voice-mail function. Although the primary services provided by the IVR function deal with private information, public information such as mortgage interest rates or the nearest ATM location is also provided. Outbound systems frequently use voice mail to capture caller response and use inbound call processing to transfer calls to the agents that are handling the outbound calls. Multiple media systems also exist. Hand-held terminals are used with a voice-processing system for the entry of alphanumeric information that is usually difficult to enter with only the DTMF keyboard. Facsimile is being integrated with voice mail and transaction processing. A subscriber in a voice-mail system can receive a facsimile in a manner similar to the way in which a voice-mail message is received. For many IVR applications, facsimile provides a hard-copy delivery mechanism for information. The caller enters his or her facsimile number, and the information requested is sent to them. Outbound call processing and IVR complement each other in many applications. Where call-back percentages are significant, users need an IVR function for handling inbound calls. A call center environment will frequently include IVR, ACD, voice mail, C-TI, outbound call processing, automated attendant, and fax response.

# Chapter 5
# Types of Voice-Processing Applications

There are many types of voice-processing applications. They are driven by the capability of providing an existing service more efficiently or providing a brand-new type of service. In many cases, voice processing is simply the automation of an existing service being performed manually. With voice processing, a service can be expanded and provided at a fraction of the cost of manual operation, while being more reliable and reproducible. The cost of training and retraining personnel is significantly reduced. A voice-processing system will perform 24 hours a day, even on holidays. In many cases, voice processing provides an opportunity to provide a new service or to accomplish things that could not have been performed without it.

The application areas of voice processing can be categorized as follows:

- Obtaining public information over the telephone;
- Obtaining private information over the telephone;
- Calling someone to provide or obtain information;
- Providing information over the telephone;
- Automatic call routing, automatic messaging;
- Hands-busy or eyes-busy environments.

The ubiquity of the telephone is the primary reason that obtaining information over the telephone is so attractive. Compared to other information delivery mechanisms, the telephone is a highly portable and available device. All a caller needs is a telephone number to call (and, in some cases, a password).

## 5.1 OBTAINING PUBLIC INFORMATION OVER THE TELEPHONE

Obtaining public information over the telephone has become a major application of voice processing. The information provided includes sports scores, store locations, hours of business, flight information, coming events, soap opera updates, and financial information. In some cases, callers pay for obtaining the information directly, by using a 900 or 976 number. In other cases, the caller is not charged for the information and a sponsor pays for providing it.

## 5.2 OBTAINING PRIVATE INFORMATION OVER THE TELEPHONE

Obtaining private information over the telephone has received widespread acceptance in the financial community. Other areas in which this application has been used extensively are universities and the transportation industry. In many cases, the primary motivation for automating this function has been an economic one. When an organization is getting many inquiries each day for certain types of information, automating the function becomes practical. The cost of employing a couple of clerical people to handle routine calls is more expensive than the purchase and support of an automated voice response system. Other reasons for providing an automatic voice-response system are related to marketing. An automated system will generally provide superior service to callers and is available 24 hours a day, 365 days a year. In addition, it does not take lunch breaks, can be programmed to be always courteous to callers, makes considerably fewer errors than a human clerk, and does not need training every few months. Systems used to provide private information are known as *interactive voice response* (IVR) systems.

## 5.3 CALLING SOMEONE TO PROVIDE OR OBTAIN INFORMATION

Automatically calling someone to provide or obtain information has become a popular application. For example, schools automatically call a student's home when the student is absent. Telemarketing, polling, market research, and collections are the major application areas that are using automatic calling techniques. Manually calling a large number of people is a frustrating, time-consuming, and inefficient task. A typical model would be that 50% of the calls are ring/no-answer, 10% are busy, 10% are telephone company intercept, and 10% are answered by an answering machine. This leaves 20% of the calls in which the caller is connected to a live person. Of these, half are answered by the wrong person, which means it takes ten calls to reach just one person. Predictive dialers free the agent from the time-consuming frustration of dialing and listening for the person being called. The primary benefit of a predictive dialer is that the agent is able to make many more customer contacts.

## 5.4 PROVIDING INFORMATION OVER THE TELEPHONE

The caller providing information over the telephone is an application in which the information provided is automatically captured and used. A caller may leave his or her name and address or telephone number by recording a voice message, or may vote on a particular topic. The caller may also identify where he or she is by entering the *area code* (NPA) and *local exchange* (NXX) of the calling telephone. With an ANI capability, the voice-processing system is able to obtain the telephone number of the calling telephone automatically.

## 5.5 AUTOMATIC CALL ROUTING

Automatic call routing is an automation of the function that is typically performed by a switchboard operator. For a small group of people who do not receive a large volume of calls, a live operator is effective. Because this live operator is often also the receptionist, the incremental cost of handling the telephone calls is not significant. However, as the number of people and calls handled by a live operator increases, the need to automate this function becomes apparent. Callers may receive busy signals or are put on hold for minutes at a time. Adding additional telephone ports and live operators to handle them is an expensive and ineffective solution. Telephone traffic patterns in a business environment are heavily skewed toward certain times of the day; just before and after lunch, the call traffic can increase by 50 to 100%. Adding operators only to handle this peak traffic is usually quite difficult, while adding telephone lines and ports to a voice-processing system is both relatively inexpensive and easy. Callers may be routed to a particular person, department, or group of TSRs. The basis for routing them may be a touch-tone input, the number that they called, their telephone number, the time of day, the availability of TSRs, or other parameters that are appropriate for a particular application.

## 5.6 AUTOMATIC MESSAGING

One of the basic limitations of telephone communications was that it required simultaneous, real-time participation by both the calling and the called parties. The familiar game of "telephone tag," in which the two parties keep calling and missing each other, often results—an inefficient way to communicate. A study conducted by AT&T in 1978 yielded the following:

- 75% of all business calls are not completed on the first attempt;
- 50% of all calls are for the one-way transfer of information;
- 67% of all calls are considered to be less important than the work they interrupt;
- 50% of all calls are longer than necessary due to unrelated discussions.

With voice mail, the need for simultaneous, real-time communication is eliminated. A caller is able to call someone and leave a message. The message is recorded and retained without the need of a secretary or receptionist to write it down and deliver it. The recipient subsequently will receive the message and respond appropriately. The basic benefit of voice mail is that it speeds up communication. Other advantages of this form of communication are

- *Confidentiality*. The voice messages are recorded privately, and the recipient needs a password to obtain them;
- *Accessiblity*. All an individual needs to obtain voice-mail messages is a telephone;
- *Low cost*. Compared to other message forms that involve written communication, it is significantly lower in cost. An estimate of the cost of a typewritten letter ranges from $7 to $16. A voice-mail message costs from $1 to $2 per message;
- *More effective communication*. The voice-mail message is in the caller's own voice, which permits him or her to express emotions such as concern, anger, and urgency much more effectively than is possible with a written message.

Obtaining a voice-mail capability can be accomplished by either purchasing, installing, and managing a system or by using a voice-mail service bureau or telephone answering service.

## 5.7 HANDS- OR EYES-BUSY ENVIRONMENTS

Hands-busy or eyes-busy environments are those in which individuals perform a job that requires that their hands or eyes (or both) be used to perform the task, and an essential aspect of the job is capturing information. Many of these environments involve manufacturing quality assurance situations [1]. For example, a person is inspecting an item, which occupies the hands and eyes, but the test results need to be recorded. The normal operation would be for the inspector to interrupt the process to record the results. This interruption significantly slows the inspection process. By using speech recognition, the inspector can input the test results with a minimum interruption of the inspection process.

Voice processing has also been used to assist individuals who are physically impaired. Blind people can use computers that talk to them. Text-to-speech converters can be used to convert computer information from a conventional terminal directly into voice form, one that a blind person can use. Individuals who are unable to speak have used text-to-speech converters to verbalize. Individuals who are unable to move their hands or legs can use speech recognition to activate equipment. These are but a few examples of the way in which voice processing can be used.

### REFERENCE

1. Pfarrer, L. A., "Using Voice Recognition for Data Collection in a Factory Environment," *Speech Tech 90 conference*, 1990, pp. 153–155.

# Chapter 6
## Specific Voice-Processing Applications

Applications in which voice processing has been most successful have one characteristic in common—the function to be automated is already being performed manually, so voice processing only accomplished the automation.

Other characteristics of a successful application are

1. Cost reduction with rapid, measurable payback;
2. Improved service without hiring additional personnel;
3. A strong competitive advantage;
4. Information for which customers are willing to pay.

If an application has one or more of the above characteristics, it has a good chance of being successfully automated. The application of voice processing can be classified as either a *horizontal type* or a *vertical type*.

### 6.1 HORIZONTAL VOICE-PROCESSING APPLICATIONS

Horizontal applications are common to many industries or environments. Customer service, sales, marketing, accounting, manufacturing, and purchasing, are functions found in most operations. For example, customer service is an area where voice processing is beneficial, and it is applied in a similar fashion to many such departments.

Personnel departments use voice processing to provide information to employees on benefits such as vacation-time earned, medical coverage available, company news, company policy, organization events, and training available. In addition, information about job postings can be provided readily with voice processing. If an employee enters a *personal identification number* (PIN), he or she

---

may obtain individual account information on 401K plans, stock-option ownership, and retirement benefits earned to date.

Salespeople must frequently and quickly communicate with a remote marketing organization, and quick contact is often critical to the success of a sale. Marketing people are often in meetings or on the phone and the salesperson is with customers, making them both inaccessible. Without voice mail, this is a classic example of "telephone tag." With voice mail, however, communication is greatly enhanced. A sales manager can communicate quickly with an entire sales force by using the group messaging feature of a voice-mail system. Such a system can also be used to provide new product information and to send pricing and delivery changes to a sales force quickly.

Marketing groups use predictive dialing to perform market research on large projects. This system allows agents to call and obtain opinions from large numbers of people efficiently. The interviewer is able to handle 50 to 60% more calls and can also concentrate on obtaining customer input. Marketing departments use audioconferencing for customer meetings, press conferences, and communication with remotely located groups within a corporation.

Sales departments use voice processing for automated order entry and for checking on the status of existing orders. Trying to determine the status of a particular order is often a frustrating and expensive process. A salesperson may try to reach an order administrator, sometimes taking days to make the connection. When they do connect, the order administrator looks up the order in the computer system and reads the information to the salesperson. With voice processing, the salesperson can call directly into the computer and obtain the desired information. Voice mail is also used effectively for communication between a salesperson and customers. Product price and availability updates are readily communicated to the sales organization with voice processing.

Voice processing is also becoming popular in telemarketing. Predictive dialing systems for outbound telemarketing and collections are used to increase the caller productivity by performing the dialing and call progress detection. The caller is only required to be on the phone after a call has been placed and a live person has been reached.

Customer service operations use voice processing for providing work assignments and customer problem reports and dispatching service people to a customer site. Field engineering changes that are critical to the proper operation of a product can be communicated quickly to an entire field service organization with a broadcast message. Customers can report problems after hours and receive immediate response by calling a mailbox programmed to page an on-call service person. The field service person receives the page, calls the voice mail box, and listens to the message.

Purchasing departments use voice processing to communicate with suppliers. Because a buyer's job involves mostly one-way communication with vendors, voice mail tends to greatly improve the order process.

Engineering departments use voice processing for automatic entry of project charges. This is particularly important to businesses in which engineering time is charged back to a customer, such as on government and consulting engineering contracts. Financial departments use voice processing to solicit proxies from stockholders. Each stockholder is called and urged to return his or her proxy vote. Collections is another area in which financial departments have used voice processing quite extensively.

## 6.2 VERTICAL INDUSTRY APPLICATIONS

Voice processing has been applied to almost every industry. The areas that have found the largest amount of applications are financial, transportation, utilities, telephone, education, publishing, retail, wholesale, medical, insurance, and manufacturing. Table 6.1 and Figure 6.1 identify the percentage of money invested in voice-processing equipment and services by each kind of industry during 1991.

**Table 6.1**
Industry Applications of Voice Processing–1991

| Industry Area | Revenue | Percent |
|---|---|---|
| Finance | $ 496.3M | 14.4% |
| Transportation | $ 248.0M | 7.2% |
| Utilities | $ 168.8M | 4.9% |
| Telco | $ 458.2M | 13.3% |
| Education | $ 199.8M | 5.8% |
| Publishing | $ 354.8M | 10.3% |
| Retail | $ 179.1M | 5.2% |
| Wholesale | $ 130.9M | 3.8% |
| Medical | $ 175.7M | 5.1% |
| Insurance | $ 248.0M | 7.2% |
| Manufacturing | $ 396.2M | 11.5% |
| Government | $ 389.3M | 11.3% |
| Total | $3,445.1M | |

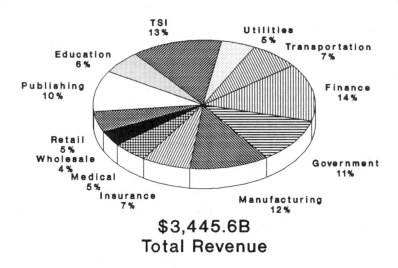

**$3,445.6B**
**Total Revenue**

**Figure 6.1** Voice-processing applications by market area.

Table 6.2 and Figure 6.2 provide a projection of the investment for each of the market areas through 1996.

### 6.2.1 Finance

Providing banking services over the telephone is one of the major applications of financial voice-processing products. This industry is both information intensive and people intensive, so it is constantly seeking ways to reduce costs, improve service, and obtain competitive advantages. See Table 6.3 for the financial applications that have proven to be the most attractive for voice processing [1, 2].

In most instances, the banks are already providing many of these services manually. A voice-response system merely automates a previously existing manual operation. In addition to the economic benefits, providing improved service is a significant factor in obtaining a marketing advantage in a highly competitive industry. More lines can be made available, and the service is available 24 hours a day. An ATM locator is a service that allows the caller to enter the NPA and NXX the telephone from which he or she is calling. The system then gives the address of the nearest ATM. For example, an ATM network was receiving over 20,000 calls per month and paying a service bureau $1.50 per call for inconsistent quality. The investment the company made in automating this function paid for itself in less than six months, and the company was able to increase the call volume in a graceful fashion. Stock-trading systems provide the caller with price and yield information on listed stocks. Financial reports on specific stocks, market news, regulatory information, interest and currency exchange, and credit ratings are

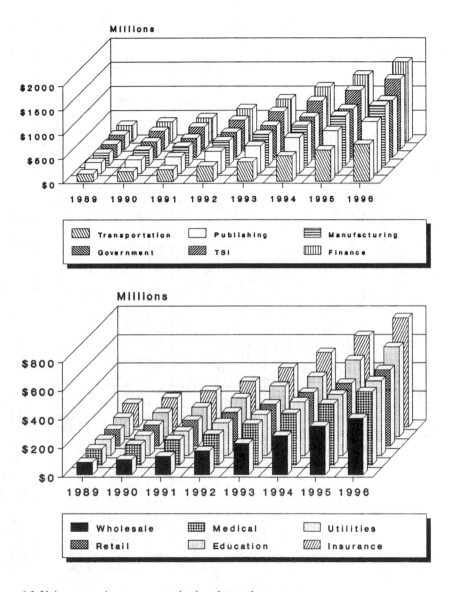

**Figure 6.2** Voice-processing revenue projections by market area.

examples of other types of information provided to callers. Validation of credit cards is readily accomplished with a voice-processing system. The caller enters the credit card number, the expiration date, and the purchase amount and the system responds that the cardholder has sufficient credit to cover the purchase. Automated collections on overdue mortgage payments and delinquent credit card accounts is accomplished by voice-processing systems that automatically call individuals from

Table 6.2
Industry Segment by Voice Processing Revenue Profile

| Industry Segment | | 1990 | 1991 | 1992 | 1993 | 1994 | 1995 | 1996 |
|---|---|---|---|---|---|---|---|---|
| Finance | $Ms | 397.9 | 482.3 | 665.9 | 864.3 | 1,110.8 | 1,357.5 | 1,630.1 |
| | % | 14.1 | 14.0 | 14.8 | 15.0 | 15.1 | 15.2 | 15.3 |
| Transportation | $Ms | 206.0 | 248.0 | 319.4 | 403.4 | 529.7 | 652.0 | 767.1 |
| | % | 7.3 | 7.2 | 7.1 | 7.0 | 7.2 | 7.3 | 7.2 |
| Utilities | $Ms | 141.1 | 172.3 | 229.4 | 288.1 | 375.2 | 428.7 | 522.1 |
| | % | 5.0 | 5.0 | 5.1 | 5.0 | 5.1 | 4.8 | 4.9 |
| Telco | $Ms | 372.5 | 458.2 | 598.4 | 772.1 | 993.1 | 1,214.6 | 1,438.4 |
| | % | 13.2 | 13.3 | 13.3 | 13.4 | 13.5 | 13.6 | 13.5 |
| Education | $Ms | 169.3 | 206.7 | 269.9 | 351.5 | 419.3 | 535.9 | 628.6 |
| | % | 6.0 | 6.0 | 6.0 | 6.1 | 5.7 | 6.0 | 5.9 |
| Publishing | $Ms | 287.8 | 344.5 | 454.4 | 570.5 | 743.0 | 884.2 | 1,065.5 |
| | % | 10.2 | 10.0 | 10.1 | 9.9 | 10.1 | 9.9 | 10.0 |

| | | | | | | | | |
|---|---|---|---|---|---|---|---|---|
| Retail | $Ms | 149.6 | 182.6 | 238.4 | 293.9 | 375.2 | 437.6 | 532.7 |
| | % | 5.3 | 5.3 | 5.3 | 5.1 | 5.1 | 4.9 | 5.0 |
| Wholesale | $Ms | 104.4 | 127.5 | 166.5 | 219.0 | 272.2 | 339.4 | 394.2 |
| | % | 3.7 | 3.7 | 3.7 | 3.8 | 3.7 | 3.8 | 3.7 |
| Medical | $Ms | 143.9 | 179.1 | 216.0 | 288.1 | 360.5 | 428.7 | 511.4 |
| | % | 5.1 | 5.2 | 4.8 | 5.0 | 4.9 | 4.8 | 4.8 |
| Insurance | $Ms | 206.0 | 254.9 | 319.4 | 414.9 | 522.3 | 643.0 | 767.1 |
| | % | 7.3 | 7.4 | 7.1 | 7.2 | 7.1 | 7.2 | 7.2 |
| Manufacturing | $Ms | 321.7 | 396.2 | 508.4 | 639.6 | 823.9 | 1,018.2 | 1,225.3 |
| | % | 11.4 | 11.5 | 11.3 | 11.1 | 11.2 | 11.4 | 11.5 |
| Government | $Ms | 321.7 | 392.7 | 512.9 | 656.9 | 831.3 | 991.4 | 1,172.0 |
| | % | 11.4 | 11.4 | 11.4 | 11.4 | 11.3 | 11.1 | 11.0 |
| Total | $Ms | 2,821.9 | 3,445.1 | 4,499.0 | 5,762.3 | 7,356.5 | 8,931.2 | 10,654.5 |
| | % | 100.0 | 100.0 | 100.0 | 100.0 | 100.0 | 100.0 | 100.0 |

**Table 6.3**
Financial Voice Processing Applications

| | |
|---|---|
| Account balance | Next payment due |
| Bill payment | Security access to building |
| Credit checking | Rate line |
| Credit card supplies ordering | 1099 interest paid |
| Funds Transfer | Prices and yields |
| Cleared check status | Cash management/lockbox |
| Stop payment | ATM lost-card notification |
| Cash and currency orders | Statement request |
| Delinquent account reminder | Line of credit available |
| Loan application status | Credit card inquiry |
| Portfolio value | |

a computer-generated list, monitor the call progress, and connect the agent to the called party when that party is reached. The agent is provided with information that describes the account status of the called party; the agent can then work with the customer to resolve the delinquency problem. The Federal Reserve Bank receives many inquiries each day on bonds. The information provided includes auction results, securities currently available for purchase, and procedures for purchasing treasury securities. Financial trades are executed by traders using speech recognition. Traders are able to look at the screen and speak transactions, so they do not need keyboard dexterity.

### 6.2.2 Transportation and Travel

This area includes trucking, airlines, railroads, and hotels—all highly competitive industries and always looking for ways to provide better service and to improve employee performance. The voice-processing applications that have proven to be the most successful in each area are shown in Table 6.4.

#### 6.2.2.1 Trucking

Identifying the location and estimating the arrival time of a truck shipment is important in every trucking business. Truckers call into a dispatcher to provide this information and to obtain new assignments. With a manual system, they are frequently placed on hold. With a voice messaging capability, truckers are able to pick up and leave messages without wasting time attempting to reach the dispatcher. The driver can enter the NPA and NXX that identifies his or her location. Further, ANI is an attractive option for automatically locating the trucker and reduces the possibility of the driver's entering an incorrect NPA or NXX.

**Table 6.4**

Transportation/Travel Voice Processing Applications

| Trucking | Tracking/dispatching drivers<br>Rate quotes<br>Driver messaging<br>Shipment tracing | DOT permit status inquiry<br>Fuel authorization inquiry<br>driver ETA reporting |
| --- | --- | --- |
| Airlines | Flight information<br>Crew scheduling | Weather information for pilots<br>Rental car return |
| Overnight shippers | Shipment trace | Account inquiry |
| Hotels | Wakeup service<br>Phone charges (HOBIC) | Guest messaging |
| Railroads | Railcar tracking<br>Crew scheduling | Train schedules |

### 6.2.2.2 Airlines

The FAA provides a voice-response service in which private pilots can identify their starting location and destination and obtain detailed flight conditions. Frequent-flier hotlines provide caller-earned award levels and answer frequently asked questions. Providing flight status information is a popular application of voice processing; 24-hour access to all flight arrival and departure times, gate numbers, and the current status of a particular flight are available by telephone. Most airlines in the United States offer voice-response services that provide fare, flight number, and estimated departure and arrival times. Facsimile-response services are available that provide weather information to pilots. A pilot can call a service and obtain a facsimile of a National Weather Service aviation weather briefing and chart in a few minutes.

### 6.2.2.3 Railroads

Voice processing is used effectively to provide train schedules to callers. The caller indicates the point of departure and the destination, and is provided with the arrival and departure times of trains between those points. Crews are automatically scheduled by the employee calling a number and being told what his or her assignment is and acknowledging it. Before automatic service, employees would call and frequently receive a busy signal or be placed on hold for long periods of time.

An ANI capability would identify the worker and eliminate the need for him or her to enter an identification number.

### 6.2.2.4 Hotels and Time-Share Guest Messaging

Automated telemarketing is used by time-share companies to contact members and arrange the exchange of vacation weeks. Time-share members are able to select alternative vacation sites and place their vacation time and site into a spacebank pool. For telemarketing applications, voice-processing systems are used extensively to automatically dial the number, monitor call progress, and connect the agent when the called party is actually on the line. Voice messaging is available in many hotels as a courtesy to guests [3].

### 6.2.3 Education

This area includes primary and secondary public schools as well as universities. The most attractive applications have been ones that (1) provide a unique improvement in the learning process, (2) attract students, or (3) enforce discipline. The applications that are often implemented include:

*The university student registration application* addresses the problem of a yearly peak-activity load. Increasing staff for short periods of time is both costly and difficult. Inadequate staff usually exists, which results in long student lines, errors, and frustrated students and educators. With a student registration system, each student is able to select courses over the telephone.

*Computer-aided instruction* has used voice processing to enhance teaching. Combined aural and visual techniques have proven effective. For individuals with dyslexia, for example, audio communication is much more successful than the conventional visual techniques.

*University voice information services* provide cafeteria menus, grade reports, and the status of an admissions or financial aid application. Callers select the topic and are guided by a series of instructional prompts.

*Voice processing* has been used extensively in the public schools to provide automatic notification of a student absence to parents. Each day, the parents of each absent student are called automatically and informed that their child was not in school.

Students for whom English is a second language often have difficulty in learning the proper pronunciation of words. They may know the meaning of a word when it is pronounced, but would not recognize it in print. Text-to-speech technology has been effectively used to assist in teaching proper word pronunciation. Using this system, a student hears a sentence while he or she is reading it.

One of the most successful uses of voice processing has been the educational toys provided by Texas Instruments. *Speak and Spell* and *Speak and Math* were released in the the early 1980s and are still very popular.

The voice-processing applications in the education area are shown in Table 6.5.

### Table 6.5
Education Voice Processing Applications

| | |
|---|---|
| University student registration | School closing |
| Dormitory menus | Absence notification |
| Financial aide status | Correspondence testing |
| Admissions status | Language learning |
| Interactive video/audio training | Voicemail |

### 6.2.4 Government

This area includes both State and Federal governments. Applications are usually oriented toward providing better service to the public and encouraging utilization of these services. Some government applications in which voice processing has been used are:

*Warning.* Many parts of the country are prone to natural disasters such as floods or hurricanes. Systems that call all of the residents to warn of an impending flood and provide evacuation instructions can rapidly call large numbers of affected people.

*Public information.* Local government offices receive many calls related to information about the town. Over 75% of these calls are repetitive and easy to answer. The information requested is often hours of operation of the public dump or library, bus schedules, or the time and place of the town meeting. Town offices usually do not have an abundance of people available to answer these questions. A person calling for some simple information may get a busy signal for long periods of time, or callers may not be able to reach someone except during specific hours. A voice information system can readily be implemented to provide basic information for a local government.

*Security.* Speaker verification has been successfully used to provide high security. Initially, the individual makes a "voiceprint" by speaking a phrase. Later, he or she repeats the phrase, and the new phrase is compared with the voiceprint. Systems of this sort often provide direct control gof locks, which open when the voiceprints match.

*Other government applications.* The Tele-Tax service provided by the Internal Revenue Service offers information on a wide variety of topics. A person calls a toll-free number and then enters a three-digit code that corresponds to a particular topic. The topics and their numbers are published in many of the telephone books. This information is also available in Spanish. In early 1992, the Internal Revenue

Service introduced a capability that permitted taxpayers to file 1040EZ returns entirely over the telephone.

The National Highway Traffic Safety Administration provides a toll-free hotline for obtaining recall information about a specific vehicle. The caller is prompted to enter the information that describes the automobile and his or her name and address.

The U.S. Consumer Product Safety Commission provides a toll-free hotline for obtaining safety information about consumer products. A directory of topics is provided from which a caller may select an item. The caller is also able to report a safety problem he or she has discovered. The state lotteries are starting to permit bet placement by calling a 900 number. A $1 bet would cost the better $1.95, where $0.95 would be the service premium.

Electronic monitoring of incarcerated individuals who are in home confinement is being used by corrections departments. A monitoring system randomly calls an individual and obtains a response. One approach is to have each prisoner wear a bracelet that generates a unique code to identify him or her. Another approach uses voice recognition, in which the called party says specific words that are compared to a template of his or her voice patterns.

Obtaining information from state motor vehicle agencies is a frustrating process. They are usually understaffed, which creates busy signals and long waits. Automated systems are being used to dispense routine information about license renewals, license plate and title processing, vehicle registration, directions to the nearest motor vehicle facilities, and the hours of operation.

Federal job information is provided by the Federal Office of Personnel Management to all callers through a voice-response system. How to apply for federal jobs, available federal jobs, how federal jobs are advertised, temporary employment opportunities, walk-in testing requirements, and overseas employment are among the topics available.

The United States Department of Labor's Bureau of Labor Statistics provides callers with the consumer price index, producer price index, employment and unemployment data, wages and earnings figures, and many other kinds of economic data. Political parties use voice processing for fund-raising and get-out-the-vote campaigns.

Speech recognition has also been used in military command-control environments, such as airplane cockpits [4]. Government applications of voice processing are shown in Table 6.6.

### 6.2.5 Medical

This area includes hospitals and other medical service providers. The primary motivation is to provide improved service and to contain costs.

Voice-processing systems permit diabetic patients to monitor their blood glucose and adjust the insulin dosage accordingly. The patient calls in and enters

**Table 6.6**
Government Voice Processing Applications

| | |
|---|---|
| Juror ascertain duty | Courthouse closing |
| Tax information | Check on disabled/elderly |
| Road closing information | Agency service available |
| Museum opening announcement | House arrest monitoring |
| Voice access to buildings | Unemployment claims processing |
| Lottery results | Voicemail |
| Building inspection scheduling | Auto attendant |
| Evacuation instructions | |

data regarding glucose, insulin, diet, activity, and illness. The system then calculates the appropriate insulin dosage and provides it to the patient [5].

Another application provides centralized dictation of radiology reporting and transcription. The radiologist dictates into a voice-processing system rather than into a cassette recorder. The transcriptionist transcribes the verbal radiology report by calling into the system. A major advantage of a system of this sort is that the verbal radiology reports are available to everyone as soon as the radiologist completes the dictation. Systems can be programmed to call individuals (such as the referring physician) as soon as the report has been dictated. The turnaround time for obtaining transcribed reports is reduced, and the time needed to fill and deliver a cassette to a transcriptionist is eliminated [6].

Speech recognition has been used to automate the radiology dictation and transcription process one step further. The radiologist enters the radiology report into the system by speaking key words. Each word corresponds to a "standardized" normal or abnormal diagnosis, which is stored in the system in text form. When the radiologist has completed dictation of the report, a printed report is immediately available. As a further extension, the text message is converted into speech form with a text-to-speech converter. This makes the final report accessible to callers in voice form and retains one of the basic advantages of the centralized dictation system.

Information services are available for patients, employees, doctors, and other callers in voice form. Patients are provided immediate access to hospital information such as services, food menus, doctors' schedules, and billing status. Employment information is available to hospital employees. People in the community can access a voice-response system to obtain general health information and information relating to hospital services, visiting hours, and patient room and telephone numbers.

Communication in a hospital environment is more critical than in other environments because of the work done there. Systems that track the whereabouts of hospital personnel on an hour-by-hour basis and provide the means to contact those individuals immediately are in place in many hospitals. They use voice mail and paging as an integral part of the communication system.

When a health emergency arises, the Food and Drug Administration must get messages to health personnel across the United States immediately. The FDA uses an outbound system that calls approximately 200 health officials per hour.

Healthcare service providers receive an enormous number of routine inquiries concerning the services they provide. Automated services now dispense information on catastrophic illness legislation, services that are covered, and participating physicians. Callers may also order claim forms and benefit handbooks by leaving their subscriber number.

Many communities usse voice processing to monitor the well-being of their senior citizens. These systems call each senior citizen each day. If the call is not answered after a few attempts, the police are alerted to check on the called party. To avoid false alarms, senior citizens call the police station when they plan to be away from home for an extended period of time.

Pharmaceutical companies conduct clinical field studies of their new products by working with doctors and clinics that are using the new product. Each participating doctor or clinic is required to track enrolled patients and to report information concerning the trial back to the pharmaceutical company. Voice response is a convenient and efficient means of reporting field test results. Doctors and dentists are using outbound systems to call patients and remind them that they have an appointment. Table 6.7 summarizes the voice-processing applications in the medical services industry.

**Table 6.7**
Medical Voice Processing Applications

| | |
|---|---|
| Self medication advice | Home monitoring of patients |
| Hospital staff assignments | Voicemail |
| Radiology results reporting | Auto attendant |
| Appointment confirmation | Radiology transcription |
| Security access to buildings | Doctor locator |
| Instrument control | Operating room reporting |
| Psychological testing | Enabling aids for the physically impaired |

## 6.2.6 Utilities

This area includes the electric power, gas, and water companies. The successful use of voice processing has improved operating efficiency and created an incremental revenue source, though they are often enforced by regulatory requirements.

Customers are able to report service outages and access information on billing and account status. Bad weather and natural disasters are not always predictable, but a voice-processing system helps alleviate staffing problems for peak periods. Vendors can inquire about invoice status by automation of the accounts payable area.

Automated collections on overdue bills for utility service use voice-processing systems that automatically call individuals from a computer-generated list, monitor the call progress, and connect the caller when the called party is actually on the line. The caller is provided with information that describes the account status of the called party. Government and State regulations require proof of notification and notification attempts, and automation of the collections process is an effective way to reduce costs and comply with these regulations.

Electric companies can use voice processing to automatically call their largest industrial customers to request reduction of power consumption during peak demand periods. Voice-mail services are provided by the telephone companies to residential customers. Voice processing is also being used to provide energy assistance information to the *Social Development Commission* (SDC). The SDC calls the utility companies voice-processing system to find out the estimated annual gas or electric usage. In turn, the SDC uses this information to determine the amount of financial assistance needed.

As part of a human resources program, many of the utility companies are giving their employees 24-hour access to information on benefits, employee stock, and investment programs. Table 6.8 summarizes the voice-processing applications in the utilities area.

**Table 6.8**
Utilities Voice Processing Applications

| | |
|---|---|
| Delinquent account reminders | Auto attendant |
| Security access to buildings | Customer meter reading |
| Auto announcement of nuclear disaster | Cable TV pay-per-view |
| Power outage announcements | Cable TV technician dispatch |
| Customer trouble reporting | Cable TV bill inquiry |
| Craftperson dispatching | Cable TV bill collection |
| Voicemail | |

### 6.2.7 Telephone Companies

The telephone companies are a major user of voice-processing technology, for both LECs and IXCs. Voice processing is used to

- Improve efficiency of telephone company services that are being provided to external customers;

- Form the basis for a service that the telephone companies sell;
- Enhance services that the telephone companies sell;
- Supplement their own internal telephone company operations.

*Automated trouble reporting* is a service that assists callers in reporting trouble. Callers are guided through a series of questions concerning the trouble; ANI identifies the caller location and pinpoints the problem.

*Bill inquiry*. Customers can automatically inquire about a bill and check how much is owed and when the last payment was received. On delinquent bill payments, customers are able to arrange a payment schedule.

*New services*. A customer can order telephone company services such as CLAS by calling into a system, selecting the services desired, and having the service deployed immediately. These voice messaging services are offered by each of the telephone companies to both residential and small business customers.

*Message delivery* is a service available when a person makes a call and either obtains a busy signal or a ring/no-answer. The option provided stores a voice message that the voice-processing system will attempt to deliver, for a fee, over the next 3 hours in 15-minute intervals. This message delivery service currently is available at many public telephones.

*Operator services* is the processing of all $O+$ and $O-$ calls. $O+$ calls are credit card calls; $O-$ calls are any calls that require operator assistance, such as person-to-person, collect, or third-party billing. Voice processing automates some of the functions that traditionally were performed by an operator. Playing a tone, capturing and validating the credit card, and then placing the call are functions that have been highly automated. Generating call-detail records for billing purposes is another function performed by the voice-processing system.

*Automatic dialing* is being added to telephone company information services. This capability automatically dials the customer-requested telephone number, again, for a nominal fee. This service is particularly attractive to callers who use cellular telephones.

*Craftperson dispatching* is a major application of voice processing in the telephone industry. Customers report trouble to a central repair dispatching facility; the information about the trouble is captured, including the name and address of the customer, and assigned to a technician. When the technician completes a current repair assignment, he or she calls the central dispatch facility to report the completion of one assignment and to obtain another. Depending upon the time of day, the technician could be placed on hold for many minutes awaiting dispatcher availability. If technician assignments are stored in voice form, the technician can report assignment completion and obtain a new one without requiring a dispatcher. Text-to-speech has been used extensively in this application. Because the information must be captured for billing and recordkeeping, a direct conversion from the stored text to voice eliminates the need for a dispatcher to record voice messages for the technicians [7].

Table 6.9 provides a summary of the voice-processing applications in the telephone service industry.

**Table 6.9**

Telco Voice Processing Applications

| | |
|---|---|
| Delinquent-account reminders | Cellular repair center locator |
| Security access to buildings | Busy line message delivery service |
| Power-outage announcements | Voicemail services |
| Customer trouble reporting | 411 call completion |
|   Location of trouble | Custom intercept |
|   Type of trouble | Operator service providers |
|   Reach number |   Third party billing |
|   Estimated time of repair |   Collect calls |
| Customer billing inquiry |   Credit card calls |
|   Current balance | Information provider services |
|   Payment arrangement |   Audiotex gateways |
|   Adjustments |   Electronic publishing |
|   Payment procedures | Cellular phone verbal dialer |
|   Location of nearest remittance center | Cellular phone voicemail |
| Order entry | Cellular information services |
|   Connect and disconnect service |   Traffic conditions |
|   CLASS service feature |   Weather conditions |
|   Product information |   Selected stock information |
|   Suspend/restore service | Cellular voicemail services |
| Craftperson dispatching | Cellular telephone voice dialers |

## 6.2.8 Retail

This area includes all retail establishments. Successful applications have displayed a solid improvement in operating efficiency or have provided a distinct competitive advantage.

*Dealer locator application* is a major one that assists a caller in locating the dealer closest to him or her. The caller simply enters the NPA and the NXX, and the system identifies the nearest dealer. With ANI, the location is determined without the caller's entering the telephone number. This is easier for the caller to use, speeds up the call process, and eliminates errors that the caller might make.

The *home shopping network* (HSN) uses voice processing on a large scale to handle the volume of calls generated by TV selling. They have in excess of 1,500 ports installed in Clearwater, Florida. Over 60% of the calls to HSN are handled by its voice-response system.

A *real estate voice response service* allows a buyer to shop for home listings according to geographic area, price range, and home features. Additional information, such as mortgage rate information, open house schedules, and moving tips are also provided.

*Automobile service messaging* is a service provided by automobile dealers to customers having their car serviced. The customer is given a repair order number; when the customer calls to see if the car is ready, he or she is asked to enter this number. The system then plays a message that indicates the car's repair status. If the repair has been completed, the system gives both the pickup times and the amount of the repair bill. One benefit this system offers is that customers can find out quickly their status 24 hours a day. Another benefit is that the repair shop can schedule phone calls to avoid constant interruption of repair work.

*Catalog sales* is a prime application of voice processing. Many customers are repeat ones, so they know what they want to order. When the sales agents are busy and the wait is long, voice processing is a very effective way to take orders. The caller is prompted to make a selection by entering the item number from the catalog and a credit card number. The credit card would be validated for the amount of purchase. If the caller is a repeat customer, the shipping address would already exist. For new orders, the caller would be switched to voice messaging and would leave his or her name and address. With an ANI capability, the past purchasing profile of the caller can be used to provide improved service.

Accurate *daily sales reporting* is critical in many businesses. Adequate stock must be maintained and cash flow must be controlled closely. Remote retail chain stores can call into a central headquarters facility and report cash receipts, credit card receipts, and items sold.

*Merchandise notification* for arrival of items ordered or being repaired is an attractive application of voice processing. Customers are automatically called and informed. If a busy signal or a ring/no-answer is encountered, the system will call again at a later date, and continue calling until it reaches the customer.

During the last few years, wholesale outlets for consumers, such as BJ's Wholesale Club and Price Club, have come into existence. The items being purchased are usually large, so conventional checkout techniques such as bar coding cannot be used. The checkout of the purchased items requires two people. One speaks the numbers, and the other listens to the numbers and enters them into the cash register. Speech recognition has been applied to permit the direct entry of the numbers by a single person. Besides saving labor, the method is also more accurate. Voice-processing applications in the retail sector are summarized in Table 6.10.

**Table 6.10**
Retail Voice Processing Applications

| | |
|---|---|
| Salesperson order entry | Dealer locator |
| Video rentals | Fast-food ordering |
| Order status | Repai-complete notification |
| Off-track betting | Merchandise available notification |
| Automobile service messaging | Daily sales reporting |
| Telephone answering services | Catalog order entry |
| Movie theater information | Voicemail |
| Real estate broker messaging | Auto attendant |
| Real estate listing | Florist birthday or anniversary message |

## 6.2.9 Publishing and Communications

This area includes major publishers and information providers. Applications have either been a new way to generate additional revenue or telemarketing ones that are oriented toward selling more publications or providing better customer service. The following paragraphs detail some of the voice-processing applications in the publishing and communications area.

*Weather reporting* is one of the most popular services. It is particularly helpful to travelers, because they are able to determine the weather status in cities throughout the world.

*Talking yellow pages* provide a capability by which the caller can access information about a particular advertiser. The information is current and may identify special sales or offers. In addition to basic telephone advertisements, most talking yellow pages offer a variety of other voice information services such as horoscopes, soap opera updates, weather reports, winning lottery numbers, news reports, sports reports, diet and nutrition news, health and fitness news, theatre information, and ski conditions.

The *CATV pay-per-view application* is one in which a large number of calls occurs just before the start of the event. With ANI, callers are identified by the telephone number from which they are calling. Based on this, the subscriber is switched on for the event without having to enter a PIN. Using this system, more calls can be handled [8].

Quick *exit poll result reporting* is critical. The television networks compete to predict the winner of an election. Voice mail is used very effectively to obtain information from pollers who are scattered throughout the country.

*News story coverage* requires that key reporters be immediately informed of, and often dispatched to, the site of a story. Voice messaging coupled with automatic paging has become an effective way for print and broadcast news-gathering organizations to accomplish this.

*Proofreading.* Organizations such as the Library of Congress proofread each document before publication by using two people—one reads and the other listens. Text-to-speech is being used to make this a process performed by one person.

*Telemarketing.* Newspapers use voice processing extensively in telemarketing campaigns. Soliciting new subscribers and advertisers is the dominant application. Predictive dialers are used to increase telemarketing efficiency. Magazine subscriber services operate similarly, and book publishers use toll-free telephone numbers for direct sales to their customers. Table 6.11 summarizes the voice-processing applications in the publishing industry.

**Table 6.11**
Publishing Voice Processing Applications

| | |
|---|---|
| Talking yellow pages | Subscriber polling |
| Magazine ordering | 976 and 900 services |
| Subscriber news service | GAB lines |
| Telemarketing for new subscriptions | Personals |
| Book purchasing | Placing classified ads |
| Proofreading | |

### 6.2.10 Manufacturing

This area includes all manufacturing activities. Applications have generally improved the cost profile of the manufacturing process or improved the product quality. Speech recognition has found some measure of success, primarily in hands-busy or eyes-busy applications.

*Data entry* of quality assurance information has already been discussed.

*Identification.* Materials handling typically requires that identification information be taken from an item and recorded. This is most efficiently accomplished while physically moving the items. With speech recognition and voice response, handlers can enter the item's identification number by speaking it.

*Restricted entry and exit.* Manufacturing operations typically have many people who enter and exit a work facility. This entry and exit need to be restricted and monitored. Voice-recognition systems automatically manage the entry and exit of workers at a manufacturing facility.

*Service contract inquiry.* The major automobile manufacturers provide service contracts that are sold by automobile dealers. Voice processing can handle inquiries from dealers and customers that have purchased the service contract. The dealer is able to determine contract validity, determine the expiration date, and identify provided coverage.

*Product literature requests* for computer peripherals are being provided by a facsimile response system. The caller connects with the system and selects the desired information. After the caller has entered his or her facsimile number, the information is sent to that number. Manfacturing applications of voice processing are shown in Table 6.12.

**Table 6.12**
Manufacturing Voice Processing Applications

| | |
|---|---|
| Security access to buildings | Inventory |
| Machine control | Service dispatching |
| Data entry of QA information | Voicemail/automated attendant |
| Order inquiry | Product support |
| Corporate conferencing | 976 and 900 services |
| Help desk | |

### 6.2.11 Insurance

All insurance companies have strived to improve efficiency and provide improved customer service. Some of the voice-processing applications in the insurance industry are highlighted in the following paragraph.

Subscribers are able to call to obtain information concerning eligibility, such as effective date of coverage, deductions, individuals covered, and types of treatment covered. The current value of an insurance policy can be obtained by calling a host computer. The major insurance companies are providing voice-mail boxes to their agents and customers. This is improving communications significantly. Table 6.13 provides a summary of the voice-processing applications in the insurance industry.

### 6.2.12 Wholesale

The wholesale area uses voice processing extensively for automatic order processing. Inventory status inquiry and order status inquiry are voice- processing applications that are popular. Voice-processing applications in the wholesale area are shown in Table 6.14.

**Table 6.13**
Insurance Voice Processing Applications

| Eligibility verification<br>Payment information<br>Benefit information | Net asset value<br>Current yields<br>Synchronized caller/record transfer |
|---|---|

**Table 6.14**
Wholesale Voice Processing Applications

| Availability information<br>Price information | Order entry (wholesale clubs)<br>Automated attendant |
|---|---|

## REFERENCES

1. Macina, C. L., "Prototyping Bank-by-Phone Services," *Speech Tech 89 conference*, New York, May 1989, pp. 246–250.
2. Lewis, C, "Phone Banking Improves Service at Fulton Federal," *Speech Technology*, Vol. 4, No. 2, March/April 1988, Media Dimensions, New York.
3. Buba, V. L., "Voice Mail: A New Solution to Old Problems," *Speech Tech 89 conference*, New York, May 1989, pp. 254–256.
4. Smyth, C. C., "Applications of Voice Recognition Devices to Air Defense Track Data Management," *Speech Tech 86 conference*, New York, April 1986, pp. 258–261.
5. Ryan, B., "Voice Technology—An Expanding Tool in Healthcare," *Speech Technology*, Vol. 3, No. 4, March/April 1987, Media Dimensions, New York.
6. Chambers, A. L., "Speech Technology in the Emergency Room," *Speech Technology*, Vol. 4, No. 1, October/November 1987, Media Dimensions, New York.
7. Schiller, T. D., "Field Craft Technician Communication with Host Computer Using Synthesized Voice," *American Voice Input-Output Society conference*, Alexandria, Virginia, September 1986, pp. 59–67.
8. Noren, R. A., "Interactive Voice Response in the Cable Television Industry," *Speech Tech 89 conference*, New York, May 1989, pp. 232–324.

# Chapter 7
# The Telephone Company's Role in Voice Processing

## 7.1 HISTORY OF THE AT&T ANTITRUST SUIT

The telephone company has a unique and preeminent position in the voice-processing area, as it is the primary provider of the transport mechanism necessary for most of the applications and the supplier of enhanced telephone network services needed for their support. The telephone company is also one of the largest users of voice-processing technology in its own operations. Finally, the telephone company has the potential to become the dominant supplier of enhanced voice-processing services.

The telephone industry has evolved from the totally noncompetitive environment that existed in the 1950s to a highly competitive environment in many areas. The only area that is still generally a monopolistic environment is the LEC services, although competition is beginning to exist in this area also. Although many of the AT&T and *regional Bell operating company* (RBOC) people still long for the "good old days" and will argue that things were better then, the reality is that services are much better and lower priced now. Competition has accelerated the deployment of new services and technology at a rate far in excess of what existed with the monopolistic environment. Business and the consumer *and* the telephone companies have been the winners.

Restrictions that were placed on the RBOCs during divestiture have been eased significantly during the last few years. Table 7.1 summarizes the present status of restrictions on the RBOCs [1].

After World War II, the United States *Department of Justice* (DOJ) became concerned that AT&T's vertical integration in manufacturing and service provision was violating antitrust laws. The DOJ wanted AT&T to divest itself of Western Electric, sell its 50% share in Bell Labs, and use competitive bidding procedures

**Table 7.1**
RBOC Restrictions

| Item | 1984 MFJ | 1991 |
|---|---|---|
| Provide voice mail | No | Yes |
| Provide electronic mail | No | Yes |
| Provide protocol conversion services | No | Yes |
| Provide billing services | No | Yes |
| Provide gateways | No | Yes |
| Provide electronic white pages | No | Yes |
| Provide electronic yellow pages | No | Yes |
| Generate electronic information | No | Yes |
| Manipulate content of electronic information | No | Yes |
| Provide long-distance service | No | No |
| Design or manufacture | No | No |

for its purchases. AT&T and the DOJ settled the case in 1956 with a consent decree. The terms of the decree were: Western Electric would limits its manufacturing activities to the production of telephone equipment; AT&T could only conduct business related to providing common-carrier communication services that were regulated by the Federal Government; and AT&T would license its patents to other organizations.

In 1982 the DOJ and AT&T announced an agreement to settle a long-standing government antitrust case against AT&T. This plan became known as the *Modified Final Judgment* (MFJ) and called for AT&T to relinquish ownership and control of the local *Bell operating companies* (BOCs). AT&T would retain its manufacturing capability (Western Electric, which was later renamed AT&T Technologies) and its long-distance capability (AT&T Long Lines, which was later renamed AT&T Communications). The BOCs were prohibited from offering products and services that were deemed to be competitive, which limited them to providing local telephone service. An early amendment of the MFJ permitted the BOCs to market *customer premises equipment* (CPE). The FCC Computer Inquiry II decision mandated that this had to be done using separate unregulated subsidiaries. Specifically, the BOCs were prohibited from

- Providing long-distance service;
- Manufacturing;
- Providing enhanced services.

The distinction between basic services and enhanced services was defined by the FCC. Enhanced services involved some form of computer processing or interaction with databases. At the beginning of 1984, the local BOCs were officially separated from AT&T and regrouped under seven separate and independent *regional holding companies* (RHCs) and became known as the *Regional Bell Operating Companies* (RBOCs). Table 7.2 summarizes the history of antitrust suits in the telephone industry.

Since the divestiture occurred, over 150 waivers have collectively been obtained by the RBOCs for relief on the line-of-business restrictions of the MFJ. These waivers allow the RBOCs to expand into real estate management, international ventures, computer software and general office equipment sales and other business activities that are not related to their regulated local exchange business. The RBOCs also gained waivers to sell certain specialized CPE (such as 911 equipment) and transmission services (data communications protocol conversion services) directly to customers [2].

## 7.2 ENHANCED SERVICES

Enhanced services were defined in Computer Inquiry II as any services other than pure transport. Computer Inquiry III required that the RBOCs submit plans for providing the interfaces for *basic service elements* (BSEs) and *comparatively efficient interconnection* (CEI) in exchange for the RBOCs' right to compete in the enhanced services market. The RBOCs were required to submit their plans by February 1, 1988.

CEI was defined as providing interconnection opportunities on an equal basis defined by technical and operational principles and a set of pricing principles. Although Computer Inquiry III permitted the RBOCs to provide transport facilities for enhanced services, they were still forbidden to offer services in which the RBOCs were the information providers. Many of the RBOCs are testing this restriction by working with third parties to provide information. One example is in the talking yellow pages area. The RBOCs are still forbidden to develop and manufacture products and provide long-distance service.

**Table 7.2**
Summary History of AT&T Antitrust Suit

| Year | Event | Description |
|------|-------|-------------|
| 1956 | Consent Decree | AT&T is required to divest of its foreign subsidiaries. The continuation of the vertical integration of AT&T is provided for, but only for production of equipment used by the Bell System for telephone service. AT&T is forced to license its inventions, including its recently invented transistor, which was the predecessor of integrated circuits. |
| 1956 | Hush-a-Phone Decision | The attachment of non-AT&T-supplied acoustic devices to AT&T telephones is permitted, provided that they present no risk to the public telephone network. |
| 1959 | Above 890 FCC Ruling | Private, point-to-point microwave links are allowed. |
| 1968 | Carterfone Decision | FCC ruling that allowed attachment of non-AT&T-supplied devices to the public telephone network, provided that they present no risk to the network. |
| 1969 | MCI Decision | Leased private microwave links allowed. |
| 1971 | FCC Specialized Common-Carrier Ruling | The MCI decision is expanded. Specialized common carriers are authorized. |
| 1971 | FCC Computer Inquiry I | AT&T is restricted from participating in the data processing business. |
| 1972 | FCC Domestic Satellite Ruling | The Specialized Common-Carrier Ruling is expanded. Specialized common carriers are encouraged to use satellite as a transmission medium. |
| 1976 | FCC Telerent Decision | Telcos are prohibited from infringing upon customer's interconnection of equipment merely because it can be defined as constituting "a substitution for telephone system equipment." |
| 1976 | FCC Docket 20097 | Unlimited resale and shared use of private line facilities are permitted. |
| 1977 | Execunet Court Decision | Indiscriminate dial up resale of MCI's long-distance network to any customer is permitted. |

Table 7.2 **(continued)**

| Year | Event | Description |
|------|-------|-------------|
| 1977 | FCC Part 68 Registration Program | Direct connection to the public network of telephone equipment previously registered and certified by the FCC to be harmless to the network is allowed, eliminating the need for costly telco-supplied protective couplers. |
| 1978 | FCC Primary Instrument Ruling | The AT&T requirement that at least one telephone per household must be supplied by the telephone company is eliminated. |
| 1980 | FCC Computer Inquiry II | AT&T is permitted to provide enhanced services only through completely separable subsidiaries. |
| 1981 | FCC Resale and Shared Use decision | Allowed unlimited resale and sharing of all interstate telephone service. |
| 1982 | Settlement of the DOJ/AT&T Anti-trust Suit | AT&T divests RBOCs. AT&T is permitted to participate in all data processing and information processing businesses (except electronic publishing through 1990). The RBOCs are prohibited from manufacturing, providing long-distance services, and providing enhanced services. Plan became known as the Modified Final Judgement (MFJ). |
| 1986 | COMPUTER INQUIRY III, PHASE I (open network architecture (ONA) ORDER). | The RBOCs are permitted to provide enhanced services under certain specified conditions. MFJ still restricts the RBOCs from offering these services. |
| 1987 | DOJ First Triennial Review of MFJ | Recommended that most of the line-of-business restrictions on the RBOCs be removed. It said that the RBOCs should be allowed to manufacture, to provide information services, go into nontelecommunications business and provide interexchange services outside their regions. |
| 1988 | MFJ court relaxing of enhanced services ban. | The RBOCs were permitted to provide gateway transmission for information services. Specifically, voice mail and audiotex gateways were permitted. Manufacturing, providing long-distance service and providing the content of information services were still prohibited. |
| 1991 | Court decision letting RBOCs provide information service | Based on a remand by the United States Court of Appeals, the MFJ court reluctantly lifted the restriction banning the RBOCs from providing information services. |

### 7.2.1 Technical and Operational Principles

The technical and operational principles that are the basis for the telephone company's providing CEI are

- Physically and functionally standardized interfaces for transmission, switching, and signaling;
- Unbundled basic services and common basic service rates;
- Common basic service performance;
- Common end-user access;
- Common knowledge of availability of basic service features;
- Common installation, maintenance, and repair;
- Minimized interconnection cost for competitors;
- Nondiscrimination among competitors.

### 7.2.2 Pricing Principles

The pricing principles that are the basis for the telephone company's providing CEI include:

- Rates for transmission facilities must be based on actual costs of installing and operating such facilities for that provider;
- An identical basic interconnection charge to recover the costs of the interconnection facilities and the unbundled basic services used by each enhanced service provided by the carrier and others;
- An equal basic concentration charge to recover the costs of the concentration facilities collocated with the carrier's basic facilities;
- Standard tariffed rates for specialized communications or signaling devices.

Providing BSEs with CEI is known as *open network architecture* (ONA).

### 7.2.3 Open Network Architecture Current Status

The current status of ONA is one of many difficult and unresolved issues. Some of the issues are detailed in the following paragraphs.

*Each RBOC taking a different approach*, using its own definition of BSEs and interfaces, independent of the other six. We expect that pressure from *enhanced service providers* (ESPs) will cause the FCC to mandate RBOC provision of BSEs that are standard from one RBOC to another.

*The cost to develop and provide BSEs*, and who will pay for this, is a wide-open area. An increase in basic service charges will not be accepted by the FCC or the *Public Utilities Commission* (PUC). Difficulty in determining the demand that would exist for a particular BSE is another serious issue.

*No solid architecture definition exists.* While the network is evolving to ISDN, ONA is being defined without any sort of specific network architecture.

*Discrepancies between service providers and RBOCs.* The FCC mandated that the development of ONA plans involve industry participants. The RBOCs have held two national forums, using Bellcore as the moderator, and a series of regional forums. The most fundamental discrepancy that exists between what the ESPs have requested and the RBOC ONA proposals is *collocation.* The RBOCs have rejected this, but the ESP position is that collocation is essential to achieving CEI.

### 7.2.4 BSEs Requested

The more commonly requested BSEs include ANI, data over voice channel, data multiplexing from the central office, DID trunks for 976 services, call forwarding for busy or no-answer, stutter dial tone, default call forwarding, suppressed ringing, directory database access, traffic statistics, and billing services.

### 7.3 RBOC Entry Into Voice Mail

The ruling by Judge Harold H. Greene (United States District Court for Washington, D.C.), which was released on March 8, 1988, let the RBOCs offer computerized information transmission and related services. The long-term effect of this ruling on the voice-processing market should be extremely favorable.

First, RBOC entry has helped to further "legitimize" and expand the market. A residential market for voice messaging, which is orders of magnitude larger than the present commercial and industrial one, could only be developed by the RBOCs. Second, the RBOCs have become major purchasers of voice-processing hardware and software. Third, the RBOCs will take a much more proactive position in the 976-type service area. Restricting the program content and promoting the services are what the RBOCs did not do well at first, but this has changed to a large extent. Finally, the reliability, quality, and usefulness of voice-processing products will improve significantly. The RBOCs are significantly more demanding buyers, which has improved current products.

Although the overall voice-processing industry will benefit substantially from RBOC market entry, some areas will witness negative results. The market for telephone answering machines will deteriorate, and service bureaus will also be affected. The *telephone answering service* (TAS) market will experience a negative effect. Voice service bureaus, however, will profit from the increased visibility and will thrive. Although the RBOCs will own the residential market, they are unlikely to penetrate the small- to mid-sized business area to any great extent. These areas require service beyond that provided by the RBOCs, which are more suitably provided by private service bureaus.

In the 4 years since the ruling that permitted the RBOCs to provide voice-mail services, each RBOC has pursued this area. As indicated in Tables 7.3, 7.4, and 7.5, the telephone companies are taking different approaches and are at different stages of deployment. Some, such as Bell Atlantic, have selected a single supplier throughout their region. Others, such as Bell South, Pactel, and NYNEX, have chosen different suppliers for different deployments. Pactel is using Unisys for residential service in metropolitan areas and Digital Sound for business services and outlying areas. NYNEX is using Octel in New York City, Centigram in Long Island, and Unisys in eastern and central Massachusetts.

**Table 7.3**
CO-based Residential Voice Mail Services Summary

| *Telco* | *Name of voice mail service* | *Date deployed* | *Monthly charges* | *Current number of subscribers (12/1/91)* |
|---|---|---|---|---|
| Ameritech | Call Minder | 11/90 | $7.95 | 35,000 |
| Bell Atlantic | Answer Call | 3/90 | $5.00 | 270,000 |
| Bell South | Memory Call | 7/90 | $3.45-$3.75 | 150,000 |
| NYNEX | Call Answering | 4/90[1] | $6-$12 | 25,000 |
| Pactel | Message Center | 11/90 | $4.95 | 160,000 |
| SW Bell | CallNotes | 9/91 | $5.50-$14.00 | <5,000 |
| US West | US West Voice Mail | 3/90 | $6.95 | 300,000 |
| SNET | Message Taker | 5/90 | $20.00 | 10,000 |
| Cincinnati Bell | | 1/91 | | 5,000 |
| GTE | Personal Secretary | 5/91 | | 20,000 |
| Rochester Telephone | Voice Mail | 9/87 | $8.00 | 10,000 |
| Centel | Voice Mail | 6/88 | $3.95 | 3,000 |

The motivation for the RBOCs to offer a voice-mail capability is extremely high. Thirty percent of all calls placed are not completed—either the line is busy or the call not answered. For the RBOCs, this means that 30% of the time telephone network resources are being used without producing any revenue. With voice mail, all calls would be completed, yielding revenue for the RBOCs. The RBOCs are enticed by the fact that this additional revenue would be obtained without any significant increase in the telephone company network facility requirement. Voice mail will also increase network traffic, because each completed voice-mail call generates two to three additional calls. The storing and forwarding of facsimile is another service the RBOCs will provide.

**Table 7.4**
CO-based Residential Voice Mail Services Supplier Summary

| Telco | Boston Technology | Centigram Commun- ications | Digital Sound | Octel Communic- ations | Tigon | UNISYS |
|---|---|---|---|---|---|---|
| Ameritech | | | | | * | |
| Bell Atlantic | * | | | | | |
| Bell South | * | | | * | | |
| NYNEX | | * | | * | | * |
| Pactel | | | * | | | * |
| SW Bell | * | | | | | |
| US West | | | | * | | |
| SNET | | | | | * | |
| Cincinnati Bell | | | * | | | |
| GTE | | | * | | | |
| Rochester Telephone | | * | | | | |
| Centel | | * | | | | |

**Table 7.5**
CO-based Residential Voice Mail Services

| Telco | Name of service | Type of service | Features provided | Price per month | Setup charge |
|---|---|---|---|---|---|
| Ameritech | Call Minder | Basic call answering | Varies by 3rd party provider | $7.95 | |
| Bell Atlantic | Answer Call | Basic call answering | | $5.00 + $7.00 for enhanced VM service | $9.00 |
| Bell South | Memory Call | Basic call answering | Call answering | $3.45-$3.75 | $8.00 |
| NYNEX | Call Answering | Basic call answering | Call answering | $5-$12 (extension MBs- $2.50/month) | $10.00 |
| Pactel | Message Center | Basic call answering | Call answering Additional extensions 30 messages | $4.95 + $2.50/extension | $7.00 |

| | | | | |
|---|---|---|---|---|
| SW Bell | CallNotes | Economy | Call answering<br>20 messages (2 min. each)<br>1 daily reminder | $9.00 | $5.50 |
| | | Standard | Call answering<br>30 messages (2 min. each)<br>2 daily reminder<br>2 extensions | $9.00 | $9.50 |
| | | Enhanced | Call answering<br>40 messages (2 min. each)<br>1 daily reminder<br>4 extensions<br>pager notification | $9.00 | $14.00 |
| US West | US West<br>Voice Mail | Basic call<br>answering | Call answering | $6.95 | $7.00-$13.00 |

## 7.4 RBOC Entry Into Voice Information

On July 25, 1991, U.S. District Court Judge Harold H. Greene issued a ruling that permitted the RBOCs to provide electronic information services. Judge Greene issued this ruling very reluctantly, citing concerns regarding RBOC abuse of power in the past. In particular, Judge Greene believed that the RBOCs have market power that they can (and probably will) use illegally to hinder competition and cheat telephone service subscribers. A 1-year stay of this order was included to give opposing interest time to appeal the ruling. In issuing this ruling, Judge Greene acted on a order from the Washington District Court of Appeals, which had requested that he reconsider his previous ruling to restrict the RBOCs from providing electronic information services. On October 7, 1991, the same court of appeals struck down the 1-year stay and ruled that the RBOCs could immediately begin offering information services.

It is unclear at this time what the impact these rulings will have. Opponents, which include most of the existing information provider industry participants, were strongly opposed. The basic argument is that RBOCs have an unfair advantage in that their control of both the information and the pipeline. The industry participants argue that it is unreasonable that they rely on a competitor for compilation of sales data, answering service calls, and collecting accounts receivable in addition to providing critical telephone network services.

The only obvious short-term benefit is that the uncertainty regrading the restriction on the RBOCs' providing electronic information services is eliminated. The only organizations that are sure to benefit are the alternate LECs such as Metropolitan Fiber Systems, Inc. and Teleport Communications Group, Inc. Information providers will prefer to do business with the bypass companies rather than with a competitor such as an RBOC. It is also likely that the RBOC effort to enter the information provider area could cause them to become distracted from their core telephone network business, which would enhance the appeal of alternative local carriers to potential users.

What will the long-term impact be of RBOC entry into the electronic information services area? An examination of RBOC performance in similar areas is not encouraging. The RBOCs have had a poor record so far with enhanced services. Voice-mail services and videotex trials have not taken the country by storm. The marketing approach was consistent with an organization that for more than 80 years had a captive customer base that did not have to be sold.

Another factor that will inhibit the rollout of new services is the presently strained billing systems. Present services are already taxing the capabilities of existing billing systems, leading to numerous problems such as late and inaccurate bills. Offering services that cannot be billed properly does not make sense. RBOCs are still restricted from the sale of long-distance service, further restricting the type of service provided. Many services depend on the resale of long-distance service for profitability. Without being able to resell long distance, the RBOCs would have to conclude that they are not economically viable services.

Another way to project the future would be to look at the history in other countries in which telephone companies have been free to offer electronic information services. The United States and Canada have been alone in not allowing the telephone company to offer electronic information services. Throughout the rest of the world, telephone companies have been permitted to offer information services with few restrictions. It appears that, almost without exception, none of these telephone company services has been successful or made any money. For example, both Germany and the United Kingdom have run a nationwide videotex service for almost 10 years and have failed to turn a profit. The French Minitel service claims to be profitable, although it benefited from an enormous subsidy from the French government in the startup phase. It is also interesting to note that the only Minitel service provided by the French telephone company is electronic yellow pages. Table 7.6 is a list of electronic information services that have been frequently identified as ones that it would be appropriate for the RBOCs to provide.

None of these services is new and exciting. They may save money, improve quality of life, and generally be quite useful, but they are not ones that would capture the imagination of an exceptionally broad market segment. If the RBOCs were to address the information services area alone, at best, we could expect some subset of services of this sort. Appealing to a broad consumer market requires a totally different orientation than what exists in most corporate environments. An appropriate corporate orientation leaves it to the companies to show that their products are necessary and useful, an effective approach in the corporate world

**Table 7.6**
Some Possible RBOC Information Services

| | |
|---|---|
| Electronic yellow pages | EDI |
| Home security monitoring | Protocol conversion |
| Media conversion | News services |
| Medical imaging | Video on demand |
| Financial information | Electronic funds transfer |
| Games | Home shopping/banking |

but unsuccessful in a consumer market. Are Nintendo games necessary and useful? Are Pump Reeboks necessary and useful? Are Teenage Mutant Ninja Turtles necessary and useful? Are they more successful than any of the information services? The sort of marketing savvy needed is totally alien to the RBOC environment.

The model of RBOC entry into the electronic information services market alone is an unlikely one. If this does occur, ROBC impact on the information provider area will be minimal. A more plausible one is that a variety of partnerships will be forged. Likely RBOC partners would be companies like Sony and Matsushita with the marketing know-how required for success in the consumer market.

## 7.5 PAST EFFECTS OF THE TELEPHONE COMPANY

The telephone company plays a major role in directing the voice- processing area. The existence of a quality telephone network is essential to most voice-processing applications. In the past, the telephone company has frequently functioned in what appears to have been a self-serving and monopolistic fashion. For over 30 years, the telephone company opposed any sort of attachment of non-Bell devices to the telephone network. In the 1950s and most of the 1960s, any non-Bell device was generally attached to the telephone network acoustically. In 1968, the Carterfone decision forced the telephone company to permit attachment of non-Bell devices. However, a coupling device had to be obtained from the telephone company. This device was priced expensively and the telephone company often took many weeks and sometimes months to provide it. The general industry viewpoint was that the coupler did not perform any useful service, but this situation made it very difficult for companies to compete with telephone company equivalent products. The primary motivation for the coupling device seemed to be as a vehicle with which the telephone company could restrain competition. In 1978, the coupler requirement was eliminated, and a registration requirement was initiated by the FCC (part 68), which now must be met by any device attached directly to the telephone network.

## 7.6 THE TELEPHONE COMPANY'S FUTURE ROLE
## IN VOICE PROCESSING

The RBOCs have control of much of the telephone traffic through their ownership of the local telephone loop. Although some bypass activities do exist, at this time it is rather slight. This puts them in a position in which monopolistic abuse can occur. The currently existing RBOC restrictions are aimed at controlling these monopolistic powers. The RBOCs continue to maintain a significant lobbying effort directed at eliminating the regulatory restrictions. However, industry trade organizations also are putting a lot of resources into lobbying to maintain the current restrictions. It is difficult to predict what will happen in this area, but it would appear likely that the restrictions will continue to be eased. Although the potential anticompetitive abuse by the RBOCs does exist, it is difficult to argue that someone should be penalized for what they *might* do. The possibility of the RBOCs being permitted to provide cable TV programming is an area that is likely to receive a good deal of attention. With the projected future growth of personal communication networks, wireless communications will become an important area for the telephone companies. One of the future projections is that things that we transmitt over wire versus what we transmitt over the airwaves will be totally reversed. The likelihood of relieving the restrictions on manufacturing will probably occur next and will be done in stages. It is unlikely that the restrictions on the RBOCs' providing long-distance services will be changed in the near term.

## REFERENCES

1. Milne, W. G., "Legal Constraints on the Regional Bell Companies," Speech Tech 90 conference, pp. 194–196.
2. Nelson, E., S. Ryba, S. Silverman, and M. Bradshaw, *Introduction to the History, Structure, and Technology of the Telecommunications Industry*, Washington, D.C., NATA, 1991.

# Chapter 8

# Voice-Processing Systems and Components

Particular types of systems correspond to each voice-processing function. Although similar in many ways, the systems differ in the details of how they work. In many cases, a particular system will perform multiple functions. Voice-processing systems are available as either preprogrammed packages configured to perform a particular function, or as a system assembled with individual components that are part of other voice-processing systems. The types of voice-processing systems are

- Voice-mail systems;
- Automated attendant systems;
- IVR systems;
- Information provider systems;
- Passive intercept systems;
- Outbound;
- Automatic call distributors;
- Multiple-function systems.

A number of suppliers exist in each category. In addition, numerous suppliers of the individual components exist. The products vary considerably in price and the capabilities that they include.

## 8.1 VOICE-MAIL SYSTEMS

The basic capability provided by a voice-mail system allows a caller to leave a message and a subscriber to receive it [1]. Beyond this basic capability, voice-mail systems have a multitude of features.

### 8.1.1 Capabilities and Features

The capabilities provided in a voice-mail system can be categorized into the following areas:

- Send messages;
- Review messages;
- Personal features;
- System management.

Send-message features that are available in most voice-mail systems include

- Pausing during message creation;
- Adding from a point;
- Review of recorded message;
- Rerecording message with one keystroke;
- Destination verification;
- Marking message to be sent as urgent;
- Restricted forwarding of a message;
- Directory of subscribers;
- Notice of message receipt;
- Notice of receipt of an urgent message;
- Message review before sending;
- Sending message to group distribution lists;
- Page repetition if not picked up;
- Leaving message in more than one mailbox without returning to the operator;
- Date and time specification for future message delivery;
- Returning operator after leaving a message.

The first four features are associated with the creating the message. Most subscribers record the message, listen to it, and then, if they are satisfied, send it. If they are not satisfied, they rerecord it. Most of the other send-message features are associated with whomever receives the message and the way it should be delivered. Some subscribers are listed on more than one group distribution list. Sending messages to more than one such list requires that subscribers of this sort be identified, and the system must be designed so that they receive only a single copy of the message.

Review-message features that are available in most voice-mail systems include

- Informing the recipient of messages;
- Skipping to the next message;
- Canceling message review;
- Pausing during message review;
- Message replay;
- Saving the message;
- Deleting the message;

- Moving backward or forward in the message;
- Speed control of message playback;
- Volume control of message playback;
- Quick scan of received messages;
- Reply to a received message;
- Forwarding a received message to another subscriber;
- Forwarding a received message to another subscriber with an introduction;
- Playing time-and-date stamp upon request;
- Informing subscriber that a message was purged.

These features permit a subscriber to identify messages that have been received, review them, and then, if appropriate, respond. The subscriber can then either retain them or delete them. Messages are either played *first in, first out* (FIFO) or *last in, first out* (LIFO) order. This capability varies from one system to the next but is consistent within each system type. Dependin on the particular environment, either the FIFO or the LIFO scheme may be more appropriate.

Checking the delivery status of a message permits the subscriber to verify whether a sent message has been received. This verification can occur by the subscriber's entering a command when the message is sent, and the voice-mail system will provide the time and date the recipient actually plays the received message. Verification can also occur through subscriber request of information about the messages that a particular recipient has received. The system will indicate the number of messages that the subscriber has sent to that recipient that have not been played, and then play them.

Personal features available in most voice-mail systems include

- Subscriber-changeable passwords;
- Subscriber-recordable greeting;
- Subscriber-recordable name prompt;
- Group lists;
- Notification of new message receipt.

Name prompts are used to both identify the subscriber by name and to verify the addresses when a message is sent.

Notification of new messages received can be accomplished in a variety of ways. Message-waiting lights are available with many telephone systems. To activate them from the voice mail system, a PBX integration must be implemented. This sort of notification is most appropriate for subscribers who usually work in an office. For subscribers that are not usually in a permanent office, a notification by pager or a direct telephone call is more appropriate. Pagers can be either simple beep or vibrating ones. When they are activated, the subscriber knows that a new voice-mail message has arrived. Numeric-display pagers indicate the telephone number of the voice-mail service. This permits a subscriber to receive pages from multiple sources and be able to identify the source of the page. A nationwide paging service is available from SkyTel Corporation, for example, which permits callers to leave a voice message and page a subscriber to indicate that a message has arrived. This service is called SkyTalk and permits subscribers to be paged almost anywhere in the country. SkyTel is expanding its coverage so that subscribers can be paged outside the United States; ultimately, a subscriber may be paged anywhere in the world. Simply dialing a subscriber-specified number is another method of informing him or her of the receipt of a new message. Temporary forwarding of all or selected (urgent) messages to another telephone number is a capability available in some voice-mail systems. In this case, when a message is received, the subscriber is called at the number he or she specified. If the subscriber answers the call, a menu is provided, permitting him or her to listen to the message just received and to log onto the voice-mail system. With some voice-mail systems, messages can also be delivered to nonsubscribers. When sending the message, the subscriber specifies the telephone number of the nonsubscriber. If the system is unable to deliver the message (e.g., busy, ring/no-answer, recipient not available), the system can be programmed to try again at regular intervals for a specified period of time.

Within the notification of new messages-received capability, the subscriber would typically be able to specify a number to be called and the notification criteria. He or she could specify that notification would be triggered by either any message being received, only urgent messages, or messages received from a specific mailbox. The ability to specify that the system notify the subscriber of new messages received at a specific time each day is one available with many voice mail systems. Notification by outdialing features are ones selectively provided to subscribers. They are typically specified as a *class of service* (COS).

System management capabilities include establishing and monitoring the subscriber database and the activity of both individual subscribers and the system. The subscriber database would include information about each subscriber such as date activated, password, PIN, system resource usage, and COS. The COS would enable different features for a subscriber. Some of the features that can typically be set by the system administrator on an individual subscriber basis include

- Maximum length of a single message that may be left;
- Maximum number of days that a message may be stored;
- Maximum length of personal greeting;
- Outdialing (internal);
- Outdialing (local calls);
- Outdialing (long distance calls);
- Allowing guest accounts;
- Group distribution list creation;
- Group distribution list usage;
- Broadcast message creation.

Most of these service parameters affect the use of system resources. For example, if the message length is long and subscribers can retain messages for long periods of time, the amount of bulk memory required for speech storage is much larger than in an environment where memory usage is controlled more tightly. If there is a level of outward dialing, the required number of telephone ports may become much greater than if dialing out were constrained.

Voice-mail systems can be set up to have more than one hundred different classes of service. Each subscriber would be assigned to a particular COS. System activity reports include port activity, subscriber activity, and system activity. System management capabilities allow the configuration of a voice-mail system for a specific telephone system environment. Parameters that can be specified are:

- Type of call transfer mechanism (e.g., hook flash, bridge);
- Hook or flash duration;
- Number of telephone lines connected to the system;
- Number of rings to wait before answering a call;
- Prefix used for dialing PBX extensions;
- Prefix used for dialing local phone numbers;
- Prefix used for dialing long-distance phone numbers;
- An incoming port is considered busy when out of service;
- Ports that may be used for dialing out;
- Message-waiting indicator clearing.

These capabilities are typically established when the system is installed. Many must be tailored to match the telephone system with which the voice-mail system is working. System management capabilities are available to configure a voice-mail system to respond to the caller in a certain way. Parameters that can be specified are

- Number of seconds to wait for a subscriber to enter the mailbox number;
- Number of unsuccessful attempts before disconnecting the caller;
- Number of seconds to wait for input from the caller before prompting again;
- Number of timeouts permitted before disconnecting the caller
- Number of rings without an answer before an outdial is aborted;
- Dial-out/try-again interval if call response is ring/no-answer Dial-out/try-again interval if call response is busy;
- Maximum number of outdial call attempts that will be made;
- Number of digits in voice-mail box numbers;
- Number of digits in the security codes;
- Administrator password for access to system management functions;
- Recording systemwide broadcast message.

The ability to set these parameters while the system is on line is a capability of many voice-mail systems. Other operational capabilities available on many systems are

- Help prompts at all decision points;
- Canceling current operation and returning to the previous menu;
- Listening to either new messages or saved messages;
- Time-and-date stamp played only when requested by the caller;
- Messages played either FIFO or LIFO.

A capability that has become available on many voice-mail systems is a *voice-form feature*. Specific mailboxes can be set up to record answers to a series of preprogrammed questions. One application of this feature is as a telemarketing or market research tool. The person being interviewed would first be contacted by an interviewer and then directed to the voice-form mailbox to complete the interview. Product promotions could be accomplished by offering a prize for providing information using the voice form. A transcription package is also provided to complement the voice-form capability.

With the multitude of features available in a voice-mail system, the caller interface must be carefully designed to avoid a system that appears complex and difficult to use [2]. Most features are hidden from the caller so he or she does not routinely have to deal with them. Callers typically send commands to the voice-mail system by pressing a single key.

System management information and statistics are provided with most voice-mail systems. The information provided identifies the usage profile of a particular system resource for a particular time period. The resources typically reported on include port usage, storage usage, and mailbox usage. In addition, many systems provide billing information.

Port usage information includes the number of system accesses and the duration of each. A typical port usage report is shown in Table 8.1. This type of report provides a good picture of the system's call traffic. For the system shown in Table 8.1, the telephone lines are configured in a *hunt chain*, whereby the caller connects with the first port not already busy. This means that the only time a caller gets a busy signal is when all twelve ports are in use.

Storage usage reports indicate the amount of disk storage being used and the amount still available. Table 8.2 is an example of a typical storage usage report.

Mailbox and feature usage reports provide a profile of each subscriber's mailbox. A typical mailbox and feature usage report is shown in Table 8.3.

Billing information is provided with many voice-mail systems used in a service bureau environment and includes the detailed usage of the voice-mail system by the subscriber. The amount of storage used, the minutes of connect time, and use of special features such as out dialing is reported. The billing information is often provided in a format compatible with an external billing computer.

System administration is performed through a system console *video display terminal* (VDT). A set of menus for selecting various functions is available. Functions that can be accomplished by the system administrator are backup and restore all mailbox information, usage information, and system configuration information. In this backup, information is typically transferred to floppy disks or a streaming tape. Support for a variety of pagers is available on most voice-mail systems. The types of pagers are nondisplay, numeric display, and alphanumeric display. Nondisplay pagers are the simplest and most common type of pager and are supported on most voice-mail systems, consisting of outdialing the specified pager number. Numeric display pagers outdial the pager number and the voice-mail number. The

**Table 8.1**
Voice Mail Usage

| Port Utilization Report | | |
|---|---|---|
| Period covered: April 2, 1992, 8:00 a.m. to April 3, 1992, 8:00 a.m. | | |
| *Port Number* | *Number of calls* | *Connect time* |
| 1 | 783 | 26,785 |
| 2 | 604 | 18,104 |
| 3 | 543 | 16,122 |
| 4 | 487 | 14,596 |
| 5 | 401 | 12,070 |
| 6 | 307 | 9,211 |
| 7 | 256 | 7,603 |
| 8 | 173 | 5,186 |
| 9 | 101 | 3,133 |
| 10 | 76 | 2,198 |
| 11 | 45 | 1,343 |
| 12 | 33 | 973 |

Total calls ................................ 3,809

Total seconds ................................................................ 117,224

Average call duration ...................................................... 30.8 seconds

All ports busy ................................................................. 507 seconds

**Table 8.2**
Voice Mail Storage Usage Report

| Storage Utilization | |
|---|---|
| April 2, 1992 8:00 a.m. | |
| Blocks used | 10,875 |
| Blocks free | 8,888 |
| Percentage free | 45% |
| Number of messages | 3,469 |

**Table 8.3**
Voicemail Subscriber Usage report

| Mailbox Usage Report | |
| --- | --- |
| Mailbox Number 0100010<br>From: March 1, 1992 to April 1, 1992 | |
| Number of messages | 4 |
| New messages | 2 |
| Saved messages | 8 |
| Total connect time | 248 |
| Total outdial time | 24 |
| Number of group messages | 1 |

system administrator can typically set parameters such as the number of paging attempts and the interval between attempts.

Mailbox setup by a subscriber is fairly straightforward. The first time a subscriber accesses the voice-mail system, he or she must establish a password and record a name prompt and greeting. The password allows the subscriber to control the access to and privacy of the mailbox. The recorded name is used by the voice-mail system to identify mailbox ownership to callers. The greeting is played to callers when they first access the mailbox. This setup is done once and in most cases does not have to be repeated often. Passwords should be changed occasionally for security reasons. Greetings are often changed when a subscriber is on an extended absence, such as a vacation or a business trip. When a subscriber has groups of people that often must receive the same message, distribution lists are used. With many systems the subscriber can set up these lists from his or her telephone. With some systems, this is not possible, and distribution lists can only be set up by the system administrator from the system console.

Some voice-mail systems provide a guest mailbox capability, which allows a subscriber to provide a portion of his or her mailbox to someone else. The guest user would have the same mailbox address as the subscriber but have a different password. The guest user can only receive messages from and send messages to the subscriber. A secretary access capability is provided with some voice-mail systems. This permits a person to access a subscriber's mailbox and review the envelope of each new message but not be able to listen to the messages. Broadcast messages are public messages available to all system subscribers. They are provided either over a separate broadcast message mailbox, or at the beginning of each session when a subscriber calls the voice-mail system.

## 8.1.2 Connection With the Telephone Network

A voice-mail system can be connected with the telephone network either through a direct connection with the central office, through a PBX, or through a hybrid combination of both.

With a direct connection to the central office, callers reach the voice-mail system by dialing either a 7- or a 10-digit number. The configuration can be either a single telephone number for the entire voice-mail system, or a DID configuration, in which each subscriber has a unique telephone number. The advantage of the DID configuration is that the caller does not have to enter the subscriber mailbox number. This is particularly attractive for callers who are at a rotary telephone, because they can leave a message without having to enter any DTMF digits. The disadvantage of this configuration is that alternate call handling functions, such as connecting with an operator or transfering to an alternate extension, are not available.

With a connection through the PBX, calls can be routed directly to the voice-mail system, answered by an operator and then transferred to the voice-mail system, or routed to the voice-mail system when the extension is busy or does not answer. Another advantage of this configuration is that any subscriber in an office being served by the PBX can access the voice-mail system by simply dialing an extension number.

With a hybrid PBX and central office connection, callers are able to reach the voice-mail system either directly with a DID number or by going through the PBX. Most PBXs offer tie lines that provide the functions of a DID service.

Connection to CENTREX is essentially like attaching to a huge PBX. CENTREX is a service provided by many telephone companies in which an organization's extension lines are connected directly with the central office. A specialized interface is available with CENTREX that provides PBX integration capabilities.

Connection with key systems is often somewhat more difficult. Capabilities to transfer a call are frequently not available, individual stations are attached by proprietary interfaces, and many do not generate the DTMF signals necessary for control of the voice-mail system. Attaching the voice-mail system directly with the central office or to the trunk ports of the key system is often the only effective way to work with a key system.

## 8.1.3 Integration With PBX

A complete (seamless) PBX integration includes the following:

*Message waiting indication* controls the PBX message-waiting indicator.

*Transfer to operator* allows the caller to exit from the voice-mail system and go directly to the switchboard operator or to another extension.

*Call forward direct to voice mailbox* permits a subscriber to forward phone calls directly into a mailbox without requiring the caller to reenter the extension or mailbox number.

Integration with the following PBX and CENTREX systems is commonly available:

- AT&T Dimension, System 25,75,85, DEFINITY G1,G2,G3
- CENTREX (1AESS)
- Ericsson
- Executone
- Fujitsu Focus 960, 9600
- GTE GTD 4600, Omni
- Harris 20/20, DL1200, H400
- Hitachi DX series
- Rolm 9751
- Intecom IBX S/10, S/40, and S/80
- ISOETEC PBXs
- ITT 3100
- Mitel SX100/200 and D200
- Mitel SX2000
- NEC 2400 MMG
- Northern Telecom SL-1
- Northern Telecom SL-100
- Northern Telecom DMS-100
- Rolm CBX (7000, 8000, 9000)
- Siemens Saturn II, IIE, and III
- Solid State Systems
- STC Starswitch
- Tandiron Coral
- Telex UTC-1001
- TIE Mercury
- Toshiba Perception II

Although the actual interfaces vary in the details, they are conceptually very similar. They obtain the number being called (usually a DID number), send back an indication that a message was received (for message waiting indication), and provide a way for the caller to escape to an operator (usually a simple hook flash or dial sequence). Most of the interfaces are inband ones, although a few use separate RS232C links.

## 8.1.4 Product Types

Voice-mail products can be separated into five distinct types:

- Voice mail as an option on a PBX system
- Departmental voice-mail products

- Corporate or service bureau voice-mail products
- Personal voice-mail products
- Central-office-based voice-mail products

Voice mail as an option to a PBX system is offered by major PBX suppliers such as Northern Telecom, Rolm, and AT&T. In the past, some of these products were more limited than free-standing voice-mail products. The human interface to the caller is often a bit awkward, and advanced features found that in many of the free-standing products have sometimes not been available with PBX-based products. They are typically highly optimized for the particular switch and the integration is excellent.

Departmental voice-mail products are oriented toward the needs of smaller companies or departments of larger companies. An automated attendant capability is usually one option that is readily available. The basic application in many cases is switchboard automation. Departmental voice-mail systems are usually based on IBM PCs. They typically include from 1 to 32 ports, 1.5- to 60-hours speech storage, easy recording of greeting and system prompts, an employee directory, and statistics on system and subscriber usage. Although networking capability does exist on some products, it is not available with most of them. Figures 8.1(a) and 8.1(b) show small voice-mail systems. They generally are relatively easy to install, set

**Figure 8.1(a)** Small-configuration voice-mail system. (Photograph courtesy of Active Voice Corporation.)

up, and maintain and are able to be expanded to larger capacity configurations fairly gracefully.

Corporate or service bureau voice-mail products have much larger port counts and storage capacities, and networking capabilities are much more sophisticated and comprehensive. Statistics reporting is generally significantly more extensive, and information about the usage profiles of each subscriber is more detailed. These

**Figure 8.1(b)** Medium-configuration voice-mail system. (Photograph courtesy of Active Voice Cor poration.)

products are suited to applications in which data must be provided to customer service representatives who deal with customers in reconciling billing discrepancies. Corporate or service bureau voice-mail products also have international accommodations, which are often not available with departmental voice-mail products. These systems support multiple languages, and regulatory approvals of national *posts, telephone, and telegraph* (PTT) administrations have been obtained. Interfaces with text-mail systems are often available, which provide both message notification among systems and the ability to read text messages over the telephone using text-to-speech converters. Call throughput per port is usually significantly higher in the corporate or service bureau systems than in the departmental voice-mail systems. Finally, the price of corporate or service bureau voice-mail systems tend to be an order of magnitude higher than departmental voice-mail products. Voice-mail service bureaus and large corporations have been the largest customers in this area.

Personal voice-mail products are board and software options that can be added to a PC DOS environment. These products support a single port and provide basic voice-messaging functions. They act as a sophisticated personal answering machine. Cost is much less than $1000.

The RBOC requirements have extended the capabilities of previously existing voice-mail systems. Previously existing largest single voice-mail systems could barely handle a single central office, thus making them impractical for use in the residential market. Systems for the RBOCs would need to provide area-wide coverage, which implies a single system that accommodates many central offices. Port counts and storage capabilities are at least an order of magnitude higher. A capability to implement message-waiting indication is required. The most effective way to do this has been with *simplified message desk interface* (SMDI) links to multiple central offices. Figures 8.2(a) and 8.2(b) show a large voice-mail systems. Appendix 1 lists many voice-mail and automated attendant product suppliers.

## 8.1.5 Standardization

The areas in which a standard set of interfaces is essential are the transmission of messages among systems and caller interfaces. For voice mail to become a ubiquitous communication media, voice-mail systems must be able to talk to one another, and the subscribers should be able to use different voice-mail systems with minimal learning. It is not unreasonable for a subscriber at one service bureau to want to send mail directly to a subscriber of another service bureau. Achieving this sort of capability is nontrivial. A first step, however, would be the standardization of basic transport communication and message formatting. However, the present situation is far from this: Each vendor with a networking capability has developed a proprietary networking scheme. The leading vendors in this area have historically displayed a highly provincial orientation in this area. Rather than make

**Figure 8.2(a)** Medium-sized voice-mail systems. (Photograph courtesy of Applied Voice Technology, Inc.)

their networking interfaces public and encourage other vendors to use them, they have attempted to discourage other vendors from doing this by not making the networking interfaces public information.

### 8.1.5.1 AMIS Standard

The drive to improve this situation has come from customers who are large users of voice mail. A group was established in 1988 called the AMIS project group. This group comprised over 30 organizations and included product vendors, service bureaus, and large voice-mail customers. The AMIS group came up with a standard for transmission of voice mail that is based on the CCITT X.400 family of recommendations for text-message interchange. The recommended transmission scheme is a digital one, using 32-kb/s encoding, defined by CCITT Recommen-

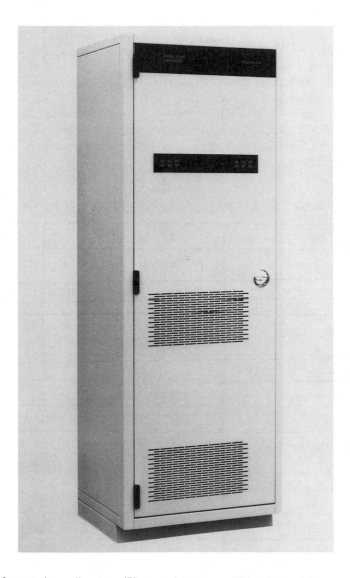

**Figure 8.2(b)** Large voice-mail system. (Photograph courtesy of Digital Sound Corporation.)

dation G.721. The specification supports networking on a "closed" basis, requiring prior administrative involvement such as the exchange of passwords.

An analog scheme has also been agreed upon as an alternative standard. This standard uses DTMF signaling and the exchange of voice messages in analog form. It provides an "open" networking between two systems on a dialup basis without prior administrative involvement. It provides a scaled-down set of messaging features, and is particularly suitable for use with small systems or in applications in which the message volumes are low.

Table 8.4 summarizes the AMIS analog and digital standards [3]. Although the AMIS specification was accomplished rapidly, compared with other standards activities, the deployment of AMIS has been rather slow. Only a few of the vendors have announced the availability of AMIS-compliant products and, two years after the standard was finalized, no known installation exists that uses AMIS to link voice-mail systems of different suppliers.

**Table 8.4**
Summary Comparison of AMIS Digital and Analog Standards

| *Feature/capability* | *Digital* | *Analog* |
|---|---|---|
| Transmission media | Modems up to switched 56 kb/s | Telephone voice line |
| Framing | X.25 | Analog |
| Compression | 32 kb/s ADPCM, CCITT Recommendation G.721 | NA |
| Address and control format | X.400 | DTMF |
| Intersystem security | X.400 password | Open |
| Send/receive/reply | Yes | Yes |
| Originating message time-stamp | Yes | No |
| Separate originator's voice name | Yes | No |
| Message privacy | Yes | No |
| Message-sending priority | Yes | No |
| Forward | Yes | No |
| Full-duplex message flow | Yes | No |
| Delivery notification | Yes | No |
| Message importance indicator | Yes | No |
| Receipt notification | Yes | No |
| Maximum number of messages per call | Unlimited | 9 |

**Table 8.4 (continued)**

| Feature/capability | Digital | Analog |
|---|---|---|
| Maximum number of messages per call | Unlimited | 9 |
| Maximum number of recipients per message | 128 | 1 |
| Maximum message length | 8 minutes | 8 minutes |
| Nonreceipt notification | Yes | No |
| Store-and-forward | Yes | No |
| Service notification | Yes | No |
| Transmission time: 1-minute message | 40 seconds @ 56 kb/s<br>230 seconds @ 9.6 kb/s | 95 seconds |
| Transmission time: 8-minute message | 5.3 minutes @ 56 kb/s<br>30.7 minutes @ 9.6 kb/s | 8.6 minutes |

### 8.1.5.2 Voice Messaging User Interface Forum

As we might expect, the interface seen by the caller is different for each voice-mail system. As a caller deals with various voice-mail systems, he or she needs to learn how each one works. This is certainly a detriment to the widespread acceptance of voice-processing technology. When a driver encounters a car that he or she has not driven before, the driver can be sure that the accelerator pedal is always on the right, the brake pedal is always next to it on the left, and the steering wheel is round. The basic operating interface is standardized. This is not so with voice-processing systems. Again, each of the vendors has purposefully developed caller interfaces that are unique and proprietary. The RBOCs have started to drive for a standard caller interface, and we anticipate that within the next few years product suppliers will define and adopt a standard. An industry group known as the *voice messaging user interface forum* (VMUIF) has developed a set of standard caller interfaces. This group is coordinated by the IIA, which recently made a preliminary specification available. The stated aims of this specification were to

- Provide voice messaging system users with a consistent interaction.
- Define common elements of the services from the user point of view.
- Facilitate the offering of voice messaging services in a way that is independent of the underlying systems.
- Promote future consistency and user transparency as extensions to the user interface are defined.

The VMUIF standard addresses four areas:

1. Commonality principles and design guidelines;
2. Universal functions and data types;
3. Voice messaging user interface core features;
4. Service flows.

*Commonality principles and design guidelines.* Commonality principles address the areas of user control, system feedback, statement phrasing, menus, key assignment, errors, and help.

In general, the system should prompt users with available options and allow the users to override the prompts. The user should receive immediate feedback in response to an action. When unprompted commands (such as *fast forward*, *rewind*, *louder*, or *softer*, during message playback) are used, their effects should be reversible. It is particularly important in these cases that the caller receive some kind of immediate feedback in response to an action.

There should be a common universal set of functions that are always available within the system. These functions should be made as easy to use as possible and should be consistent throughout the interface. An example is Help. The caller should have control of the system wherever possible. This includes the ability to control the start and end of the actions such as *recording* and *playback*, the ability to pause or cancel transactions in process, and the ability to enter and exit Help.

Caller input should terminate or preempt prompts asking for the input, and input should be stacked for processing when the caller is working ahead of the system. In the event that invalid input is encountered while input remains stacked for processing, the stack should be cleared at the time the user starts to receive error feedback.

System announcements, including error messages, can be broken into two parts. The first part of an announcement would not be interruptable; caller input entered at this time is ignored. This prompt should be as short as possible. The second part of the message would be preemptable and caller input should be acted upon immediately. For example, the caller enters an incorrect password, and the system responds with the message, "Invalid password. Please reenter." The first phrase would not be interruptible by the caller input, but the second phrase would be interruptible.

Feedback would be provided to the caller to confirm actions, to warn about dangerous actions, to echo caller input, or to explain error conditions (such as an option's not being available). Tones may be used as feedback. The voice messaging system should have a *record* tone. A nonirritating tone may be used to indicate an error. If other tones are used, they should be distinct from these.

System prompts should be of the form "function followed by instruction." For example, *to do X, press Y*.

Terminology should be consistent throughout the voice-processing interface and subscriber documentation. Wording should be chosen that is clear and unambiguous, while avoiding the use of jargon. System wording should be simple. If possible, terminology should allow graceful addition of future functionality. If a metaphor is used (e.g., post office), it should be used consistently throughout the system.

Menus should be limited to a maximum of four prompted choices. Prompted choices should be given in ascending numerical order. They may also include an indication that additional options are available through some other action (not counted in the four). This limit applies only to prompted menu choices and not to unprompted commands such as Help or Cancel that are available as well. If the caller has asked for additional options, this system may give more than four choices.

The caller should not hear prompts for commands that are not currently available. (This could result in numbers being skipped when a menu is spoken.) Whenever possible, actions should be available by pressing single keys rather than by typing multikey commands.

Menu choices should be numbered to correspond with the numbers on the telephone keypad, rather than named with mnemonics. The choices within a menu should be numbered consecutively in ascending order, starting with *1*. Gaps may appear in menus when some choices are not offered in some situations. When possible, make key assignments consistent across functions.

Choices should appear on menus by order of frequency (i.e., most common choice first), or in a "natural" order if such a strong order exist (e.g., creating an item before editing an item).

When a core function is not implemented, it is recommended that consideration be given to reserving its assigned key for possible future implementations of that function. In the event that a key associated with a core function is used for a different function, it is recommended that consideration be given to the effects on users who may have come to associate that key with the core function.

If a directional metaphor is used, numbers on the left side of the standard 3-by-4 keypad should indicate Previous, Lower, Slower, Backwards, and so forth, and numbers on the right side of the keypad should indicate Next, Higher, Faster, Forward. This provides the best possible match with cultural stereotyping and minimal conflict with other factors.

Avoid time-dependent (without caller action) system state changes. For example, a key should not mean one thing while a message is playing and something else when the message finishes. If a timeout does change the state, the system should inform the caller.

In some cases it might be desirable to provide functions by having a single key pressed twice quickly, or two different keys pressed in quick succession. This mechanism should be implemented with caution and with consideration for the following issues: the ability of some callers to complete the two key presses within the interval and thus being unable to access these functions; the requirement for callers to delay when they want one function twice or two functions, rather than the function invoked by the combination of keys; the possibility of invoking the wrong functions; and the system's ability to determine which functions were intended when the user has typed ahead.

Functions relying on the * and # keys should be available in alternate ways (e.g., timeouts) when possible, to accommodate callers whose telephones disable these keys.

Error statements and prompts should be of the following format, though any of these parts may be omitted:

- Error tone;
- What went wrong;
- Current state (system status);
- What to do next (possibly including more information than in the original prompt).

An example is "<Tone>. Greeting too long. Discarded. Please rerecord your greeting at the tone."

After so many errors in a row, the system should take some special action (e.g., prompt for a transfer to an attendant). Counts may also be kept on timeouts and requests for help.

Help should be context sensitive and available whenever possible. In addition, the caller should be able to receive help on generic system commands that apply in that context. Help in the system may consist of

- Further description of menu choices;
- Additional menu items;
- Repetition of menus or prompts;
- Connection with a TSR.

The VMUIF commonality principles and guidelines are summarized in Table 8.5.

*Universal functions.* Universal Functions are system functions that are available to the subscriber anywhere in the system flow. The universal functions that are addressed by the VMUIF are Cancel, Backup; Help, Operator; and Terminate, Skip Ahead.

In general, the * key stops the current action or input and takes the caller one or more steps backward in the system structure. If an action is incomplete and the system goes back to a state before that action starts, the action is canceled; completed actions are generally unaffected. It is left to each vendor to decide how far back the * key will take the user at each point in the interface. Suggested examples of using the * key include:

*Cancel recording.* If the caller is recording a message, pressing * might stop the recording, discard what had been recorded, and return the user to the prompt preceding the record tone.

*Cancel input string.* If the caller is entering a string such as a password or mailbox number, pressing * might discard the digits that had been entered and return the caller to the prompt preceding the entry of digits.

*Back up to previous action.* In a function that requires many individual steps, such as sending a message that requires both addressing and recording, pressing

**Table 8.5**
VMUIF Commonality Principles and Design Guidelines

| *Area* | *Description* |
|---|---|
| User Control | 1. Prompt users with available options. <br> 2. Prompt override. <br> 3. Unprompted commands reversible. <br> 4. Immediate system feedback in response to an action. <br> 5. Common universal functions available. <br> 6. Caller has control of system. <br> 7. Stack caller input. <br> 8. Two part system announcements: first-part nonpreemptable and second-part preemptable. |
| Feedback | 1. Feedback to confirm actions, warn about dangerous actions and echo input. <br> 2. Record tone. Nonirritating tone for errors. Should be distinct tones. |
| Statement Phrasing | 1. System prompts in form "function followed by action." <br> 2. Consistent terminology throughout. Wording clear and unambiguous. No jargon. |
| Menus | 1. Menus limited to four choices. |
| Key Assignment | 1. Single-key actions. <br> 2. Choices should be numbered, not lettered, in ascending order. <br> 3. Key assignments consistent across functions. <br> 4. Menu choice in order of frequency of use. <br> 5. Right-side keys for Next, Higher, Faster, Forward; left-side keys for Previous, Lower, Slower, Backwards. <br> 6. Meaning of key not time dependent. <br> 7. Two-key sequences should be implemented with caution. <br> 8. Functions relying on * and # keys available in alternate ways (e.g. timeouts). |

## Table 8.5 (continued)

| Area | Description |
|------|-------------|
| Errors | 1. Error tone, what went wrong, current system state, what to do next.<br>2. Count number of errors in a row and take special action. |
| Help | 1. Context sensitive and available at all times.<br>2. Additional menu items.<br>3. Repetition of menus or prompts.<br>4. Connection with a TSR. |

* might take the user back past the last completed step and return the prompt to perform that step over again.

*Exit submenu.* If the caller is at a lower level menu, pressing * might take the caller back to a higher level menu, perhaps even to the:&$0*((system's main menu. Note: Interface testing has shown that callers may have trouble exiting unless explicitly prompted to do so.

*Terminate call.* Some use of the * key may cause the system to exit the caller from the system.

The 0 key stops the current action and takes the caller to a help facility in the system. The help facility should be context sensitive whenever possible. It may include prerecorded Help messages and/or access to a TSR (which does not preclude that a transfer to a TSR may be a menu choice on a given system). The Help system may include prompts to clarify what kind of help, in content or in format, the caller wants. (Related commands, such as 00, may also be used to access specific kinds of help.)

During input of numeric parameters, the 0 key is not normally available for help; to get help, the user must first press * and then 0. The only exception is the 0 by itself, followed by a timeout, is interpreted as a request for help.

Timeouts and errors may also be interpreted as requests for help. The specific help that is given might vary depending on history, such as repeated errors or help requests. After the help, the system state is usually the same as that before the request for help. One exception is that an incomplete action, such as a partial recording, may be canceled, and the caller may have to start it over. Another exception is that the user might have done something during help to ask to be moved elsewhere.

In general, the # key tells the system that the user is done with the current activity and takes the user one or more steps forward in the system structure. It is left to each vendor to decide how far forward the # will take the caller at each point in the interface. Suggested examples of using the # key are:

*Numeric or recording delimiter.* When a terminator is required for a typed or recorded entry, the caller presses #. A timeout (no keystrokes, or silence) may be accepted as the terminator. Terminators may not be required in fixed-length strings. However, inconsistent use may cause caller confusion.

*Skip to record.* If the caller is listening to a prompt that precedes a record tone, pressing # might skip the rest of the prompt and take the caller to the record tone. This also applies if the caller is listening to:& a subscriber's greeting; the # skips the greeting and goes straight to the record tone to leave a message for the subscriber.

*Next message.* If the caller is listening to a series of messages, pressing the # might take the caller to the next message.

The VMUIF universal functions are summarized in Table 8.6.

*Voice-messaging user interface core features.* The VMUIF has identified a core set of features for inclusion in the standard. These core features were selected according to the following criteria:

*Frequency of use.* Is the feature used repeatedly by the subscriber as he or she uses the system?

*Aids to rote use.* Does the feature allow the subscriber to perform a routine function quickly?

*Unprompted.* Is the feature used without spoken instructions, and does the subscriber require immediate access to it?

*Ubiquity.* Is the feature available on most systems?

*Minimum feature set.* Would a subscriber expect this feature in common applications?

The core features defined by the VMUIF are summarized in Table 8.7.

Features that were not included as core features include

- Initialization
- Personal options

**Table 8.6**
VMUIF Universal Functions

| Function | Keypad assignment | Description |
|----------|-------------------|-------------|
| Cancel, backup | * | Stops current action and takes caller backward in the flow. |
| Help, operator | 0 | Stops current action and takes caller to a system help facility. |
| Terminate, skip ahead | # | Tells system that caller is done with the activity and takes caller forward in the flow. |

- Record name
- Record greeting
- Change passcode
- Listen to recording
- Header
- Envelope
- Multiple addressing
- Send a copy
- Skip to end of message
- Skip to beginning of message

**Table 8.7a**
VMUIF Core Features

| Features associated with: | Core Feature | Description |
|---|---|---|
| Entering the mailbox | Enter mailbox | After reaching a voicemail system, the subscriber follows a protocol to enter the mailbox. This may or may not include the use of passcode. |
| Sending a message | Send | The subscriber is prompted to press a specific key to send a message. The prompts then instruct the subscriber to enter an address(es) where the message will be sent, and begin recording. The subscriber then records and transmitts the message. |
| Other features | Call answering | When a call is answered by the voice messaging service, the caller hears the subscriber's greeting or a system greeting, followed by a tone, and then leaves a message that will be stored in the subscriber's mailbox. |
| | Terminate call | The subscriber presses a specific key(s) to disconnect from the voice mail system and return to dial tone. |
| | Revert to Login | While listening to a greeting, the subscriber presses a specific key to begin login to his/her mailbox. The prompt then provides instruction on how to login to the mailbox and access mailbox features. |

## Table 8.7a (continued)

| Features associated with: | Core Feature | Description |
|---|---|---|
| Listening to messages, and taking action on these messages | Listen | The subscriber is prompted to press a specific key to listen to messages. The subscriber then hears message that have been stored in the mailbox. |
| | Repeat | The subscriber is prompted to press a specific key to repeat the message. The message is replayed from the beginning. |
| | Save | The subscriber is prompted to press a specific key to save the message. The action "save" is to explicitly mark and indicate the message as receieved by the subscriber. The saved message is kept in the subscriber's mailbox, so that at a later point in time, it can be listened to, replied to or copied, and then saved or erased. |
| | Erase | The subscriber is prompted to press a specific key to erase the message. The message is tagged for removal from the mailbox and is no longer stored by the system. |
| | Reply | The subscriber is prompted to press a specific key to reply to the message that has just been played. A prompt then instructs the subscriber to record a message that will be transmitted to the sender's mailbox. |
| | Rewind | While listening to a message, the subscriber presses a specific key to rewind to a previous point in the message. |
| | Pause | The subscriber presses a specific key to stop listening or recording for a brief period of time. The action resumes after a timeout or after the subscriber presses the same key. |
| | Fast-Forward | While listening to a message, the subscriber presses a specific key to fast-forward to a later point in the message, without having to listen to its entirety. |

**Table 8.7a (continued)**

| Features associated with: | Core Feature | Description |
|---|---|---|
| Universal keys | Cancel | The subscriber who wishes to take corrective action presses a specific key to end an ongoing activity and go back to the previous action. |
| | Back-up | The subscriber presses a specific key to back up, so that an action previously available can be selected. The prompt the subcribr heard earlier is played again. |
| | Help | The subscriber presses a specific key for help, and is given assistance or additional information about the service. The help feature may be available on a prompted or unprompted basis. |
| | Numeric delimiter | The subscriber presses a specific key to indicate that a string of numbers just entered is complete. After a string, if there are no further key presses, the string may be considered complete. A prompt then gives instructions for the next activity. |
| | Recording delimiter | The subscriber presses a specific key to indicate that a spoken recording is complete. Alternately, after a period of silence, the spoken recording may be considered complete. A prompt then gives instructions for the next activity. |
| | Skip to record | The subscriber presses a specific key to override a call answering greeting, and to begin to record. The subscriber hears a record tone immediately after pressing the key. |

The VMUIF has recommended that if vendors or service providers decide to offer these features, they should do so in a manner consistent with the general design principles.

*Service flows.* The VMUIF service flows describe in detail how the core voice mail features work.

*Call answering* is a service that is offered when the voice-mail system is reached, except when a subscriber is accessing his or her own mailbox. Examples of call answering include when an outside caller is forwarded to the voice-mail

**Table 8.7b**
VMUIF Core Features Key Assignments

| Menu | Function | Keypad key assignment | Description |
|------|----------|----------------------|-------------|
| Listen | Repeat | 1 | The caller is prompted to press the 1 key to repeat the message. The message is replayed from the beginning. |
| | Save | 2 | The caller is prompted to press the 2 key to save the message. The action of "save" is to explicitly mark the message as received by the subscriber. The saved message is kept in the subscriber's mailbox, so that at a later point in time, it can be listened to, replied to or copied, and then saved or erased. |
| | Erase | 3 | The caller is prompted to press the 3 key to erase the message. The message is tagged for removal from the mailbox and is no longer stored by the system. |
| | Reply | 4 | The caller is prompted to press the 4 key to reply to the message which has just been played. A prompt then instructs the caller to record a message that will be transmitted to the sender's mailbox. |
| | Rewind | 7 | While listening to a message, the caller presses the 7 key to rewind to a previous point in the message. |
| | Pause | 8 | The caller presses the 8 key to stop listening or recording for a brief period. The action resumes after a timeout or after the user presses the 8 key again. |
| | Fast-forward | 9 | While listening to a message, the caller presses the 9 key to fast-forward to a later point in the message, without having to listen to its entirety. |

**Table 8.7b (continued)**

| Menu | Function | Keypad key assignment | Description |
|------|----------|-----------------------|-------------|
| Main | Listen | 1 | The caller is prompted to press the 1 key to listen to messages. The caller then hears messages that have been stored in the mailbox. |
|      | Send | 2 | The caller is prompted to press the 2 key to send a message. The prompts then instruct the caller to enter an address where the message will be sent, and begin recording. The caller then records and transmits the message. |

system because the person that the caller was trying to reach either was on the phone or did not answer; when a subscriber gives out a number attached to the voice-mail system as if it were his or her own number; or when someone calls a common number to leave a message for the subscriber. The overall flow is shown in Figure 8.3. In general, the system plays the greeting recorded by the subscriber to whom the caller intended to talk, then gives the caller an opportunity to record a message.

*VMUIF greeting the caller and confirming the mailbox.* If the subscriber's address is not automatically known by the system, the system prompts the caller to enter the phone number of the subscriber's address. This entry can be terminated with either a # or a timeout. Afterward, the sequence continues as if the address had been delivered to the voice-mail system automatically.

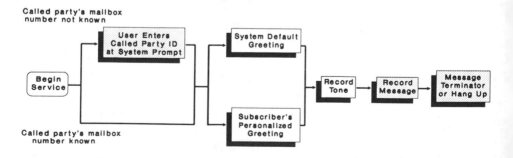

**Figure 8.3** Functional diagram of call answering—nonsubscriber view.

If the subscriber has recorded a greeting, the system plays the greeting now. If there is no recorded greeting, the system plays a default greeting. It is recommended that the default greeting include some information to help the caller ensure that he or she dialed the correct number. This might include the subscriber's recorded name if it is available or the mailbox number.

*VMUIF recording the message and terminating.* The system plays the record tone and records whatever sound the caller makes. If the caller then hangs up, the system delivers the message to the subscriber's mailbox (available either immediately or the next time the subscriber logs on). If the caller presses #, the system quits recording. If the recording exceeds a time limit, the system quits recording and gives a suitable announcement. If the system detects a period of silence without the caller's ever having said anything, the system may break in with help. If the system detects a period of silence after recording some sound, it may terminate the message as if the caller had pressed #.

*VMUIF universal functions.* The caller can get help by pressing 0.

In the call answering mode, if the caller presses * any time before the record tone, the system switches to voice messaging and proceeds with the sequence for entering a mailbox. If the caller's intent is to cause the system to terminate the call, the caller keeps pressing * until the system hangs up.

In call answering mode, if the caller presses # any time before the record tone (after having typed in the subscriber's mailbox if necessary), the system provides the record tone immediately.

*VMUIF Voice messaging/subscriber call.* This is the service in which a subscriber calls in to retrieve messages, send messages, or perform other functions. First, the subscriber enters the mailbox, depicted in Figure 8.4. Once that has occurred successfully, the subscriber is given the main menu (Fig. 8.5) from which he or she can listen to messages (Figure 8.6) and send messages (Figure 8.7).

*VMUIF enter mailbox.* Under some circumstances, the number from which the caller is calling is automatically passed to the voice-mail system: that number may be assumed to be the subscriber's mailbox number (a correct assumption if

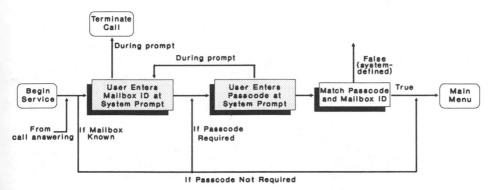

**Figure 8.4** Functional diagram of service entry—subscriber view.

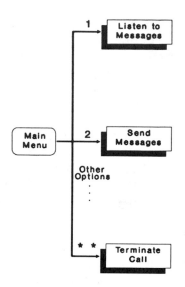

**Figure 8.5** Functional diagram—main menu.

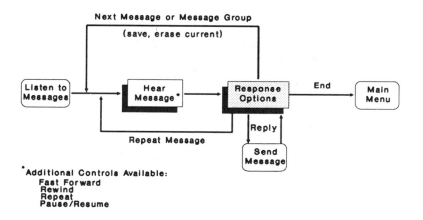

**Figure 8.6** Functional diagram—listening to messages.

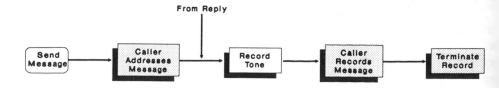

**Figure 8.7** Functional diagram—sending messages.

the subscriber is calling from the phone with which the mailbox is associated). However, there could be a problem that prevents the calling number from being transmitted to the voice-mail system. In that case, or if the calling number is not a valid mailbox number on the system, or if the voice-mail system does not assume that the calling number is a mailbox, the voice-mail system will ask the caller for his or her mailbox number. The caller types the mailbox number, optionally terminating it with a #.

If a passcode is required (it might not be required if the subscriber has called from home, for instance), the system asks the subscriber to enter it, optionally terminating it with a #. If the subscriber knows that the system is assuming the wrong mailbox number, he or she types * during the passcode prompt, making the system go back to ask for the mailbox number and then return to the passcode prompt. If the subscriber presses * during the mailbox prompt, the system terminates the call. The system compares the passcode that the subscriber typed with the one associated with the mailbox. If they do not match, it is up to the system provider to decide what to do to correct the problem.

After the subscriber has logged in correctly, the system plays the main menu (refer to Fig. 8.5). This gives the subscriber the choice to listen to messages (key 1) or to send a message (key 2), and possibly some other choices. If the subscriber presses ** at the main menu, the system terminates the call.

*Listening to messages.* If the subscriber chooses to listen to messages, the system goes into a mode in which it plays the messages in the subscriber's mailbox (refer to Fig. 8.6). For each message, it does the following:

It plays the message itself. During message play, the subscriber can press

1 to start over at the beginning of the message;
2 to quit listening to the message and save it;
3 to quit listening to the message and erase it;
4 to quit listening to the message and reply to it;
7 to rewind the message (start playing earlier in the message);
8 to pause the playback;
8 to resume playing after a pause (a system may restart playing after a timeout); or
9 to fast-forward (start playing later in the message).

After the message is complete, the system plays a menu of items that the subscriber can do to the message. This may include some subset of the above functions or vendor-specific functions.

If the subscriber chooses to repeat the message, the system plays the message and then repeats the menu of choices. If the subscriber chooses to reply to the message, the system goes through a procedure like that in sending a message to record and send a reply. After a reply has been sent, the system repeats the above menu for the original message. If the subscriber chooses to save or erase this message, the system moves on to the next message and goes through the same sequence. If there is no next message, the system returns to the main menu.

*VMUIF sending a message*. If the subscriber chooses to send a message, the system goes through the sequence shown in Figure 8.7. It prompts the subscriber to address the message. The subscriber enters an address terminated with a # or a timeout. The system gives feedback on the address, preferably by playing the recorded name that is associated with that mailbox. If the address is incorrect, the subscriber can press * to cancel that address and type in a new one.

Next, the system prompts the subscriber to record a message and provides the record tone. The subscriber speaks the message and presses #. When the process of sending the message is complete, the system returns the subscriber to the main menu (or to the listen menu if the subscriber had invoked reply).

A summary of the core actions from the main menu on is shown in Figure 8.8. A summary of the key presses in the main menu and in the listen menu is shown in Figure 8.9.

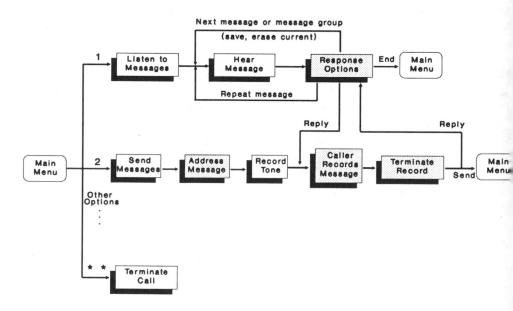

**Figure 8.8** Functional diagram—System summary.

## 8.1.6 Future Voice-Mail Products

Existing voice-mail products are stand-alone devices that provide a minimum interface with the rest of the environment in which they coexist. Voice mail is simply another communications vehicle as are pagers, text mail, facsimile, and cellular telephones. The seamless integration of voice mail with other communications mechanisms will be one major accomplishment that sets future voice-mail products

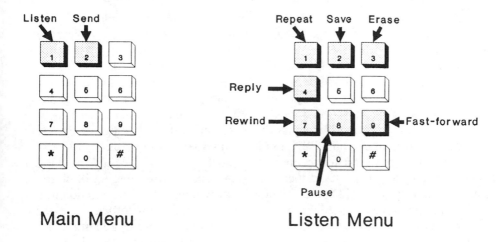

**Figure 8.9** Key-press summary.

apart from existing systems. Functions such as telemarketing, providing information, telephone accounting control, telephone answering services, switchboard operator, and dictation services are all areas in which voice mail can perform a useful,
although often secondary, function. The seamless integration of a voice-mail capability into such functions will be a leading attribute of future voice-mail systems.
The capacity (number of telephone ports, speech storage, call throughput, and
number of subscribers) will increase significantly in future voice-mail products.
Digital telephony will become commonly available, with the inclusion of switching
functions such as a drop-and-insert capability. The caller interface will become
standardized, primarily through RBOC efforts. Networking will become both commonly available and standardized.

Store-and-forward of facsimile messages is a natural addition to a voice-mail
product. In its present state of use, however, facsimile does have some shortcomings, such as lack of security for transmitted information. Received facsimiles are
often displayed in the open, so any number of people are able to see the facsimile.
Alternative routing if the facsimile machine is busy is not yet available. If the
called machine is busy, the calling machine gets a busy signal. Automatic notification of recipient upon receipt of the message is also not available, so most
recipients are notified manually. If the recipient is not in the office where the
facsimile was received, he or she is often not notified upon return. Facsimile
machines can also become junk mail receptacles. Advertisements and solicitations
of all sorts are being sent to facsimile machines. This ties up the facsimile machine,
wastes its paper, and buries the legitimate mail. Using a voice-mail system for
receiving and storing facsimile messages provides a potential solution for these
problems and enhances facsimile as a messaging mechanism. The facsimile message

would be deposited in the recipient's mailbox, and he or she could be notified in a manner identical to that used to notify subscribers of a new voice-mail message. The subscriber could then have the facsimile message routed to a destination of choice. A facsimile-messaging capability is available in a few voice-mail systems, and we anticipate that most systems will have this capability in the future.

The areas in which the departmental and the corporate or service bureau products differ will tend to disappear. As international standards such as X.400 become generally accepted, many systems will have the capability of integrating with large text-mail systems. PBX and keyswitch system integration will be common. As more powerful microcomputers and larger low-cost disks and RAIDs become available, the port and speech storage capacity differences will disappear. Multifunction systems will become common, providing automated attendant, voice mail, and telephone call accounting in a single product in one of the most popular configurations. We anticipate that the RBOCs will continue to penetrate the residential area and increase the penetration significantly from the less than 1% that presently exists. This should have a strong, positive impact on the voice-mail area, because it will tend to further legitimize this capability and significantly broaden the market by extending its availability into the residential area.

Digital telephone interfaces (such as T-1) will also be available, primarily to support the RBOC market. Consolidation through merger and acquisition will increase. Suppliers in other market segments will pursue an acquisition as a mechanism for business expansion.

## 8.2 AUTOMATED ATTENDANT SYSTEMS

Automated attendant systems are products designed to automatically process incoming calls. They essentially perform the telephone handling function of the switchboard operator. These systems are designed primarily for the caller's convenience and improved efficiency, in contrast to voice-mail systems, automatic call sequencers, and automatic call distributors, which are designed primarily for the convenience and improved efficiency of the called party.

A basic automated attendant performs the following functions:

- Answers the telephone and greets the caller with a welcome and a set of options;
- Permits the caller to choose any of the following:
- Dial the called party's extension;
- Obtain a list of available extensions;
- Transfer to a department or group; revert to a live operator; or transfer to a voice-mail center.

Note that the caller has complete control of the call. Other options available with many automated attendants include information bulletin boards, service information, caller name identification, alphanumeric called-party identification, transaction processing, and accounting systems for telephone usage.

When a caller is connected with an extension and it is either busy or no one answers, the automated attendant plays the voice-mail greeting of the called party. The caller can then choose to leave a message for the subscriber or be transferred to the operator. One option, call screening, allows the subscriber to find out who the caller is before accepting the call. This function is available on many automated attendant systems. The subscriber hears the name of the person calling, and then decides to either accept or reject the call. This is generally a subscriber-selectable option. A subscriber can also specify that calls be blocked, in which case calls would be sent directly to his or her mailbox.

Different call-processing sequences can be specified for each port. These call-processing sequences can be programmed to change automatically at certain times of the day or week. Calls could automatically be handled one way during working hours, and another way during nonworking hours.

Automated attendants can be connected to a PBX on either the trunk side or the station side. Most automated attendants attach to the station side. Trunk-side attachment provides more supervision and accountability for each call, but it is more expensive because it requires a port for each PBX trunk line.

Other features of automated attendants include:

- Alphanumeric subscriber index;
- Menu-driven software;
- Programmable number of rings before answer;
- User-recordable prompts;
- Support for DID lines;
- Management reports.

Further, the subscriber can specify that calls are not to be transferred to his or her extension. Calls are then routed directly to his or her mailbox.

The alphanumeric subscriber index is a subscriber-identification capability in which the caller can enter the first few letters of the called party's surname. The system then looks up the subscriber names and attempts to match them against the digits entered by the caller. If a single individual is identified, the system attempts to connect with that subscriber. If more than one subscriber is found for the digit sequence entered, the system will identify each found subscriber to the caller, and request that he or she choose one of them. After the caller selects one of the subscribers, the system attempts to connect with that subscriber.

When a call is being transferred, the system typically monitors the telephone progress tones to determine if the call was answered or if the phone was busy. If the extension is busy or does not answer within a specified number of rings, the system will give the caller the option to leave a message in the called party's mailbox. The user is able to easily configure the system from a menu of options, which usually includes creation and editing of the voice prompts. DID lines are supported by most automated attendants, which means that each subscriber has a unique telephone number, so the caller does not need to enter the subscriber's extension number. The number of ports can vary from 1 to 48, and prices for an automated attendant system range from $249 to $80,000. They are available as free-standing products, with voice mail as an option, or are frequently an option on a voice-mail system. Figure 8.10 shows an automated attendant system.

**Figure 8.10** Automated attendant system. (Photograph courtesy of Dytel Corporation.)

## 8.3 INTERACTIVE VOICE RESPONSE

IVR is a capability that provides real-time access to dynamic databases and allows the caller to order something, obtain information or instruction, leave information, or obtain specific account information. The information being obtained, being provided by, or delivered to the caller is private. For example, a caller ordering an item is a private transaction, while a caller providing an opinion on a topic is a public transaction.

### 8.3.1 IVR Hardware and Software Characteristics

The type of host environment and the method used to access it is the key product parameter. Interfaces to IBM mainframe and Series 3X (AS/400) computers are the most commonly supplied capabilities. Asynchronous interfaces are also typically available with most IVR products. The number of ports, stored speech available, and call throughput are the basic items that separate many of the products. Direct emulation of a terminal versus being a voice-peripheral device is a significant product characteristic differentiator. The ease with which the host linkage is set up and the flexibility in creating prompts are other key product features. In many applications, security of system access by the caller is a key feature. The availability of tools that permit a user to implement his or her own script is another key capability, as are the number of different applications and the number of hosts that can be simultaneously supported. Statistics and reports on system usage is another area in which the systems differ. For applications in which the information being accessed is confidential, many systems offer a password encryption capability. Support of data terminals and *telecommunications devices for the deaf* (TDDs) is found with many products. An automated attendant capability is provided with most of the IVR products. Fax response and voice mail are optionally available with most of the IVR products, as are speech recognition and text-to-speech options. Most IVR products have a call-switching capability, but it varies considerably in terms of its capability and capacity.

### 8.3.2 IVR Features and Capabilities

The ability to create and edit prompts; usage statistics and transaction reporting; password encryption; and an application generation facility are key capabilities in a IVR system.

#### 8.3.2.1 IVR Speech Creation and Editing

Each of the IVR systems allows the user to create and edit prompts. The simplest provides prompt recording, listening, and then rerecording if the user chooses. No real editing capability exists. More advanced features include the ability to edit a specific prompt and to create multiple prompts from a single audio file. The most basic editing capability is to slice silence from either end of a prompt. The resolution with which this can be done varies from one product to the next. It is typically 0.1 seconds, although some systems are able to resolve to 0.01 seconds. The ability to listen to a sequence of prompts as they would be heard in a live application is important, and it is found in most systems. The capability to create and edit prompts while the system is running is an area in which most systems have significant limitations. Some of the systems do not provide use of the prompt editor without taking the system down but do provide a "remote rerecord" capability, which means specific prompts can be designated as "remotely recordable." These prompts can then be recorded over the telephone while the system is running.

Being able to record all of the prompts as a continuous audio string and then breaking this string into individual prompts is a capability that exists on a few systems. For applications that have a large vocabulary, this capability is invaluable. The capability to cut and paste is found in a few systems, and can be useful in fine tuning an application. The ability to control the recording volume is another valuable capability that is found in some products.

### 8.3.2.2 IVR Usage Statistics and Transaction Reporting

Providing reports on the system-loading profile and caller use patterns is a capability that is provided with most transaction-processing systems. Telephone traffic reports will typically include

- Number of calls on each line:
    - On a per hour basis;
    - For a designated period (typically the last 24 hours).
- Percentage of time each line is used:
    - On a per hour basis;
    - For a designated period (typically the last 24 hours).
- Other information about each line on either an hourly or 24 hour basis:
    - Average call length;
    - Percentage out-of-service;
    - Call transfers attempted;
    - Call transfers completed.

A typical hourly summary call statistics report is shown in Table 8.8.

Caller usage reports permit the tracking of the usage patterns of the caller to be accomplished. Specific menus can be chosen for report. The reports typically include the following:

- Number of times a menu was accessed AHA;
- Average caller response time;
- Number of retries;
- Number of errors;
- Average prompt time.

**Table 8.8**
IVR Hourly Summary Report

| CALL STATISTICS | | | | | |
|---|---|---|---|---|---|

Time run: 8:00 a.m. on April 2, 1992

| Hour of day | Calls received | Average call duration (minutes) | Utilization % | Call transfers | |
|---|---|---|---|---|---|
| | | | | Attempted | Completed |
| 1 | 20 | 0.82 | 1.43 | 0 | 0 |
| 2 | 34 | 1.10 | 3.23 | 0 | 0 |
| 3 | 27 | 1.34 | 3.14 | 0 | 0 |
| 4 | 28 | 1.26 | 3.05 | 0 | 0 |
| 5 | 27 | 1.21 | 2.84 | 1 | 0 |
| 6 | 27 | 1.35 | 3.15 | 0 | 0 |
| 7 | 59 | 1.51 | 7.48 | 2 | 0 |
| 8 | 116 | 1.58 | 15.45 | 4 | 4 |
| 9 | 160 | 1.33 | 17.93 | 6 | 5 |
| 10 | 264 | 1.42 | 31.66 | 12 | 11 |
| 11 | 262 | 1.38 | 30.41 | 13 | 12 |
| 12 | 254 | 1.42 | 30.44 | 11 | 9 |
| 13 | 217 | 1.32 | 24.15 | 9 | 9 |
| 14 | 187 | 1.40 | 21.97 | 9 | 7 |
| 15 | 148 | 1.31 | 16.38 | 8 | 8 |
| 16 | 149 | 1.22 | 15.40 | 7 | 7 |
| 17 | 164 | 1.24 | 17.01 | 9 | 8 |
| 18 | 119 | 1.57 | 15.82 | 8 | 6 |
| 19 | 89 | 1.54 | 11.58 | 7 | 7 |
| 20 | 87 | 1.62 | 11.94 | 7 | 6 |
| 21 | 90 | 1.32 | 9.95 | 7 | 5 |
| 22 | 80 | 1.49 | 9.96 | 7 | 5 |
| 23 | 59 | 1.11 | 7.05 | 5 | 2 |
| 24 | 56 | 1.43 | 7.23 | 4 | 0 |

A typical caller usage report is shown in Table 8.9. This report is helpful in identifying the services most popular with the callers. If problems exist with the script, this report is often a valuable tool in identifying them. If callers are making

**Table 8.9**
Caller Usage Report

| Time run: 8:02 a.m. on April 2, 1992 | | | | | |
|---|---|---|---|---|---|
| *Transaction step label* | *Usage count* | *Retry count* | *Mean caller response time (seconds)* | *Caller input error count* | *Mean speech time (seconds)* |
| Rates | 87 | 9 | 8.5 | 2 | 6.54 |
| Savings | 678 | 98 | 6.6 | 12 | 4.33 |
| Checking | 983 | 108 | 5.4 | 16 | 7.44 |
| Loans | 143 | 19 | 8.3 | 4 | 9.77 |
| ATM | 107 | 3 | 3.6 | 2 | 5.32 |

too many errors or the response time is long, this usually indicates that the instructions are not clear enough and callers are becoming confused.

A trace report capability allows information to be tracked based on a key such as a caller PIN, a specific type of transaction, or a specific time interval. For example, the system administrator would enter the PIN of a particular caller, and the system would generate a report that lists all of the transactions associated with that particular PIN.

The ease with which reports can be generated varies significantly from one product to the next. Easy-to-use menu choices are provided with some of the products, while others require the system administrator to work at the operating system command-line level. Reports are available either on demand, or they can be scheduled to run at a particular date and time. The ability to create custom reports is a capability that exists with many of the IVR products. The primary variable is the ease with which custom reports can be created. The ability to store the statistics in a format that is compatible with commercially available database language processors is available with some of the products. This provides the user with a great deal of flexibility since the power of a full-fledged database processor is available for the reporting and analysis of statistical data.

### 8.3.2.3 IVR Password Encryption

Password encryption is needed for many applications, such as banking, in which access to the database must be kept secure. Most suppliers use the *Data Encryption Standard* (DES) of the *National Institute of Standards and Technology* (NIST), formerly the *National Bureau of Standards* (NBS). Typically the caller is able to change his or her (confidential) password as often as desired.

### 8.3.2.4 IVR Telephonic Capabilities

The basic telephone interface supported by all IVR systems is *loop start*. Some vendors provide ground start, E & M, and DID as either options or as part of the basic product. A few vendors provide support for MF signaling, DNIS, and ANI. Different interfaces are needed for connection with different telephone systems: the AT&T network is an ISDN PRI; MCI and Sprint provide DNIS and ANI using inband signaling. Most systems include a call transfer capability.

A T-1 capability is available from most vendors and is accomplished with either a channel-bank-type configuration or a direct connection. The completely digital approach (non-channel bank) typically costs less and provides a more comprehensive and flexible switching capability. The ability to mix analog and digital circuits on a single system is available on some of the systems.

### 8.3.2.5 IVR Application Generators

Most suppliers provide some sort of application generator for script development and editing. A procedural language oriented toward the voice application is commonly available, and menu-driven capabilities are often provided. Menu-driven application generators tend to limit system flexibility but often may be used by nonprogrammers. The implementation often consists of simply putting a front end on the procedural language processor. They are designed for easy use, and some have a *graphical user interface* (GUI). Although menu-driven packages are suitable for certain types of applications, in many cases their primary value is as a selling point. Procedural language application generators generally have more flexibility than the menu-driven variety but do require more real programming skills. The primary disadvantage of an application generator is that it requires the programmer to learn and support another programming approach. In many cases, the implementing organization has a strong programming environment already in place and is not interested in going to another programming environment. In this case, a library of functions may be more appropriate and is available from some of the suppliers.

### 8.3.2.6 IVR Networking

Most vendors offer networking to expand beyond the limits of a single computer. Existing LAN capabilities, such as NetWare or TCP/IP, are typically used. This networking is usually of an administrative nature, such as centralization of reporting, script updates, and prompt updates. The physical transport is typically a standard one such as Ethernet or Token-Ring, although some vendors have gone with proprietary ones. Performing remote administration and diagnostics is a capability that is provided with most of the products. See Figure 8.11 for examples of IVR networking.

### 8.3.2.7 IVR Product Capacities

IVR systems range in capacity from 4 to 96 ports for a single node; most PC-based systems have a total of 24 ports. Many systems that claim large port capacities in reality display significant response degradations at large call-volumes per port. The limiting factor (assuming that the processor and operating system is fast enough) is the disk access time. Prompt storage capacity is generally tied directly to the size of the hard disk; 11 Mb/hour of speech, at 24 kb/s, is typical. Prompt storage typically provided ranges from 3 to 10 hours. The amount of storage required varies dramatically with the type of application. A bank account balance application would require only a few minutes of speech, while a nationwide locator system for an organization with 10,000 locations would require many hours of recorded speech.

### 8.3.2.8 IVR Host Interfaces

The most commonly available interface is the IBM 3270. Most products emulate an IBM 3274 cluster controller. Support of either BISYNC or SDLC is usually available. A direct emulation of the 3270 screen is most commonly available. Some systems offer programming the voice-response product directly from the CICS environment. Other host environments supported by many products include IBM 5250, NCR polled terminal emulation, Burroughs (UNISYS) poll/select, and Asynchronous XON/XOFF.

The ability to have multiple applications, with each interfaced to a different host environment or able to access multiple-host environments, exists on many systems. The number of such host interfaces typically ranges from two to six.

### 8.3.2.9 IVR Facsimile and Data

Integrating facsimile and voice processing provides a powerful information delivery capability. In the basic capability the caller selects a particular document for delivery over facsimile. The caller may be required to enter the facsimile number, but for a subscription service, a password is adequate. The facsimile-response

**Figure 8.11(a)** New IVR product. (Photograph courtesy of AT&T.)

**Figure 8.11(b)** Old IVR product. (Photograph courtesy of AT&T.)

capability that is provided with most IVR systems is linked directly to the information that is being obtained from the host: the same or an expanded version of information available in voice form can be faxed to the caller.

Handling of data terminals is available on many systems. Frequently, specific ports are designated as data terminal ports and are used exclusively for communicating with terminals. In data-gathering applications that require the entry of alphanumeric information, this capability is essential. TDD support is becoming commonly available, driven by compliance with the *American Disability Act* (ADA). It is an essential capability for any of the vendors that are doing business with the Government.

### 8.3.3 IVR Application Categories

IVR applications can be broken into four different application areas:

- Remote database access and retrieval
- Automation of operator services

- Local database access retrieval
- Data collection

IVR systems for these areas have some similarities but are architecturally and functionally different from one another.

### 8.3.3.1 Remote Database Access and Retrieval

This is the classic environment in which a host database already exists and is being accessed on line by operators with VDTs. The effect is to automate the function of the human operator. In most cases, a user is reluctant to change any of the host software, so the product must provide a direct emulation of an existing terminal. The system accepts a PIN from the caller and then accesses the host to obtain the caller-requested information. In some cases, access to multiple-host environments during the course of a single call is required.

### 8.3.3.2 Automation of Operator Services

Operator services are provided either by the telephone company or by *alternate operator service* (AOS) providers. AOS providers or *operator services providers* (OSPs), as the industry prefers to be called, were created from the divestiture of the Bell System. The automation of operator services provides handling of all operator-assisted calls, as described in Chapter 6. The OSP area calls typically emanate from a public facility, such as a pay phone, hotel, or convention center, and are intercepted by OSP system, which would perform the operator function. For calling-card calls, the system plays a tone, accepts the calling card number, and validates it. If the card is validated, the call is placed. The OSP would make a business out of this by reselling long-distance lines (which are purchased in bulk from an IXC) and assessing a premium charge for each call. To improve the efficiency of this service, products have been developed to allow automatic handling of much of this traffic. When live operators are involved in a call, these systems provide information to them about the call's source and destination. The systems perform credit card validation, generate detailed call records, rate the calls, and put them into a form that can be used by the billing organization. The RBOCs have extensively deployed a system called *automated alternate billing service* (AABS) that, in addition to the automation of the calling card, also automates collect and bill-to-third-party calls. In most deployments, speech recognition has been used to automate these calls.

### 8.3.3.3 Local Database Access and Retrieval

In many applications, the database is created specifically for the voice-processing application and thus is often relatively stable. Examples of this are the locator systems that let a caller locate the nearest ATM, pizza shop, or auto dealer. The caller enters the NPA and NXX numbers, and the system searches the database to locate the facility nearest that phone number. Note that with ANI, the caller does not even have to enter the telephone number—he or she simply makes a call, and the locator system responds automatically. Entering the Zip code is another approach that has been used. This works well for residents who know their local Zip codes, but it does not work well for travelers who might not. Express mail companies use this approach for identifying the location of the sender or recipient of a package. Telemarketing campaigns are another type of local database access application. Callers will typically leave their name and address, which then must be transcribed. Some systems can transcribe the messages on line, while others dump the audio messages and perform the transcription off line.

### 8.3.3.4 Data Collection

These systems focus on the real-time collection of data. Factory data collection is one area in which the primary application is the gathering of quality control data in real time. For many applications, speech recognition has been used because of the hands-busy and eyes-busy nature of the function, as described in Chapter 5. The user is prompted to enter data in a structured manner. The system gathers this information and puts it into a database for analysis and statistical reporting. Trouble and attendance reporting and building security are other applications in this area.

### 8.3.4 Turnkey Versus Toolkit Suppliers

The suppliers of IVR systems can be categorized as either AGTK suppliers or turnkey system suppliers. Turnkey system suppliers typically provide a fully operational system programmed for the customer's specific application. The script is created, prompts are recorded, and the system is tested in the customer's environment. The vendor creates the interface with both the telephone system and the host computer database.

The individual components of an IVR system are available from a variety of sources. Voice and telephonic interface boards that plug directly into a PC are also available, as are AGTKs for developing the script, defining the telephone interface, recording and editing the prompts, and defining the host interface. A customer with system engineering skills may implement a system with the tools available. The advantages of this approach are that the external cost is lower, and the customer has direct control over system implementation. The customer can also make any changes required after the system has been commissioned. The disadvantage of this approach is that a level of technical skill is required that many customers do not have. A voice-response system is complex, and getting it to work in a reliable fashion requires significant system engineering skills. Appendix 2 lists the suppliers of voice transaction processing systems and categorizes them. Figures 8.12(a), 8.12(b), and 8.12(c) show typical IVR systems.

**Figure 8.12(a)** Large-configuration IVR system. (Photograph courtesy of InterVoice, Inc.)

**Figure 8.12(b)** Small-configuration IVR system. (Photograph courtesy of InterVoice, Inc.)

## 8.3.5 IVR Trends and Future Directions

The trend toward standardized systems that are easy to configure and customize will continue. A few years ago, most voice transaction-processing systems were rigid, custom-engineered products. Any changes to the system, even changing a single prompt, required going back to the supplier. This situation was a significant hindrance to market growth, systems were too expensive, and not enough engineers and programmers could implement them. Establishing the interface to the host application correctly is one of the main activities of creating an IVR system. The host application environment varies from one site to the next. It does turn out, though, that many of the host applications within a particular market segment (such as banking or education) are provided by the same vendors. This means that the applications within a particular market segment are standardized to the extent

**Figure 8.12(c)** Large-capacity IVR system. (Photograph courtesy of Perception Technology Corporation.)

that the screens that the IVR system needs to emulate are the same from one site to the next. Vendors that focus on specific market segments and organize to take advantage of this are able to create a custom IVR application with a minimum of effort.

The introduction of standardized systems designed for ready customization has greatly expanded the application area. The differences between the transaction-processing and information-provider areas will blur, and suppliers will work in both areas.

Most of the vendors have either gone to a direct T-1 all-digital interface or are in the process of going to it. When analog ports are needed, a conversion device, similar to a channel bank, is provided. The cost, even to provide analog ports, turns out to be significantly lower. Performance is better and a great deal of additional flexibility is available for call switching.

Telephone switching capabilities will become integral in most voice transaction-processing systems. Support for telephone network features such as ANI and DNIS will become a standard feature of a voice transaction-processing system. If the address of the calling station can be determined, a variety of services can be developed. Most inbound telemarketing services need to identify the calling party. The response to the call could be different depending upon who the caller was or where the call originated. CATV pay-per-view, 911, and shop-at-home systems are a few services already using this capability. Being able to route a call to the proper service facility will find many applications. The frustration and expense of calling a number and reaching a modem or a facsimile machine could be eliminated. Having calling features available to the user at any station in the network will be an attractive capability, and many services will be built around it. Voice-processing products will become multifunction systems that integrate a variety of communications and information-delivery mechanisms. Facsimile response will become a popular delivery mechanism in a transaction-processing system.

Facsimile has become a ubiquitous communications vehicle in the business community. For many applications, it is a highly appropriate means of providing information to a caller. For applications in which hard copy is appropriate or required, a combined voice-response and facsimile-response capability is attractive. The use of facsimile with voice response will permit systems to address a set of new applications, in addition to existing applications now being served with video display or printer terminals, the United States Postal Service, or express delivery services.

## 8.4 INFORMATION-PROVIDER SYSTEMS

Information-provider products are defined as systems that provide access to public information. The information-provider market is a relatively small segment for CPE suppliers. Distribution is almost all direct sales, with only a small number of *original equipment manufacturer* (OEM) relationships. Space brokers and service bureaus, which provide everything that an information provider needs to start, are readily available. Most suppliers also work in other segments such as transaction processing, automated attendant, or voice mail. In some cases, the supplier of the information-provider product also provides a service as a separate business activity.

### 8.4.1 Hardware and Software Characteristics

Many products are PC based, and they all have the ability to create a tree that can be traversed by the caller in an interactive fashion to obtain information. Menu-driven packages for creating trees are commonly available; the ability to modify the tree quickly and to change prompts rapidly is a key capability. Other important features include automatic prompt rotation, remote prompt updating, predigitized prompt updating, switch caller, accept messages from callers and transcribe them quickly, and remote call counts.

One requirement that distinguishes information-provider systems from transaction-processing systems is that the application is changed frequently. The information content also changes more rapidly.

### 8.4.2 System Features

Some of the features available with many information provider systems include:

- Time-based rotation of prompts and programs;
- Time-based deletion of prompts and programs;
- Message rotation per call;
- Skipping days;
- Random and rotational prompt play;
- Area code and zip code tables;
- Conferencing;
- Capture and store program feeds from DowPhone, AP StockQuotes, or other information services;
- Security for remote prompt recording;
- Dynamic port allocation to meet particular program needs.

The ability of the system to change its features dynamically is a characteristic of most information-provider systems. Prompts can be changed or rotated on each call, or at specific times. To record a prompt remotely, the user calls the system and enters a password. This permits access to a prompt rerecord facility, and the user can then rerecord any of the prompts from a remote site.

Multiple programs can run simultaneously on a single information-provider system. Dynamic port allocation provides the available ports to the program that has the most traffic and needs the capacity.

### 8.4.3 Speech Phrase Creation and Editing

Voice prompt quality is particularly important in an information-provider system. Each system allows the user to create and edit prompts. Advanced capabilities include the ability to edit a specific prompt and to create multiple prompts from a single audio file. The most basic editing capability allows the user to slice silence from either end of a prompt. The resolution with which this can be done varies from one product to the next. It is typically 0.1 seconds, although some systems are able to resolve to 0.01 seconds.

The ability to listen to a sequence of prompts, as they would be heard in a live application, is an important capability and is found in most systems. Creating and editing prompts while the system is running the application is an area in which most systems have some significant limitations. Many systems do not allow use of the prompt editor without taking the system down, but they do provide a remote rerecord capability. With this, specific prompts can be designated as remotely recordable. These prompts can then be recorded over the telephone while the system is running.

Recording all the prompts as a continuous audio string and then breaking this string into individual prompts is a capability that exists on a few systems. For applications that have a large vocabulary, this capability is invaluable. The capability to cut and paste is also found in a few systems and can be useful in fine tuning an application. Control of the recording volume is another valuable capability that is found in some products.

### 8.4.4 Usage Statistics Reporting

Usage statistics and the reports generated from them are critical aspects of an information-provider environment. The success of a service is directly tied to the volume of call traffic. Knowledge of the topics that interest callers is of utmost importance to the information provider. Unpopular topics are eliminated quickly and replaced with new ones. The system's ability to handle peak loads is also important. The information provider wants to know if callers are getting busy signals. A call to an information service is often based on an impulse decision. A caller getting a busy signal means the system loses the call and the associated revenue. The information provider uses port-usage profiles to determine if more ports should be added.

Reporting on the system-loading profile and caller use patterns is provided with most information-provider systems. Telephone traffic reports typically include

- Number of calls on each line:
  - On a per hour basis;
  - For a designated period (often with fine granularity).
- Percentage of time each line is used:
  - On a per hour basis.
- Other information about each line on either an hourly or 24-hour basis:
  - Average call length;
  - Percentage out-of-service.

Obtaining call counts sorted on a regional basis (by zip code and area code) is available on many information-provider systems, as is remote access (by telephone) to call counts.

Having a great deal of flexibility in specifying the reporting time interval is important in an information-provider system. Advertising triggers many of the calls. The effect of a television advertisement is most dramatic during the first few minutes after the advertisement is run. Being able to relate the call volumes that occur directly to an advertisement allows the system administrator to make a judgment advertising value.

Caller-usage reports track caller-usage patterns, selecting specific menus for reporting. The reports typically include

- Number of times a menu was accessed;
- Average response time of the caller;
- Number of retries;
- Number of errors;
- Average prompt time.

This information helps identify subjects that are most popular and shows how easily the caller can use them.

### 8.4.5 Telephonic Capabilities

The basic telephone interface supported by all information-provider systems is *loop start*. Some of the vendors provide ground start and DID as either options or as part of the basic product. A few vendors also provide support for MF signaling and ANI. The ability to detect far-end call disconnect is also provided on many systems. Most vendors offer a T-1 capability. The dialogic board set, for example, provides a fairly graceful capability in a channel bank fashion. Only a few vendors provide a completely digital interface.

### 8.4.6 Application Generator

Most suppliers provide some sort of application generator for script development and editing. A procedural language oriented toward voice application is also commonly available. Vendors also often provide menu-driven capabilities, which tend to limit the system flexibility, but often are usable by nonprogrammers. Implementing this often means simply putting a front end on the procedural language processor. Although menu-driven packages are suitable for certain types of applications, they are more useful as a selling tool.

### 8.4.7 Networking

Most vendors advertise a networking capability for expansion beyond the limits of a single computer. Existing LAN capabilities, such as NetWare or TCP/IP, are typically used. Administrative in nature, networking includes such examples as centralization of reporting, script updates, and prompts updates.

### 8.4.8 Product Capacities

Information-provider systems (see Figure 8.13) range in capacity from 4 to 96 ports. Most PC-based systems have a total of 24 ports. Many systems that claim large port capacities, in reality, display significant response degradation at large port-count call volumes. Prompt storage capacity is generally tied directly to the size of the hard disk; 11 Mb/hr of speech is typical. Prompt storage usually provided ranges from 3 to 10 hours. Appendix 3 lists many information-provider product suppliers.

**Figure 8.13** Information-provider system. (Photograph courtesy of Brite Voice Systems.)

### 8.5 PASSIVE INTERCEPT

Passive intercept products are also known as digital announcers. These devices are a special type of information-provider product. They answer the telephone and play an announcement and are used in environments that use a single voice message played frequently. The number of applications is enormous. A few are listed in Table 8.10.

The telephone company application is one of the largest. Any time a caller is intercepted, a digital announcer is used. "The number you have reached . . . has been changed. The new number is . . ." is a common interception announcement. Information service number announcements are accomplished using digital announcers. The market is a mature one. The products are of almost a commodity nature and are readily available from a variety of distribution sources. Many suppliers of digital announcers also provide IVR systems such as automated attendants, information-provider systems, or transaction-processing systems. The

**Table 8.10**
Digital Announcer Applications

| | |
|---|---|
| Building evacuation | Music-on-hold |
| Canned agent announcements | Rental car return instructions |
| Dial-a-prayer | School closings |
| Exhibit announcements | Ski conditions |
| Exhibit explanations | Stock reports |
| Fire alarm messages | Telephone company intercepts |
| Hours of operation | Automatic call distributor front-end greetings |
| Interest rates | Utility service outage |
| Jury duty assignments | Wake-up calls |
| Movie theatre times | Weather reports |

telephone company intercept is different than most of the applications shown in Table 8.10, since it uses a database lookup to identify the appropriate message to play to the caller. Appendix 4 lists many of the suppliers of passive interception products.

### 8.5.1 Product Characteristics

These products are stand-alone devices that are fundamentally characterized by three items:

1. The number of ports;
2. The length of the message or messages;
3. The number of messages.

Digital announcers either have a single port, or a small number of ports (five to six) in a box. Prices range from a few hundred dollars per port to over a thousand dollars per port. The length of a message varies from a few seconds to over five minutes. The ability to set message length is usually an optional feature. For multiline units, multiple messages can be created and one assigned to each port.

Other features that differentiate passive intercept products are remote re-record of messages and the ability to start at the beginning of the message on each call. Some devices can be programmed to either play continuously or to start the message from the beginning when the telephone is answered. Call-count reporting is available on a few products.

For many applications, the units must interface directly with telephones on the headset side. Compatibility with the various ACD telephone sets is an issue with these units because no standardization exists at this end. Many units are designed to run on batteries during a power outage and will operate on the −48V provided in the central office.

### 8.5.2 Trends and Future Direction

These products will continue to be an appropriate solution for applications that require a repetitive message at a low cost. We do not anticipate that the profile of these products will change dramatically. Appendix 4 lists many of the providers of passive intercept products.

### 8.6 OUTBOUND CALL-PROCESSING SYSTEMS

The outbound voice-processing area contains two different product types. Devices that can be programmed to automatically dial a group of numbers and play a message (and frequently obtain a response from the recipient of the call) and TSR-based dialers, which can be programmed to dial a group of numbers and connect the called party with a telephone service representative. The former are known as *automatic dialer recorded message players* (ADRMPs). The ADRMP units are given a list of telephone numbers to dial and a message to deliver. They can then be turned on to dial large numbers of people automatically. These units are frequently stand-alone devices that dial a single line at a time. Price is typically less than $5,000 for a single-port unit. These products have been used in applications that typically have either a low volume and steady outdialing requirement or an emergency-only requirement.

Many applications are highly specialized and address a particular market niche. Multiple-port units are primarily used where there is a need to dial a large number of people in a short period of time, such as in emergency-notification situations. TSR-based dialing units perform all the number dialing, call-progress detection, and getting a person on the line. The dialer connects an operator with the line when a person has answered, which frees the operator from dialing the number and monitoring the call progress. These units are usually connected with a host database that contains the information about each person being called, including the telephone number. TSR-based dialers cost between $6,000 and $10,000 per operator station. The benefits of a TSR-based dialer are: increase in call center productivity, better customer service results from screen information available on each customer, automatic dialing and connection, callback scheduling, and automatic call wrap-up. The campaign list broadens and increases, and more customers can be called per hour. Call center management and discipline improve through monitoring the real-time operation of the center and comprehensive statistics reporting. The effectiveness of a campaign can be evaluated much more quickly and modified if necessary to optimize results. The use of telephone network resources can be optimized by selecting the least costly line.

Four different types of TSR-based dialers are available: preview dialers, progressive dialers, power dialers, and predictive dialers. With preview dialers, sequential call records are brought to the screen of the TSR. After reviewing the record, the TSR pushes a button to initiate the call. The TSR monitors the call progress and initiates a conversation when the call is answered by a person. Progressive dialers dial numbers from a list, and the TSR does not see the call record before the call is being dialed. When the call is completed, another call is automatically initiated. Power dialers initiate multiple calls at a rate that is controlled by the supervisor of the call center. The intent is to initiate more calls than there are TSRs available to assure that the TSRs are always busy. The call rate is adjusted so that a small number of occurrences of an answered called with "no TSR available" happen. If the rate is too high, many "no TSR available" situations will occur. If it is too slow, the TSRs will not be kept busy enough. A predictive dialer is similar to a power dialer. It shares the benefit of maximum TSR productivity and enhanced monitoring and supervision, but reduces the occurrence of "no TSR available" situations. Predictive dialers use automatic pacing algorithms to control the dialing rate. The dialing rate is adjusted automatically by parameters such as: average length of conversation, percentage of answered calls, and number of available TSRs [4].

### 8.6.1 Product Characterization

Most ADRMP products are single-port units able to dial a large set of preprogrammed telephone numbers and perform extensive call-progress detection. The length of message delivered, number of messages, number of dialed phone numbers, and call-status reports are among key product features. Many dialers can accept responses from the called party, and a few have the ability to deliver the caller-obtained information to a remote system through a data link. TSR-based dialing products are either single- or multi-port systems that support individual or a group of TSRs in making large volumes of calls. These systems obtain information (typically from a host database) about the called party and provide it to the operator at a VDT. The system automatically dials the telephone number and connects the called party with the TSR after the connection is made. The predictive dialing and power dialing product are conceptually similar to ACDs, but in reverse.

### 8.6.2 Applications

Collections is one of the primary market applications for both ADRMP products and predictive dialers. Schools use ADRMP products to notify parents of absent or tardy children, a major application of such products. Automatic electronic monitoring of convicted criminals in a home-confinement sentencing program is also a growing market area because of prison overcrowding. Notification of repairs being complete is another significant application area. ADRMP products have been used for emergency notification of events such as a nuclear disaster or a flood. For predictive dialing products, telemarketing, polling, and market research are major areas. Predictive dialing significantly increases the operator productivity— some companies claim increases of as much as 300%.

### 8.6.3 Product Features

TSR-based dialing products are able to

- Determine particular telephone numbers to be called, according to type (e.g., delinquent more than 60 days).
- Perform least cost call routing.
- Screen and list all nonconnects (e.g., busy, telephone company intercepts, ring/no-answer) for recall.
- Restrict calling numbers based on time zones (specific sets of numbers belonging to a particular time zone can only be called during certain hours).
- Recycle busy, ring/no-answer, and not-home results (Different algorithms are available for recycling and the number of times that the number is to be retried).
- Perform secondary number dialing (supervisor distinguishes times for which primary and secondary customer numbers are dialed by the system).
- Specification of messages used by the operator.
- Transfer instantaneously a live contact, with all customer information, to the operator.
- Issue extensive reports that reflect system operations and provide details on operator performance.
- Schedule callbacks to a customer.
- Capture call result.
- Permit agent modification of a customer's record.

The results of a call can usually be categorized readily. Single keyentries are provided for each of these results, which could be: promise, no promise, left message, wrong number, disconnected number, and request callback. Calls that do not reach the agent, such as busy and ring/no-answer, are also categorized and scheduled for recycling.

The TSR's ability to modify the customer's record is used primarily for changes to a customer telephone number or address. A least-call-routing capability determines the telephone facility that would provide the lowest telephone cost for a call.

A supervisory workstation is used for establishing call lists, changing line-to-operator ratio, adjusting call pacing, viewing operational data, starting up or shutting down the system, monitoring any call by listening in, or listening and talking in a three-way conversation. Determining how the calls are to be distributed within the agent workgroup permits the workload to be distributed to accommodate special situations, such as an inexperienced agent.

Calls may be traced to a particular agent. The feature is particularly useful in environments where the agents receive sales commissions. Real-time displays are available that report agent and campaign statistics. These displays are used to make operational decisions as the shift progresses through a call list. Automatic pacing of the call rate is a capability available with many predictive dialing products. This tends to optimize the call rate to the particular environment.

Automatic dialers can function independently of the host environment or be configured to operate interactively on line with the host computer. Typical predictive dialing system configurations are shown in Figures 8.14(a) through (c). The systems range from those in which the workstation is directly coupled to the host, and has very little local intelligence, to those that are almost totally stand-alone. For the ones that are most dependent on the host computer, the host must be able to keep up with the calling sequences. Free-standing dialers typically have the entire campaign database resident on a minicomputer, which is part of the dialer. Interfaces to load the database from a host system are also available. A preview capability is available with most predictive dialing systems, which allows the agent to obtain the customer's records without actually calling the customer. Prerecorded messages can be provided for the operator to use as appropriate. These would be used for repetitive voice messages, such as greetings or closeouts.

In ADRMP products, the following features are commonly found:

- Remote activation from any DTMF telephone;
- Security on activation;
- Identification entry of individuals to be called;
- Call-back to verify that message is correct;
- Remote cancel;
- Passcode for recipient's option;
- Redial of uncompleted calls (i.e., busy, ring-no-answer, answering machine);
- Dialing of alternative numbers for unanswered phones;
- Random dialing of telephone numbers from a list;
- Programmable telephone number length (up to 22 digits);
- Multiple lists;
- Priority levels for calling.

The capacity of an ADRMP system varies from one product to the next. The specifications that will vary are:

- The number of telephone numbers that can be stored ranges from 5,000 to 200,000.
- The number of telephone lines that can be dialed simultaneously varies from 1 to 24.

**Figure 8.14(a)** Predictive dialing system. (Photograph courtesy of International Telesystems Corporation.)

- The number of prerecorded messages varies from 10 to 200.
- The length of prerecorded messages varies from 30 seconds to 5 minutes.
- The number of calls that can be made per minute depends upon the percentage of completions, the length of the prerecorded messages, and the number of ports.

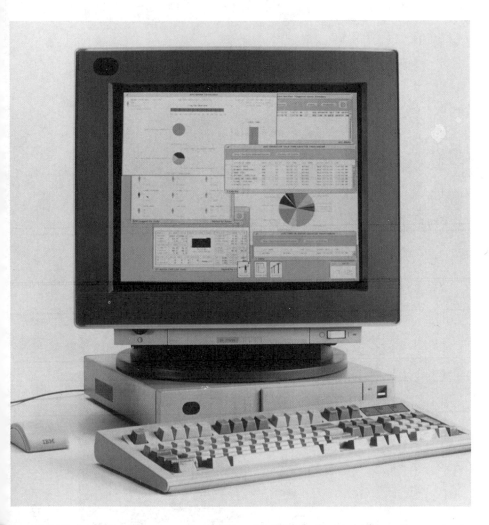

**Figure 8.14(b)** Predictive dialing supervisor station. (Photograph courtesy of Davox Corporation.)

## 8.6.4 Reports

System summary reports are typically provided, listing the number of records that were worked and the number that were busy, ring/no-answer, answering machine, telephone company intercept and sent to an agent, promises obtained, promises not obtained, and the agent action. Table 8.11 is an example of a system summary report.

System efficiency reports are also provided, listing the total number of records, the number that were worked, the number of dials, the number of contacts,

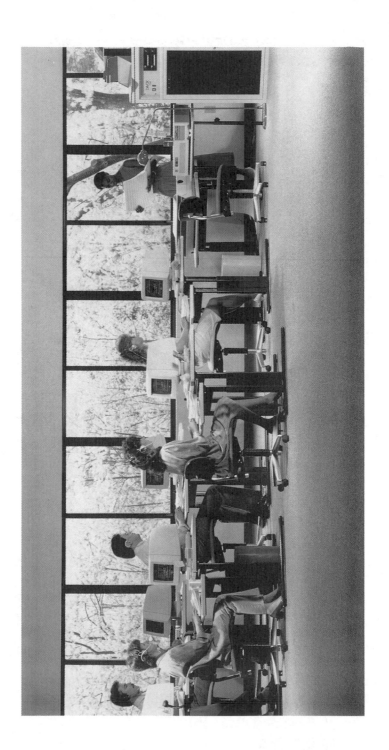

**Figure 8.14(c)** Predictive dialing operating environment. (Photograph courtesy of Davox Corporation.)

**Table 8.11**
Outbound Call Processing Typical Project Summary Report

OFFICE ID: 3
CLIENT NAME: ABC Bank
PROJECT NAME: Credit Card Collection
DATE PRINTED: April 2, 1992

| Item | Number | Percentage of calls | Time spent (HH:MM:SS) | Percentage of time |
|------|--------|--------------------|-----------------------|--------------------|
| Total number of records | 20,978 | | | |
| Total number of numbers dialed | 20,554 | 100% | | |
| Number of promises | 6,655 | 32.4% | 9982:30:05 | 56.0% |
| Number of no promises | 3,339 | 16.2% | 4730:15:45 | 26.6% |
| Number of no answers | 5,893 | 28.7% | | |
| Number of left messages | 4,667 | 22.7% | 3111:18:25 | 17.4% |
| Totals | | | 17824:04:15 | |

total hours worked, average records per hour, contact rate per hour and percentage of no answers. Agent efficiency reports list the elapsed work time of each operator, total calls received, average duration of each call, promises obtained, and allocation of time. Table 8.12 is an example of an agent efficiency report. An abandoned call report lists the number of calls that are abandoned before and after the agents answer a live call, average wait, and longest wait. Appendix 5 provides a listing of many of the outbound voice-processing product suppliers.

## .6.5 Trends and Future Direction

inbound call processing will become a more significant portion of the outbound call-processing area. Systems will become more standardized and readily configurable. The port capacity of systems will increase to handle the needs of a large service bureau environment. Product costs will decrease to less than $5,000 per agent station.

**Table 8.12**

Outbound Call Processing Agent Efficiency Report

| Agent | Active duration (minutes) | Calls made | Contacts per hour | Promises | Promises per hour | Allocation of time (Minutes) | |
|---|---|---|---|---|---|---|---|
| | | | | | | Connect | Idle |
| Abbot, Jill | 143.44 | 87 | 31.88 | 43 | 19.1 | 135.2 | 8.2 |
| Bishop, Sue | 128.88 | 75 | 30.26 | 39 | 19.5 | 120.1 | 8.8 |
| Brere, John | 176.65 | 104 | 30.57 | 40 | 18.0 | 163.5 | 13.2 |
| Cameron, Jan | 155.99 | 96 | 29.32 | 49 | 21.1 | 144.7 | 11.3 |
| Harn, Sharon | 143.88 | 90 | 29.19 | 51 | 19.2 | 134.6 | 9.3 |
| Thoms, Karen | 206.09 | 114 | 29.04 | 43 | 18.8 | 194.5 | 11.6 |
| Wilson, Mary | 164.08 | 101 | 30.49 | 61 | 19.4 | 158.4 | 5.7 |

Growth in this market segment will be driven by telemarketing industry growth. The service bureaus are currently at a low automation level—less than 6%. Distribution channels will be expanded to include a significant VAR and dealer effort. This will provide the total solutions needed for this market area to register significant growth.

## 8.7 FACSIMILE RESPONSE AND DISTRIBUTION

We anticipate that requesting information and receiving it over facsimile will be a major information delivery vehicle. The ubiquity of the facsimile machine will make it an efficient and rapid way of obtaining information. Facsimile messaging will also become popular in specialized situations [5].

The remote retrieval of information by facsimile has application in a variety of situations. Some of the kinds of information that have been provided over facsimile are shown in Table 8.13.

The very best applications are ones in which the information is changing regularly and is important to obtain immediately. For example, pilot weather flight information is in this class. Information that is fairly unchanging (such as a report) could be a good application if the information were needed immediately.

The dramatic growth of express delivery services such as Federal Express and immediate delivery devices such as facsimile machines indicates an enormous market for this capability. The facsimile market has experienced phenomenal growth during the last few years. Table 8.14 is a profile of the working installed base of facsimile units. Note that the average use of each facsimile machine is increasing steadily.

The percentage of business lines that have a facsimile connected to them is a good measure of the penetration of facsimile into the business environment. In Japan, over 20% of all business lines are for facsimile; in the United States it is 4%, and in Europe it is only 2%. Ignoring the language difference, which causes facsimile to be even more of a business necessity in Japan, this would indicate that major growth will occur in the United States and Europe. We anticipate that by the end of 1995, over fifty million facsimile machines will be in use throughout the world. Sending documents by facsimile is the fastest way, and usually the least expensive way as well. Table 8.15 shows document delivery costs for a variety of methods [6].

Facsimile-response products will have many of the same requirements as the purely voice-based transaction-processing systems. The ability to obtain documents to be sent is one of the areas in which the systems will differ. Appendix 8 lists many of the suppliers of facsimile-response messaging products and facsimile service bureaus. Some of the ways in which a document could be obtained are to

- Send a facsimile to the system;
- Scan a document;

**Table 8.13**
Facsimile Response Applications

| | |
|---|---|
| Ad layouts | Newsletters |
| Art approvals | Newspaper clippings |
| Bills of lading | Newspaper summaries |
| Boating condition reports | Order status |
| Buy and sell orders | Packing lists |
| Car loan applications | Plane tickets |
| Circuit diagrams | Press releases |
| Company news | Price lists |
| Contracts | Product specifications |
| Credit card authorization | Purchase orders |
| Credit forms | Questionnaire |
| Damage reports | Racing form updates |
| Delivery receipts | Real estate information |
| Engineering sketches | Rental information |
| Financial instrument prices | Repair information |
| Financial statements | Research papers |
| Flight weather information | Resumes |
| Government publications | Sales reports |
| Installation orders | Sandwich shop menus |
| Insurance applications | Signed receipts |
| Insurance binders | Sketches |
| Interest rates | Ski condition reports |
| Earned interest statements | Specifications |
| Invoices | Stock market advisories |
| Legal papers | Technical manual revision sheets |
| Manuscripts and corrections | Theater tickets |
| Maps | Trucking permits |
| Medical coverage information | Weather maps |

- Create the document with a graphic language processor;
- Obtain the document through a floppy disk file;
- Obtain the document using a remote host computer.

## 8.8 AUTOMATIC CALL DISTRIBUTORS

An ACD accepts incoming calls and directs them to the TSR that has been idle
the longest or to the TSR that has had the fewest number of calls. TSRs are usually
grouped into functional units, which are called groups, gates, splits, or queues.
With the basic ACD function, calls are routed to the agent group that is associated

**Table 8.14**

Facsimile usage

| Year | Working installed base | Average pages/day | Pages sent/year |
|------|------------------------|-------------------|-----------------|
| 1985 | 2.0M | 1.8 | 0.8B |
| 1986 | 3.2M | 2.1 | 1.5B |
| 1987 | 5.5M | 4.3 | 5.2B |
| 1988 | 9.6M | 5.7 | 12.0B |
| 1989 | 14.8M | 6.1 | 19.9B |
| 1990 | 20.5M | 7.6 | 34.3B |
| 1991 | 27.0M | 8.6 | 51.1B |
| 1992 | 33.6M | 9.9 | 73.2B |
| 1993 | 40.2M | 10.9 | 96.4B |
| 1994 | 49.2M | 12.3 | 133.1B |
| 1995 | 56.5M | 14.3 | 177.7B |

with a particular telephone trunk or group of trunks. If TSRs are not available to take a call, the ACD system holds the callers in a queue and plays an announcement or series of announcements to the caller. If a caller is in a queue for a predetermined length of time, the ACD can be programmed to route the call to another TSR group.

**Table 8.15**

Document delivery costs (5 pages from Boston to San Francisco)

| Delivery Service | Cost |
|------------------|------|
| Federal Express | $14.00 |
| Express Mail | $ 8.75 |
| United Parcel Service | $ 8.50 |
| Telex | $17.70 |
| Group 3 facsimile | $1.25 |

**Figure 8.15** Facsimile-processing system. (Photograph courtesy of AudioFax Corporation.)

### 8.8.1 ACD Components

The basic components that compose an ACD are

- Incoming line interfaces;
- Switching system;
- Call-routing processor;
- TSR stations;
- Supervisor stations;
- *Management information system* (MIS).

### 8.8.1.1 Incoming Line Interface

Included in the lines that are commonly supported are local exchange lines, 800 service lines, PBX extensions, T-carrier trunks, tie trunks, and ISDN PRI trunks.

### 8.8.1.2 ACD Call-Routing Processor

This portion of the ACD routes the calls through a series of steps that depend on the caller (who it is and what they want), the number that was called, and the loading status of call center. Routing capabilities and features include

- Date/time programmed routing;
- Conditional routing;
- Telephone-network-directed routing;
- Caller-directed routing;
- Data-directed routing;
- Overflow;
- Intraflow;
- Interflow.

### 8.8.1.3 ACD TSR Stations

These are often specifically designed to support the operation of a TSR in a high-call-volume environment.

### 8.8.1.4 ACD Supervisor Stations

These permit the supervisor to monitor the operation of a TSR or TSR group, communicate with that TSR or TSR group, adjust the call center environment to match the nature of the call traffic and obtain real-time information on system and TSR activity.

### 8.8.1.5 ACD MIS Capability

These provide details, reports, and charts on TSR, trunk, and overall system performance.

### 8.8.1.6 Other ACD Capabilities

Capabilities that are offered with many ACDs include

- Networking;
- Distributed architecture;

- Voice mail and automated attendant;
- IVR;
- Remote diagnostics/alarming;
- Redundancy.

### 8.8.2 ACD Characteristics

ACD charactistics are determined by the call-processing techniques, supervisor station capabilities, TSR station capabilities, and the MIS reports available.

### 8.8.2.1 Call Processing

ACDs provide a variety of ways to process a call. Commonly available techniques include conditional routing, network-directed routing, data-directed routing, intraflow, and interflow.

*Conditional Routing.* Conditional routing provides for the calls to be routed differently based on dynamic conditions such as the hold time of the longest queue, the number of calls in queue, and the number of available TSRs. Dependent on these conditions, an ACD system can play different announcements, divert or forward calls to other TSR groups, or encourage callers to leave a recorded message that would result in a call-back from a TSR at a later time. ACDs can often be programmed to route differently depending upon the date and time.

*Network-Directed Routing.* Network-directed routing uses information obtained from the telephone network such as DNIS or ANI. With DNIS, the last four digits of the dialed number would be used to route the call to a particular TSR group. With ANI, the entire number of the caller is available and calls could be routed to a specific TSR group based on either the specific number or some aspect of the callers number (e.g., route all calls with certain area codes to a particular TSR group).

*Caller-Directed Routing.* Caller-directed routing requests that the caller select the service that they are trying to reach. This is essentially an auto-attendant function in which the caller is presented with a series of choices and is prompted to select the desired service by entering touch-tone inputs. Based on the caller input, the caller is routed to the appropriate service. This could be a specific TSR group, an automated information line, a voice-mail system, a facsimile-response system, or an IVR system for database access.

*Data-Directed Routing.* Data-directed routing obtains information from the caller such as an account or identification number, references this information against a customer database, and routes the call to the TSR group that is appropriate for this caller. Information from the database is typically sent to the TSR. This is usually the caller's name and account number, but could be other information about the caller, such as past buying profiles or credit history. The information being provided to the TSR is synchronized with the arrival of the call.

*Intraflow.* Intraflow provides for the routing of calls from one TSR group to another within the same ACD. The criteria for intraflow occurring is programmed by the system administrator to occur when certain thresholds are reached based on the length of time a call is queued and the number of calls that are in queue. In some of the systems when intraflow occurs, callers may be queued into separate TSR groups, and if the first group becomes available before the second one, the caller is taken by the first TSR group.

*Interflow.* Interflow is the routing of calls to other, often remotely located ACDs based on system conditions. The capability to make the determination whether it is appropriate to route the call to a remote ACD is based on a calculation to determine if the call would be completed more quickly if interflow occurred. This requires that conditions at each ACD be analyzed, which is called look-ahead interflow.

Emergency alert is a capability that permits a TSR to quickly respond to a threatening phone call. Most ACD systems provide a single-button capability and a way for the TSR to communicate the nature of the threat to a supervisor.

### 8.8.2.2 Supervisor Stations

Supervisor stations are typically special consoles that permit the supervisor to view the activity of each TSR (e.g., idle, active on a call, doing postcall work, doing an outbound call, out to lunch). The amount of time that TSRs are spending in specific work states referenced to specific target parameters is provided. Information about the number of calls in queue and call holding time is provided at the supervisor station. The ability to silently monitor a call of a particular TSR is another feature included with most supervisor stations.

### 8.8.2.3 TSR Features

Features that are commonly provided for a TSR include

- Supervisor assistance;
- Direct outward dialing;
- Entry of type of call;
- Call conferencing;
- Call transfer;
- Information;
- Supervisor messages;

- Trunk group number;
- Number of calls in queue;
- Wrap-up prompting.

### 8.8.2.4 MIS Information Provided

Standard reports are typically provided to address seven basic areas: performance, users, trunks, applications, lost calls, queued calls, and exceptions. The reporting time period can be specified as hourly, daily, weekly, or monthly. The reports reflect statistics for the time period just ended or for a time period specified by the user.

Real-time information is also provided, which displays the performance of the ACD in real time. The current activities of individual TSRs and ACD groups are provided. In addition to the status of each TSR, information provided includes total calls-waiting service; length of time the oldest call has waited for service; average speed of answer; percentage of calls abandoned during the last 10 minutes; number of TSRs signed on; number of idle agents; number of TSRs performing postcall work; number of TSRs engaged in outgoing calls; number of TSRs handling incoming calls; and number of TSRs ready to accept incoming calls.

Many of the ACD MIS systems use color to highlight special items such as a critical threshold being exceeded. For historical information, many of the ACD systems show the information in a graphic (histogram) format. The ability to create custom reports is a capability that is commonly available with most ACD MIS products, although it is often priced as an option.

ACDs are available as either stand-alone systems or as a PBX option. Figure 8.16 shows an ACD system. Appendix 11 provides information about many of the ACD product suppliers.

### 8.8.3 ACD/Computer Interface Standards

Data-directed routing suggests a communication between the ACD and a host computer that contains the customer database. Each of the ACD products does have a ACD-to-computer interface. Each of the suppliers has taken his or her own approach, and, as expected, no standard interface exists at this time. Two standards bodies are presently engaged in the development of standards recommendations for computer-telephone interfaces: the *European Computer Manufacturers Association* (ECMA) is working on a standard known as *Computer-Supported Telephony Applications* (CSTA); and the *American National Standards Institute* (ANSI) is working on a standard referred to as *Switch-Computer Application Interface* (SCAI). Although some coordination of the work of these two bodies is occurring, it is unlikely that these two standards will converge for some time yet.

**Figure 8.16** ACD system. (Photograph courtesy of Aspect Telecommunications Corporation.)

## 8.9 MULTIFUNCTION VOICE-PROCESSING SYSTEMS

Future voice-processing systems will be different from the currently existing systems in the following ways:

- More storage;
- More ports;
- Standardized user and caller interfaces;
- Lower cost;
- Standardized and more comprehensive networking.

At this level, products will provide cost and performance characteristics and simply be able to do what they originally were designed to do, properly. This is one of the characteristics of a maturing market area. The more interesting aspect is in the new capabilities that will be provided:

- Multifunction systems;
- Use of telephone company enhanced services;
- Facsimile response.

Multiple voice-processing functions can be provided as options within a single voice-processing architecture as follows:

- IVR;
- Information providing;
- Automated attendant;
- Voice mail.

Voice-processing functions can be linked with other complementary functions to provide a much more powerful overall capability:

- ACD;
- Paging;
- Telephone answering service;
- Text mail;
- Facsimile response;
- Inbound telemarketing;
- Telephone usage management and accounting.

Specific vertical market areas will often need certain types of functions but not need others. For example, a field service organization may need voice mail, paging, information provision, transaction processing, and TAS but not have any need for a telemarketing or text-mail capability. Another vertical market area may require voice mail, text mail, and facsimile but not have any need for paging, TAS,

**Figure 8.17(a)** Multifunction voice-processing system. (Photograph courtesy of Digital Sound Corporation.)

The concept of a multifunction system will also be needed to provide a competitive advantage over the voice-mail service that the telephone companies will offer. Some of the functions the RBOCs are prohibited from providing. Others, such as TAS, it is highly unlikely that the RBOCs would ever provide them.

The concept of a multifunction product is appealing but does have some drawbacks. The complexity of the caller interface will increase. For the caller that or telemarketing. Identifying the specific needs of a particular vertical market area and then putting together a product optimized to satisfy those requirements is clearly a way to achieve a leadership position. Some of the multifunction systems are shown in Figures 8.17(a) and (b).

**Figure 8.17(b)** Multifunction voice-processing system. (Photograph courtesy of Microlog Corporation.)

is only using one of the functions, this is an annoyance. In many cases, the performance of any one of the functions will be compromised. Many of the first-generation multifunction products are ones in which additional functions are an added as an afterthought, and the cost and performance is unattractive [7].

## 8.10 VOICE-PROCESSING SUBSYSTEMS AND DEVELOPMENT TOOLS

A voice-processing system comprises separate subsystems and peripheral devices that are connected to form a voice-processing system. Development tools are used to make the system perform a particular set of functions. The voice-processing subsystems and development tools area can be split into four distinct areas:

1. Voice and speech recognition;
2. Text-to-speech;

3. System components and development tools;
4. Product development tools.

The developer of a voice-processing system has a variety of tools and subsystem components from which to choose.

### 8.10.1 Voice and Speech Recognition

Speech-recognition devices recognize spoken words, while voice-recognition devices recognize a particular speaker. Although some similarities exist in the technologies, the products, suppliers and applications are totally different.

#### 8.10.1.1 Speech Recognition

Over two dozen speech-recognition products exist. The products are usually devices that are peripheral to a larger voice-processing function. In many cases, the entire application is based on speech-recognition technology. In other cases, speech recognition is simply an optional way to communicate with a voice-processing system. The basic products range from units having recognition vocabularies of a few words to thousands of words. Most are discrete utterance devices, although a few are capable of handling connected speech. The majority are *not* designed to work properly over the telephone network. A few suppliers have products that are designed to work over the telephone network, but these have small vocabularies. The products are either speaker dependent or speaker independent. The ability to function in a noisy environment and to accommodate slight variations in the speech of the speaker are other parameters that vary considerably from one product to the next.

The purpose of speech recognition is to permit a computer to recognize spoken words. Using speech as a means of communicating with a computer has a number of positive aspects. Speech is the most natural human communication; it is both convenient and familiar. Most individuals are able to speak, while relatively few people are able to type. Specific benefits that can theoretically be obtained by speech recognition are:

*Minimization of training*. Users need not be taught to type; speaking is quicker—normal speaking rate is 180 words per minute. This is considerably faster than most people are able to type.

*Fewer errors*. A transcription step, with attendant errors, is eliminated.

*Mobility*. Typing requires physical proximity to the keyboard.

*Simultaneous functions*. Using voice frees the user's hands and eyes for performing other tasks.

Speech recognition has been a cause of much user frustration. Despite all the theoretical benefits, the reality of the technology's limitations is a source of much disappointment. A user expects to be able to talk to a computer in a natural fashion and have it understand what is being said. The present technology status is far from achieving this ideal state. Limitations that exist are:

*Words must be spoken discretely.* Except for a few small vocabulary devices that exist, the recognizer will only recognize words that are distinctly separated from other words. This means that the speech is very unnatural and slow. Vocabularies are limited. The largest commercially available recognizers have vocabularies of approximately 30,000 words, and most of them have vocabularies of a few hundred words or less.

*Dependent upon an individual speaker.* Except for a few of the small vocabulary devices that exist, most speech recognizers must be trained to the voice of a particular speaker. The training process is time consuming. The fact that it can only recognize a specific speaker tends to eliminate many applications.

*Speaker-independent devices are designed to work with a specific language.* Development of a speaker-independent product requires that a database of voice samples be gathered that is representative of all of the various dialects that will be encountered. Obtaining this database is a tedious process.

*Input is constrained.* The user must speak into a microphone in a controlled fashion. This requires a user discipline.

*Sensitive to speech variation.* A speaker may pronounce a word slightly differently or have a cold, and the recognizer will not recognize the words. A person who says a word when fatigued or under stress will pronounce it quite differently than usual. Discipline in pronouncing words exactly the same way is required for most speech recognizers.

*Sensitive to external noise.* This could be another person speaking in the vicinity of the user, a PA system announcement, or any other stray noise. These limitations have severely restricted the application of speech-recognition technology. Applications that have been successful are those in which no other alternative exists. Applications in which the hands, eyes, or both are busy are the only areas in which some measure of success has been obtained. Even in these areas, the amount of effort required to implement the application has necessitated a major system development and user training effort. In environments in which DTMF service is not available, voice input has been used with some success. In these cases, speech recognition is not a better input modality than DTMF input—it is simply the only approach available.

Beyond the technology limitations, other factors have limited the potential use of speech-recognition technology. Speaking to a terminal or a PC has very limited utility. Although speaking is a natural human communication mode, the natural communication mode with a terminal or PC is using a keyboard and monitor. The additional noise of people speaking to their PCs could be a distraction in most office environments. Speech-recognition products are shown in Figures 8.18(a) through (e).

The primary performance measurement of a speech recognizer is its accuracy, which is defined as the percentage of correctly recognized words. The types of errors encountered with a speech recognizer are substitution errors, rejection errors, and spurious response errors. *Substitution error* is the mistaking of one word for another. *Rejection errors* occur when a system is not able to recognize the

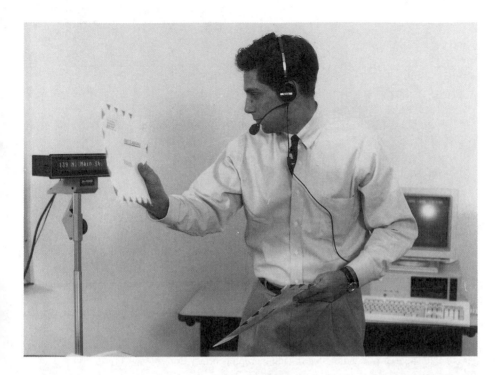

**Figure 8.18(a)** Speech-recognition system. (Photograph courtesy of Verbex Corporation.)

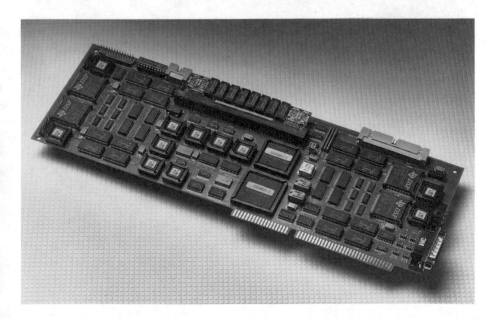

**Figure 8.18(b)** Speech-recognition board. (Photograph courtesy of Voice Processing Corporation.)

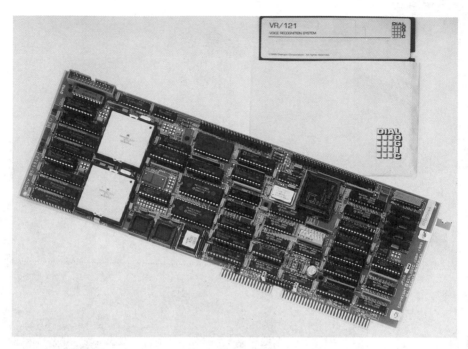

**Figure 8.18(c)** Speech-recognition board. (Photograph courtesy of Dialogic Corporation.)

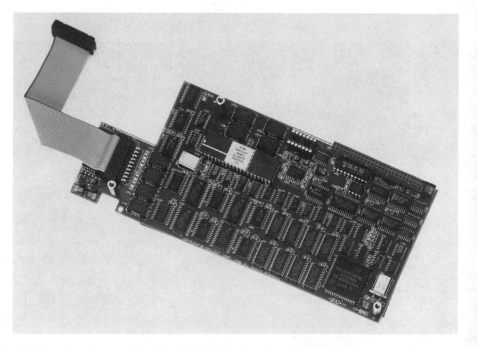

**Figure 8.18(d)** Speech-recognition board. (Photograph courtesy of Dialogic Corporation.)

**Figure 8.18(e)** Speech recognition. (Photograph courtesy of InterVoice, Inc.)

spoken word. *Spurious response errors* occur when the recognizer hears a word that has not been spoken (this is often an outside noise). Although vendors will specify a recognition accuracy (usually in the high-90th percentile), its meaning is subjective. Standardized quantitative tests do not exist. Texas Instruments has a set of recordings that has come to be accepted as a standard of sorts [8]. In any event, the only accuracy measurement that has any meaning is one obtained from experience in a specific user environment.

### 8.10.1.2 Voice Recognition

The number of voice-recognition products is quite small. The applications tend to be specialized and confined to access security. Within this area, they have been applied in environments in which traditional access security techniques such as keys and locks or cards are not appropriate. Voice recognition can provide an excellent level of security. Like a fingerprint, a person's voiceprint is unique and distinguishable from anyone else's. An advantage over other techniques is that it is integral to the person and need not be carried around. One of the major disadvantages is that a person's voiceprint is different when they have an illness, in which case the voice recognizer will not recognize that person. The products are usually provided as complete systems with physical doorlocks and associated controllers. The military is one of the major users of this technology. Appendix 9 provides a listing and categorization of many speech- and voice-recognition product and system suppliers.

### 8.10.1.3 Trends and Future Direction

Speech recognition has been one of the few areas in computer technology in which user expectations have been considerably higher than the realities of the technology. Although improvements in the technology will happen, the focus will be on properly applying the technology within the constraints that exist. Providing total system solutions for specific vertical market areas is the direction that many suppliers will take. Value-added resellers will become a strong supplement to this activity. Speech-recognition products that work over the telephone network will find a strong market in the telephone industry in the automation of operator services and in the international area.

### 8.10.2 Text-to-Speech Products

Text-to-speech products accept ASCII text and output continuous speech. They are similar to a printer; the difference is that the output is speech rather than a printed page. The major difference between one product and the next is the speech quality—it ranges from robotic and almost unintelligible to human-like with a slight accent. Prices range from a few hundred dollars to a few thousand dollars. A text-to-speech product is shown in Figure 8.19.

**Figure 8.19** Text-to-speech product. (Photograph courtesy of Digital Equipment Corporation.)

The major disadvantage of text-to-speech, when compared to digitized speech, is the speech quality obtained. If we ignore this disadvantage, text-to-speech is superior to digitized speech in many ways. The speech storage requirement is 300 times less. The direct conversion from computer files is possible. However, the reality is that speech quality *is* important, or at least perceived to be important. Despite the technical advantages of text-to-speech, the voice-processing area is dominated by digitized speech for speech output.

A primary application area for text-to-speech is where the database being accessed is either changing very rapidly or is extremely large. The automatic *customer name and address* (ACNA) service from the telephone companies is a good example of this, as is text-mail access from a telephone. The lower end units find their primary application in educational areas. For the ACNA application, the caller enters the telephone number and the system speaks the name and address of the individual associated with that telephone number. Appendix 10 provides a listing of the text-to-speech product and system suppliers.

### 8.10.3 Voice-Processing System Components and Development Tools

This segment of the voice-processing industry includes suppliers of software packages used to develop voice system applications, as well as boards that perform telephonics and speech digitization and playback. VARs and OEMs, as well as end users, purchase these components and tools and use them to build a voice-processing system. The types of different subsystem components and tools are

- Voice-response boards;
- Application generation toolkits;
- High-speech-quality boards;
- Headset microphones;
- Wireless subsystems.

### *8.10.3.1 Voice-Response Boards*

These are boards that plug into a PC or a minicomputer and include a telephonic interface for handling all call-processing functions. These boards receive commands from and provide information to the computer system. The functions typically performed include:

- Loop-start interface;
- Ringing detection;
- Taking phone off-hook after a specified number of rings;
- Placing phone on-hook;
- DTMF signal decoding;
- Digitize speech;
- Digitized speech playback;
- Call progress tones detection;

- Dial tone;
- Busy signal;
- Reordering;
- Answer detection;
- Hook-flash performance;
- Out-dialing DTMF or pulse string;
- Switching calls to other destinations;
- Silence detection.

These are the basic functions. Other functions that are performed by some of the telephonics controllers include wink detection, answer detection, DID interface, ground-start interface, far-end hangup detection, trunk-side interface, and DNIS and ANI interface. Most products are designed to work with the IBM PC ISA bus. A few are for the VME bus, *micro channel architecture* (MCA) or designed for use with the Apple computer. Operating environments that are supported include MS-DOS, UNIX, and PS/2. A set of drivers is typically provided for a specific environment and is used by developers to implement a voice-processing application.

In addition to the basic analog telephone interface boards, other boards are available, including T-1 and E-1 capability. Digital and analog switches are available to complement the basic voice-processing boards.

In order for different boards (speech recognition, fax processing, text-to-speech) to be able to seamlessly operate in the same environment as the basic voice-processing boards, a standardized interface needs to be available. Two interfaces of this sort presently exist: Dialogic Corporation has an interface called *PCM expansion bus* (PEB), and Natural Microsystems Corporation has an interface called *Multi-Vendor Interface Protocol* (MVIP). Both work into a TDM interface in which devices connect with timeslots. Figures 8.20 through 8.23 show voice-processing boards.

### 8.10.3.2 Application Generator Toolkits

These are either menu-driven packages or procedural language processors. Functions performed by most of the AGTKs are:

1. Define the individual steps of the script.
2. Define the logic flow between the steps.
3. Define the action to take at each step.
4. Define the parameters associated with each step.
5. Provide a display of call status.
6. Set up the interface with external databases.
7. Capture statistics and generate reports.

AGTKs are available to support most of the prominent voice-processing boards and run in MS-DOS, PS/2, UNIX, and VAX VMS environments. *Graphical user interfaces* (GUIs) are available with some of the AGTKs.

**Figure 8.20** Voice and analog telephonics board. (Photograph courtesy of Dialogic Corporation.)

### 8.10.3.3 High-Quality-Speech Boards

These products are designed for recording and playback of speech and can record at a variety of sampling rates. The fidelity of the speech recorded is better than that for telephone-based applications. Its applications are training systems, audio and visual broadcasting, point-of-sale, and computer workstations.

### 8.10.3.4 Speech Transmission Boards

These devices transmit speech at relatively low bit rates and yet maintain good speech quality. Their primary use is to improve the efficiency of telephone line usage. A compression of up to 8:1 is typically achieved, which permits eight voice signals to use a single voice line. These devices are frequently used with fractional T-1 services. Fractional T-1 services provide individual DS0 slots of a DS1 T-1 service.

### 8.10.3.5 Headsets and Microphones

These devices are either used in speech-processing applications or by agents in ACD or outbound predictive dialing environments. The speech-processing appli-

**Figure 8.21** T-1 board. (Photograph courtesy of Dialogic Corporation.)

cations are primarily for speech recognition. An important headset characteristic is its weight. Units that weigh less than an ounce are available, as are headsets in a variety of configurations, which include binaural, monaural, wire-band, or over-the-ear. The noise-canceling capability of a microphone is an important consid-eration in most environments; 8 to 12 decibels of noise cancellation is typically provided. Appendix 7 provides a listing and categorization of the suppliers of voice-processing subsystems and tools.

Figure 8.22 ISDN board. (Photograph courtesy of Dialogic Corporation.)

## 8.10.4 Voice-Processing Product Development Tools and Components

Voice-processing development tools and components are used to design and implement the basic elements of a voice-processing system. They are also used for signal analysis and simulation. Included in this area are the semiconductor vendors

**Figure 8.23** Fax-processing board. Photograph courtesy of Dialogic Corporation.

that provide specialized speech processing and telephonics devices such as codecs and DTMF detectors and generators. Customers are speech researchers and developers of voice-processing products.

Products include a variety of tools for engineers or programmers to use in developing voice-processing products. Hardware and software that permits the acquisition and analysis of speech signals include capabilities for spectrum analysis, amplitude extraction or analysis, pitch extraction, and *linear predictive coding* (LPC) analysis or synthesis. Tools for developing DSP applications include assemblers, compilers, and simulators.

## 8.11 NATURAL VOICE-PROCESSING USER INTERFACE

The existing user interface for voice-processing systems is awkward and inappropriate for the vast majority of the users.

The touch-tone telephone is the control and data-entry device in most voice processing systems despite its shortcomings:

- Frequently not available;
- Not usable with many telephones (T-T pad in handset);
- Not an acceptable interface for the majority of the user population.

The use of the touch-tone keypad was driven by the fact that it was a economical solution that worked in a reasonably reliable way. Despite its seemin acceptance, we should not lose sight of the fact that its shortcomings tend to severel restrict the usage of voice processing to a relatively small percentage of the tota potential user population. Many potential users are simply not able or willing to deal with the use of the touch-tone telephone as anything other than a device for dialing telephone numbers. Rotary pulse detectors do nothing to address this problem. Aside from having a severe set of technical limitations, the user would be even less willing to use a rotary dial for anything other than dialing a telephone number. Speech recognition systems that have been implemented to date are not any better. They require that the user speak in a very structured and unnatural manner.

The "telephone answering machine syndrome" is another major limiting factor in the use of existing voice-processing systems. Many callers simply do not like talking to machines. They will either hang up or wait in silence until they are switched to an operator.

The ultimate user interface for a telephone dialogue is one in which the caller converses with the voice-processing system in a completely natural way. The first thing that the caller hears is "Hello, can I help you?" From that point on, the caller speaks and the voice-processing system responds in an appropriate fashion. To be truly successful, the voice-processing system needs to be intelligent enough to accommodate the likely responses of the caller and not force the caller to adapt to what the voice-response system would like to see.

An example of a service, using systems, that successfully automates the caller voice interface in a completely natural way is ConServIT, a telemarketing service bureau that is provided by *Conversational Voice Technologies Corporation* (CVTC). Typically, the ConServIT system answers the telephone, greets the caller, accepts orders, and then captures the name, address, telephone number, and credit card number of the caller. The applications that are routinely handled include locator services, customer service and information, literature and sample requests, order entry, and overflow call handling. The caller is typically not aware that he or she is not talking to a human operator. Amazingly, the ConServIT system does not even use speech recognition. It uses a patented technique relying solely on the duration of caller response and the duration of pauses in the conversation to determine the next response that is most appropriate to provide. The performance that is achieved by the ConServIT system is significantly superior to that achieved with TSRs or conventional voice-processing systems. The performance criteria that are used are the percentage of calls completed successfully. A comparison of these approaches in a typical telemarketing application is summarized in Table 8.16. The telemarketing application that is shown is a lead-generation one in which the goal is to develop lists of customers that are interested in a specific product or service [9].

The *caller records incomprehensible* is where critical information is incorrect to the extent that information sent to the caller would have a low probability of being delivered. The fact that the TSR has an error rate that is higher than ConservIT comes as a surprise since the TSR has the option of asking the caller

**Table 8.16**

Telemarketing Application – Different Approaches

| Item | ConServIT | TSR | IVR |
|---|---|---|---|
| Responding callers | 100% | 100% | 100% |
| Callers lost to non-T-T | 0% | 0% | 40% |
| Caller Hangup (machine syndrome) | 1% | 0% | 20% |
| Callers unanswered | 0% | 20% | 0% |
| Caller records incomprehensible | 5% | 10% | 20% |
| Returned undelivered | 1% | 10% | 20% |
| **Successful calls** | **93%** | **65%** | **31%** |

to repeat the response if there is uncertainty. The reality is that TSRs are typically measured on call throughput and are not motivated to ask a caller to repeat something of which they were not certain. Another factor is the sheer monotony of a TSR job that leads to high error rates. On the surface, it would also seem that ConServIT and the IVR should be equal since they are both recording the caller response digitally. The reasons that the ConServIT has a significantly lower error rate are:

A 64-kb/s encoding is used with ConServIT. Most IVRs use 32 kb/s or less. Although 32 kb/s is perfectly acceptable for most voice-processing applications, for certain words and certain speakers, the recorded speech will be unclear.

A phenomena that has been observed is that callers speak clearly when they think that they are talking to a person. If they are talking to a machine, they typically talk in a constrained, unnatural, and unclear manner. The concept of ConServIT is to not let the caller be aware that he or she is talking to a machine. IVRs take the other approach and tend to emphasize that the caller is talking to a computer.

Most IVRs have a finite time period for switching from the outgoing to the incoming mode that often measures in the seconds. They will frequently use tones to signal when the caller is to start speaking. In some cases the caller will start to speak before the switch to incoming mode has been accomplished, and the first word or so of the caller's input is lost. ConServIT has an instantaneous switching capability that will not lose the first word of the caller.

*Returned undelivered* is the caller that seemed as though he or she had a good address, but for some reason the address was not correct enough to deliver and the package was returned to the fulfillment center.

The information on the performance of ConServIT service was obtained from CVTC. The information on the TSR and IVR approaches was obtained from a survey of approximately three dozen of the leading telemarketing service bureaus, ad agencies, and fulfillment centers that used these techniques. For obvious reasons, service bureaus are not anxious to publicize weaknesses in their services, which these items surely are. On the other hand, none of the service bureaus disagreed with the figures and most suggested that the actual losses were much higher. The figures presented represent a consensus of the information that was obtained.

The ConServIt system is able to handle any two-way branch condition based on the *thought* of the caller. It cannot branch based on discrete information, such as if the caller gave an invalid account number. The system can duplicate the way the courteous, well-trained nightguard would handle an after-hours call (he or she knows nothing but can take the information).

CVTC is a licensee of Theis Research, Inc. Theis Research is offering licenses of the patented technology to the trade. The technology is known as *intuitive call processing* and is being developed further by Theis Research.

Implementation of a natural, conversational user interface, requiring that the likely responses of a caller be well understood. Data need to be obtained that are statistically significant, and then the system response needs to be designed to accommodate the caller. A critical requirement is that the caller responses be as though the caller were talking to a person and not a computer. Without this, the caller response database will not be valid and the response of the caller will be unpredictable. The techniques that are used for a natural, conversational interface are the antithesis of the techniques used with traditional voice-processing products. Conventional voice-processing products require that the caller adjust to the requirements of the computer system. The design of a natural user interface requires that a major effort be put into understanding the response of the caller community to a particular prompt and careful design of the dialog to cause the caller to respond in a predictable fashion.

A natural user interface has the potential to attract the 80 to 90% of the population that would not deal with the present touch-tone interface, do not have the use of T-T available, or will not talk to a machine. The use of speech recognition in addition to pause and length detection and a design approach that is oriented to the voice-processing system accommodating the caller would appear to be capable of doing this. The suppliers that recognize this as an opportunity an act upon it should do quite well.

## 8.12 VOICE-PROCESSING PRODUCT FUTURE TRENDS

Products will become significantly easier for the end user to operate. The ability for the end user to customize the product to meet specific requirements will become necessary. This is one sign of a market maturing. The needs of the customer (and how they tend to vary) are well understood by the suppliers and the products are designed with the flexibility to meet these needs. The passive interception area is presently at this stage of maturity. The transaction-processing area is currently the furthest removed from this level of maturity. Product trends will initially lower the price while maintaining constant product functionality and will then reach a stage of constant product cost with an increase in functionality. This increase in functionality will include the incorporation of multiple voice-processing functions within a single, integrated architecture and the use of multiple voice-processing technologies within a single architecture.

Existing voice-processing products are stand-alone devices that provide a minimum interface with the rest of the environment in which they need to coexist. Voice mail is simply another communication vehicle, as are pagers, text mail, facsimile, and cellular telephones. The "seamless" integration of voice-processing functions with other communication mechanisms will be one of the major characteristics that set future voice-processing products apart from today's products.

Functions such as telemarketing, information provision, telephone accounting control, telephone answering services, switchboard operation, and dictation services define areas in which voice processing can perform a useful, although often secondary, function. Transaction-processing systems that include facsimile as a response mechanism are becoming increasingly prevalent. Systems in which the sole information transfer is by facsimile will claim a significant market segment. Improvements in processor power and storage will tend to increase call throughput and prompt or message storage. Systems with port counts greater than 64 will be common, and voice-mail storage capacities will go beyond 500 hours. The most significant change will be in the area of telephony. The major things that will drive this are digital telephony and enhanced telephone services.

Digital telephony direct T-1 interfaces will become readily available. The major immediate advantages are improved speech quality and lower cost. The lower cost will be obtained both in the subscriber's line costs and in the cost of the interface between the voice-mail system and the telephone network. The cost of a 24-port interface will be a small fraction of the cost of the analog equivalents that exist today. Voice-processing system interfaces will include a drop-and-insert capability, which will permit them to perform as the front end to a variety of other services and also to let the voice-processing system use a smaller number of the 24 ports and make the unused DS0 slots available for other functions within an organization. The significant long-term advantage to a digital telephony interface is that the products are being positioned to accommodate ISDN services.

The physical interface will be the same, and much of the architecture to support T-1 service will be transportable to an ISDN environment. The basic data rate of ISDN will be fully compatible with the 64-kb/s PCM coded voice of a T-1 DS0 channel. The speech-coding techniques that are used within a voice-mail system will become 64-kb/s PCM or a lower bit rate technique that can be readily transformed to and from 64-kb/s PCM. ISDN will make available a variety of new capabilities. The caller station address can be delivered to the destination during call setup. This capability would permit the development of selective call-acceptance systems. Service identification will be available, which would identify the type of digital data (coded voice, facsimile, video, and data). This permits routing to the proper destination facility for service, or rejecting the connection if no such facility is available. Expanded call services such as call forwarding, transfer, call holding, and conference calls can be supported from any station in the network.

## REFERENCES

1. Gould, J. D., and S. J. Boies, "Speech Filing—An Office System: for Principles," *IBM Systems Journal*, Vol. 23, No. 1, 1984, pp. 65–81.
2. Richmond, R. L., "Complexity in Call Processing Systems," *American Voice Input/Output Society conference*, San Francisco, California, October 1988.
3. Walters, R. E., *Voice Information Systems*, NCC Blackwell Ltd., Oxford, England, 1991, pp. 276–283.
4. Varney, R. C., "Predictive Dialers and Other Dialing Technologies—How They Differ," *Telemarketing*, January 1992, Technology Marketing Corporation, Norwalk, Connecticut.
5. Tetschner, W. C., "Update: Fax Server Technology," *Business Communication Review*, February 1992, Hinsdale, Illinois, pp. 52–56.
6. McConnell, Bodson, and Schaphorst, *Fax: Digital Facsimile Technology and Applications*, Norwood, Mass., Artech House, 1989, pp. 178–189.
7. Tetschner, W. C., "Multifunction Voice Processing: Who Needs It?" *Voice News*, July 1991, Stoneridge Technical Services, Rockville, Maryland.
8. Leonard, R. G., "A Database for Speaker-Independent Digit Recognition," *IEEE International Conference on Acoustics, Speech, and Signal Processing proc.*, March 1984, pp. 42.11.1–11.4.
9. Tetschner, W. C., "Improved Caller Interface," *Voice News*, July 1991, Stoneridge Technical Services, Rockville, Maryland.

# Chapter 9
## Computer-Telephone Integration

### 9.1 BASIC COMPUTER-TELEPHONE FUNCTION

*Computer-telephone integration* (C-TI) links telephone systems, TSRs, and computer environments to improve call-handling efficiency. C-TI is a concept that enables organizations to functionally integrate both telephone (voice) and terminal (data) environments to create fully integrated business solutions. Supporting database information is used to improve the efficient flow of the call.

Chapter 8 described predictive dialing. This is one example of an application in which a computer database is coupled with the telephony function. The TSR is given access to the record of the individual being called. Complementing the basic ACD function with this computer database access can significantly improve call handling, with more calls handled by the same call center staff and better customer service.

C-TI provides one or more of the following functions:

- Automatic caller identification by telephone number or by caller-provided information;
- Automatic identification of caller's purpose, based on the DNIS, and appropriate routing of call;
- Automation of routine caller-information gathering;
- Routing of call to the appropriate department;
- Transfer of caller records with the call;
- Providing information to the caller;
- Updating caller's record based on results of the call.

Each of these items contributes to overall efficiency, saving time for the caller and the TSR. Automatically identifying the caller from an ANI saves the time it takes for callers to either say their names or enter an identifying code. In many applications, the number that was called specifically identifies the caller's intent. Based on the DNIS, the call can be automatically routed to the appropriate resource.

Simultaneous transfer of the caller's records with the caller is a fundamental aspect of computer-telephony integration. In many cases, the caller needs to be transferred to another resource to complete the call. Transferring the caller's records (including the history of the current call) permits the call to proceed in a positive fashion and avoids the need to reobtain data previously obtained. This also avoids the frustration of having to say who you are and describe what you are calling about to one person, then being transferred and having to repeat it.

In many cases, callers or people being called desire information. This can be provided either verbally by the TSR, or automatically with voice response, data, or fax. The caller's record can be updated based on information that the caller entered with the IVR or by the TSR.

## 9.2 CALL CENTER SYSTEM CONFIGURATION

Figure 9.1 depicts a C-TI call center system configuration. The particular role of each element varies depending upon the particular call center environment and the nature of a particular call.

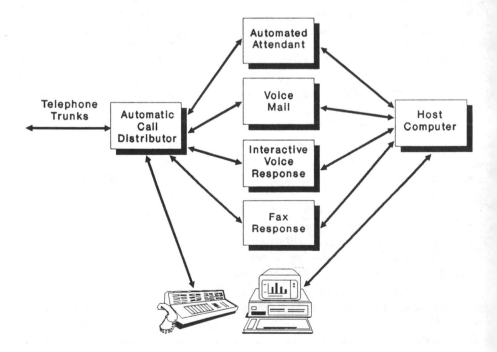

**Figure 9.1** Call center configuration.

The automated attendant frequently performs front-end call screening. The caller is given a menu and can select a desired option. This selection is then used to route the call. Voice mail is often provided as an option to a caller who is in a queue but does not want to await TSR availability. This caller is able to leave a message, which the TSR will later return. Facsimile response delivers information to a caller when a hard copy is required or is more appropriate than voice information.

## 9.3 C-TI CALL-PROCESSING SEQUENCE

Figure 9.2 shows the flow of a typical call. The call-processing sequence is as follows:

1. Call center receives a call. Caller and DNIS are transferred to the IVR unit.
2. The IVR prompts caller to enter own account number.
3. Caller enters account number.
4. The IVR sends account number and the DNIS to the host computer and requests caller's record.
5. The host computer searches for record and sends information to the IVR.
6. Based on information obtained from caller's record, the IVR prompts caller for additional information.

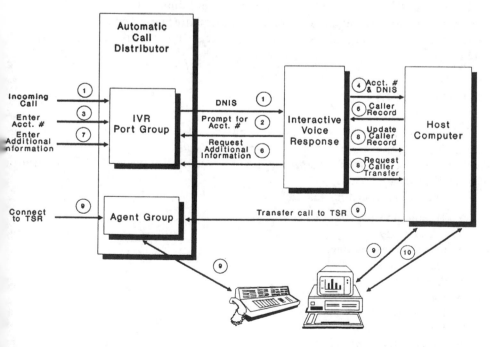

**Figure 9.2** C-TI call flow.

7. Caller provides requested information.
8. When the IVR has obtained requested information from the caller, it requests that the caller be transferred to a TSR.
9. The host computer determines which TSR or TSR group should take the call and simultaneously transfers call and caller record to the appropriate TSR.
10. The TSR updates caller record, based on a conversation with the caller, and transmits it to the host computer.

The sequence shown in Figure 9.2 is a simplified one. In step 1, ANI is provided to identify the caller and could possibly eliminate the need to perform step 2. In step 4, the IVR may need to access multiple host computers and multiple databases to obtain a complete record for the call. In step 5, the information that is obtained will vary depending upon the particular application. For a customer service application, the record may contain information that characterizes the product that the customer owns, such as the serial number and purchase date. The result of step 6 provides information to the caller in voice, data, or fax form. The transfer of the caller to a TSR can be accomplished in a variety of ways. The IVR unit could directly request that the ACD transfer the call to the appropriate agent group, requiring that the IVR be attached to the C-TI link of the ACD. The IVR (or the ACD) would still need to request that the host transmit the caller record to the terminal of the TSR synchronized with the caller-TSR connection. In this case, the ACD determines the routing that the call should take. The host performs the routing, such decision being based on caller information contained in the host database. For example, callers with a specific area code could be routed to a specific TSR.

## 9.4 APPLICATIONS

C-TI is applicable to environments that handle a large volume of calls and where accessing database information is a part of the call process. To handle large call volumes efficiently, most organizations have a centralized call-handling operation to which calls are routed.

The C-TI applications include

- Telephone sales and marketing;
- Order entry;
- Order status inquiry;
- Reservations;
- Collections;
- Registration;
- Fundraising;
- Information access;
- Emergency services;
- Customer service;

- Account management;
- Messaging;
- Telephone company operator services.

Calling to generate additional revenue is a major telemarketing activity. Predictive or preview dialing is used to automate the dialing process. Orders are taken, customer records are updated, and information is provided to the person being called in an efficient manner. Ordering of goods and services is another major C-TI application. The caller's ANI and the called DNIS are delivered to the application, and the caller is routed to the proper TSR. Information about the caller is provided to the TSR at the initiation of the call dialog. Collections is another C-TI application that uses predictive dialing. TSRs are able to accomplish many more completed calls and enter information into the caller records to provide an update of the customer account status.

Providing quality customer service is a corporate imperative. With C-TI, the customer can call and make known his or her identity and the specific product of interest. Based on this information, the caller is routed to an appropriate TSR, with the caller's information available to the TSR at the moment of connection.

Calls to 911 emergency service use ANI to identify the caller's location. The TSR is able to handle an emergency situation more quickly this way. C-TI is also used extensively in fundraising campaigns to call prospective donors and solicit contributions. *Telephone Answering Services* (TAS) use C-TI extensively to automatically link the number that was called to information about the person or organization that is being called. Call completion and information services are two examples of the telephone companies' broad use of C-TI.

## 9.5 SYSTEM COMPONENTS

A C-TI system consists of the following basic components:

- A telephone switch (PBX or ACD);
- A switch interface that provides information about a call and a means to control call routing;
- A host computer;
- A host computer interface that connects with the switch interface;
- Host software able to respond to and manage the call flow and provide access to caller records.

These components are shown in Figure 9.3.

### 9.5.1 Telephone Switch

Telephone switches take a variety of forms. The PBX concentrates many telephone sets onto relatively few public telephone lines. An ACD is a specialized type of PBX that is designed to handle a high level of calls of a uniform or specific nature: the caller is not calling to reach a particular *person*, but rather, is calling about a

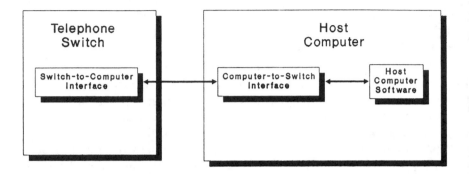

**Figure 9.3** C-TI system components.

specific *something*. The public telephone network is a massive telephone switch. When equipped with the capability to manage the call flow through it, each of these switches can be part of a C-TI environment.

### 9.5.2 C-TI Interfaces Provided by Switches

C-TI Interfaces are provided by most of the switch suppliers. These interfaces have been developed independently by each of the suppliers and are proprietary. The physical transport used varies from one to another but is a standardized interface. Although the protocol varies from one C-TI link to the next, the information and control functions are similar. The basic functions that are provided by a computer-switch interface include:

- Answer call: allows a call to be completed to a telephone set.
- Create a conference bridge: prepares to build a call having more than the usual two parties.
- Disconnect call: terminates an in-progress telephone call.
- Join existing calls: creates a connection between two or more calls already in progress.
- Make call: initiates a connection.
- Place call on hold: temporarily disconnects a call from a telephone set without terminating the call.
- Report call progress: informs the application of call-processing events, such as party disconnect.
- Report station status: informs the application of the state of a telephone set such as off-hook.
- Retrieve call from hold: reconnects a held call to the original telephone set.
- Transfer call: moves a connection from one telephone set to another.

The C-TI link consists of information that is sent by the switch to the host computer or information that is sent from the host computer to the switch. Switch-to-computer information is either a positive or negative acknowledgment of a host command to request routing assistance from the host or to inform the host of some occurrence in the progress of a call. Host-to-switch information consists of commands directing the switch to do something. Tables 9.1(a) and (b) summarize the commands and status information that exists in typical C-TI links. Table 9.2 (page

**Table 9.1a**
C-TI Link Host-to-Switch

| Command | Description |
|---|---|
| Add party | The host application instructs the switch to add an additional party to an existing call. This command is useful in predictive dialing applications after the application has been informed that the called party has answered the call. |
| Alternate call | The host application instructs the switch to place an active call on hold and then reconnect a held call. |
| Answer call | The host application instructs the switch to answer an incoming call on behalf of a particular TSR. |
| Conference call | The host application instructs the switch to join the parties in a held call with the parties in some other active call. |
| Disconnect | The host application instructs the switch to disconnect a party from a call. |
| Invoke feature | The host application instructs the switch to invoke a switch feature (e.g. call forwarding) for a particular TSR station. |
| Make call | The host application instructs the switch to initiate a call between two parties. |
| Monitor | The host application instructs the switch to send certain events (e.g. all setup or disconnected events) as a result of call activity at the switch. |
| Redirect call | The host application instructs the switch to change the destination of an incoming call from one party to another. |
| Reject call | The host application instructs the switch to reject an incoming call. |
| Retrieve call | The host application instructs the switch to reconnect a call that is presently on hold. |

**Table 9.1a (continued)**

| Command | Description |
|---------|-------------|
| Return control | The host application instructs the switch to use its normal routing algorithm to route an incoming call. |
| Transfer call | The host application instructs the switch to transfer the call to a third party line. |
| Trigger | The host application instructs the switch to take some specific action when a specific event occurs. For example, the host may issue this command to cause the switch to send a Request Instruction command to the host for all calls destined for a particular DNIS. |

221) shows the API support that is currently being provided by the major computer vendors. Table 9.3 (page 223) shows the available switch C-TI interfaces.

### 9.5.3 Host-to-Switch Interface

The host systems that have been used in C-TI applications range from mainframes to PCs. A variety of physical interfaces has been used and includes asynchronous, X.25, SNA, and ISDN BRI.

### 9.5.4 Host-to-Switch Software

The host-to-switch interface typically consists of two components: a link-layer software package and an *application programming interface* (API). The link-layer software performs all of the low-level functions associated with the host-to-switch interface. The details of various protocols and physical connectivity methods are handled. The link-layer software shields the application programmer from the specific formats and protocols used to communicate with the various telephone systems. The API is typically a set of function calls that can be directly usd with language processors such as COBOL, PL/I, and C. Figure 9.4 (page 222) shows C-TI software.

### 9.5.5 Host-to-Switch Interface Standardization

As might have been expected, each of the switch suppliers has developed their own proprietary interfaces. To overcome the enormous cost of developing and supporting host computer software for multiple switch interfaces, a standards activity is under way. Two prominent standards organizations, the *American National*

## Table 9.1b
### C-TI Link Switch-to-Host

| Command | Description |
|---------|-------------|
| Call alerting | The switch informs the host that a call is ringing at a particular destination party. |
| Call conferenced | The switch informs the host that two calls, with at least one common party have been conferenced. |
| Call connected | The switch informs the host that a party previously in an intermediate state (in progress between call setup and connection) is now actively participating in the call or that a party previously on hold has now been reconnected to the call. |
| Call held | The switch informs the host that a particular call has been placed on hold. |
| Call parked | The switch informs the host that a call has been transferred to a specified party and has placed the call on hold without ringing the specified parties phone. |
| Call picked | The switch informs the host that a call has been either answered or retrieved by a party other than the party for whom the call was alerting or on hold, respectively. |
| Call rejected | The switch informs the host that a call was rejected and could not be completed. |
| Call routed | The switch informs the host that a call has been successfully routed to a specified party. |
| Call transferred | The switch informs the host that the transfer of two calls involving a common party has been successfully completed. |
| Disconnected | The switch informs the host that one or more parties have disconnected from a call. |

*Standards Institute* (ANSI) and the *European Computer Manufacturers Association* (ECMA) are developing switch-computer interface standards.

The two standards-setting bodies are TC32-TG11 (technical committee 32, task group 11) of ECMA and the ISDN networking subgroup of the T1S1.1 committee of ANSI. The informal name of the ANSI standard is *Switch Computer Application Interface* (SCAI) and the informal name of the ECMA standard is *Computer-Supported Telephony Applications* (CSTA). The recommendations of each of these standards bodies were released in mid-1992.

The two groups share the same goal, which is to establish standard protocols and message formats that will enable computers and switches to work together in a reliable fashion. The two groups have some of the same members participating in both standards activities, but they are taking significantly different approaches.

**Table 9.1b (continued)**

| Command | Description |
|---------|-------------|
| Feature invoked | The switch informs the host that a TSR has invoked a particular switch feature such as call forwarding. |
| Network reached | The switch informs the host that the switch has progressed in its call-processing to the point where it is sending a call establishment request out on a trunk. |
| Party Status | The switch informs the host of the current status of a specified party. |
| Request Instruction | The switch sends this command to request that the host provide routing assistance. This command is issued as a result of a previously issued Trigger command from the host. |
| Response | The switch acknowledges the acceptance or rejection of a command from the host. Depending on which switch command is being responded to, the response will vary. As a minimum, positive response would indicate that the switch has found no obvious error with the command and is attempting to process the request. For other commands, a positive acknowledgement may also mean that the switch has successfully executed the command up to a different point. |
| Setup | The switch informs the host that a call has been initiated on some switch interface that can be involved in calls. |
| Switch Status | The switch informs the host of a change in status of the switch or a change in the status of the communications link to the switch. |

One of the major differences between the two approaches is that the ANSI activity is addressing both public and private telephone networks, while the ECMA committee is focusing exclusively on interfaces for PBXs and ACDs. The differences in the approach being used by the two groups appear to stem from the composition of each group. ECMA is composed primarily of switch and computer manufacturers. ANSI includes manufacturers but also includes the RBOCs, which are very active in the ANSI standards development process.

The differences between the two standards are that the ANSI standard will have a much higher level of specificity than the ECMA standard. For example, in a call-forwarding application, the ECMA standards would not specify the contents of the message field used to distinguish between a busy or a ring/no-answer re-

**Table 9.2**

PBX/ACD Suppliers Computer Vendor API Support

| Supplier | Switch Product Name | Name of Computer Interface | Computer Vendor API Support |
|---|---|---|---|
| Aspect Telecommunications | CallCenter | Application Bridge | |
| AT&T | Definity G1/G2/G3 | CallVisor ASAI | IBM Direct Route/2 IBM CallPath DEC CIT Stratus Adjunct Interface (SAI) Tandem Call Application Manager (CAM) H-P ACT |
| Ericsson | MD110 | MD110 Application Link | *IBM CallPath* *DEC CIT* |
| Mitel | SX2000 | Host Command Interface (HCI) | DEC CIT |
| NEC | APEX/NEAC | OAI | IBM CallPath |
| NTI | DMS-100 | CompuCall (SCAI) | |
| NTI | Meridian PBX | Meridian Link | DEC CIT HP ACT IBM CallPath Tandem CAM |
| Rockwell | Galaxy | Galaxy Transaction Link | DEC CIT |

sponse. Individual switch suppliers would specify their own values for these fields. By contrast, ANSI standards activity is attempting to define the interface so that any two switches and computers can communicate, in both public and private networks. The ECMA standards will have a broader scope in terms of specified

**Table 9.2 (continued)**

| Supplier | Switch Product Name | Name of Computer Interface | Computer Vendor API Support |
|---|---|---|---|
| Rolm | 9751 CBX | CallBridge | IBM CallPath DEC CIT |
| Siemens | Hicom 300 | CallBridge Applications Connectivity Link; ACL | DEC CIT |
| Teleos | IRX 9000 | | IBM CallPath |

application functionality. The basic disadvantage of the ECMA standard is that it limits the portability of an application. The two standards groups are attempting to reconcile their differences and align the two.

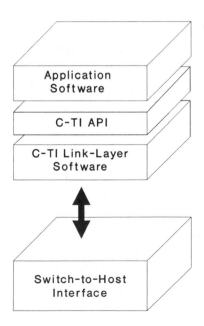

**Figure 9.4** C-TI software architecture.

**Table 9.3**

PBX/ACD Suppliers Computer Interfaces

| Supplier | Switch Product Name | Name of Computer Interface | Type of Computer Interface |
|---|---|---|---|
| Aspect Telecom- munications | CallCenter | Application Bridge | SNA, ASYNC |
| AT&T | Definity G1/G2/G3 | CallVisor ASAI | ISDN BRI |
| Ericsson | MD110 | MD110 Application Link | |
| Fujitsu | F9600 | TCSI | X.25 |
| Harris | VoiceFrame | Host Interface Link (HIL) | Async @ 9.6 kb/s |
| InteCom | IBX/80 Telari | OAI | Async @ 9.6 kb/s |
| Mitel | SX2000 | Host Command Interface (HCI) | 64 kb/s |
| NEC | APEX/NEAC | OAI | X.25 |
| NTI | DMS-100 | CompuCall (SCAI) | |
| NTI | Meridian PBX | Meridian Link | SNA, LAP-B, LU6.2, |
| NTI | Northstar | ACCESS | |
| Redcom | SBX | | |
| Rockwell | Galaxy | Galaxy Transaction Link | SNA or X.25/BX.25 |
| Rolm | 9751 CBX | CallBridge | Async or LU6.2 @ 9.6 kb/s |
| Siemens | Hicom 300 | CallBridge Applications Connectivity Link; ACL | Async @ 9.6 kb/s |

## Table 9.3 (continued)

| Supplier | Switch Product Name | Name of Computer Interface | Type of Computer Interface |
|---|---|---|---|
| Solid State Systems (Cortelco) | SR96,224, 1000 | Telecommunications Applications Bridge (TAC) | Async, 9.6 kb/s |
| SRX | VisionMS | Remote Applications Computer (RAC) | Async, 19.2 kb/s |
| Summa Four | SD1000 | | SNA, Async @ 9.6 kb/s |
| Telcom Technologies | ECD-6000 | Universal Data Link (UDL) | Async, 9.6 kb/s |
| Teknekron Infoswitch | ISD/ACD | InfoExchange | Asynch or SNA |
| Teleos | IRX 9000 | | ISDN |

## 9.6 ARCHITECTURAL ISSUES

ACDs have historically been special-purpose switches that have performed routing decisions and other call center control functions. Another approach is to place all of these functions on a general-purpose computer and use a dumb switch. The benefits of the latter approach are that users are able to link their databases more closely into the call center applications. Another benefit is that a secondary investment in learning how to program, support, and manage a special-purpose system such as an ACD is eliminated. The same people that program and maintain the general-purpose computer would handle the call routing functions.

A few companies are fielding products that eliminate the ACD and PBX altogether. They are using ISDN PRIs or BRIs as well as the control that is provided by the D-channel for all of the call routing. At present, the lack of ISDN lines is one factor holding back this application from significant deployment. Although the use of a general-purpose computer to perform all of the call routing functions is appealing, performance that can be achieved is questionable. ACDs are specifically designed to have the call routing function optimized. Looking at history, it is tempting to compare this situation to the word processing world. In the late

1970s and early 1980s, word processors were dedicated machines. By the mid-1980s, these products were totally supplanted by word processing software that could run on a personal computer. What is wrong with this comparison is that the word processing users were willing to suffer some decrease in performance as a tradeoff for a much lower price, and it is unlikely that any degradation of the call routing function will be acceptable. A more relevant model might be the data communications area. This has severe real-time requirements, and the approach has been to take functions that previously resided on a general-purpose computer and offload them to special-purpose products such as terminal servers, X.25 gateways, file servers, and LANs.

It is unlikely that the stand-alone ACD and PBX will disappear in the future. The more likely event is a broader range of system architectures available that will range from dedicated call routing products to routing software entirely on a general-purpose computer.

# Chapter 10

# Cost Justification of Voice Processing

The purchase of a voice-processing system can be justified in several ways. Typical benefits are improved employee efficiency, improved communication with customers, better customer service, reduced telephone bills, and personnel staff reductions. Each benefit can be quantified in terms of dollars [1].

## 10.1 VOICE-MAIL SYSTEM COST JUSTIFICATION

With a voice-mail system, telephone bills can be reduced by reducing the number of calls, shortening the length of each call, and by moving the call to a lower rate calling period. Because 50% of all calls involve the one-way transmittal of information, voice processing eliminates a callback for half the messages left on a voice-mail system. The number of calls to remote field employees can be dramatically reduced by having employees make local calls to leave messages, and then pick up their mail later with a single call made during a lower-rate calling period. Suppliers with which a company has a lot of contact can be assigned a mailbox, which reduces the number of calls made to that supplier. When live people talk to each other, the call length is increased by individuals making unnecessary conversation. Individuals tend to discuss the weather and other stray topics that are not relevant to their jobs. We estimate that 20% of the call length is devoted to extraneous conversation. Approximately 25% of all calls to a voice-mail system occur before 8 a.m. and after 5 p.m. local time. Because rates during these hours are significantly lower (25 to 50%) than during business hours, this shift in calling profiles yields a 6 to 12% reduction in telephone toll charges. Some of these benefits can readily be translated into hard dollars, while others are more difficult to translate because they are soft dollar savings. Determining a hard-cost justification of a voice-processing system is usually necessary and is certainly worthwhile. A cost-justification model for a voice-mail system is given below.

Reduction in the number of incomplete calls:

$$\text{Annual cost saving} = n(c)(0.75)r(235)$$

where

    n = number of employees
    c = number of calls per employee per day
    r = dollar cost per minute of an employee

For a company with 100 employees, in which each person makes four calls per day at a per minute rate of \$0.30, the annual cost saving is \$21,150.

Reduction in call length:

$$\text{Annual cost saving} = n(c)(0.25)(l)r(235) + n(0.25)(l)t(235)$$

where

    l = average call length
    t = cost of telephone line

With an average call length of four minutes and a cost per minute of the telephone call of \$0.25, the annual cost saving is \$12,925.

Reduction in the number of written memos:

$$\text{Annual cost saving} = n(c)0.1(m)235$$

where

    m = cost of a typed memo

With a cost of \$3 per memo, the annual cost saving is \$28,200.

A total cost saving calculation is:

| | |
|---|---|
| Reduction in the length of each call | = \$21,150 |
| Reduction in the length of each call | = \$12,925 |
| Reduction in the number of written memos | = \$28,200 |
| Annual cost saving | = \$62,275 |

The cost of voice mail must be deducted from this savings. If the voice-mail system costs \$36,000, an annual lease rate would be approximately \$12,000. Managing the system does require some dedicated effort. If we assume 50% of a person this would add another $20,000. Lighting, power, and space would add $4,000. The total cost would then be as follows:

Annual Expenses
Lease of voice mail system     = $12,000
Managing of voice mail system = $20,000
Lighting, power, and space    = $ 4,000
Annual cost of voice mail     = $36,000

We calculate the net annual cost saving as follows:

Total cost saving                          = $62,275
Total cost of owning a voice mail system = $36,000
Annual net cost saving                     = $26,275

Other cost savings that could be added to this model include message center staff reductions, the cost of time spent in meetings obtaining information that could be transmitted over voice mail, and the efficiency improvements of employees not having work interrupted and being able to obtain all of their voice messages at the same time.

## 10.2 COST JUSTIFICATION OF A PREDICTIVE DIALING SYSTEM

The major advantage of a predictive dialing system is that it eliminates the TSR's having to dial the number and monitor the call. Using a predictive dialing system, an individual TSR can make 100 to 200% more customer contacts. This translates into either fewer TSRs required or more customers contacted. In collections area, the benefit of contacting a customer in the early stages of account delinquency is significant because then the probability of working out a plan for eliminating the delinquency is high. With predictive dialing, customers can be reached faster and more effectively.

Assume that the TSR spends 2 minutes talking to a customer about his or her account. It would take the TSR 30 seconds to obtain and dial the customer's telephone number. The ringing and recognition of the call progress (i.e., ring/no-answer, busy, telephone company intercept, answering machine, customer not there, or customer answers) would take another 30 seconds.

Because 75% of all calls are not completed successfully, making one customer contact and talking for 120 seconds would require 180 additional seconds just for call connection. If the TSR only has to perform the customer contact portion of the call, he or she is able to make 150% more contacts over a period of time.

Assume that a collections center has 15 TSRs who are making 10 customer contacts per hour. For a 40-hour week, this amounts to $15 \times 10 \times 40 \times 52 = 312{,}000$ customer contacts per year. With a predictive dialing system, this center would be able to make the same number of customer contacts with 6 TSRs rather than 15. If each TSR costs $20,000 in salary and benefits, this yields a cost savings of $9 \times \$20{,}000 = \$180{,}000$. If a predictive dialing system costs $10,000 per TSR station, the equipment would pay for itself in just over three months.

Annual Expenses
Lease of predictive dialing system                     = $16,666
Lighting, power, and space                             = $ 4,000
Total cost of owning a predictive dialing system = $20,666

Thus, we subtract the total cost of the system ($20,666 from the savings in TSRs' salary and benefits ($180,000) to yield:

Total annual cost saving = $159,334

## 10.3 COST JUSTIFICATION OF C-TI

The integration of the computer database access with the telephone system can reduce the amount of time that a TSR spends on each call. This permits a TSR to handle more calls per hour. The setup time for each call is usually the easiest portion of the call to automate. This includes obtaining a caller's account number and matching it to the customer data and then learning what the caller is interested in and routing the call appropriately. The call setup time is typically 25% of the entire length of a 2.5-minute call.

Assume that a call center has 60 TSRs who each handle 10 calls per hour. For a 40-hour week, this amounts to $60 \times 10 \times 40 \times 52 = 1{,}248{,}000$ calls that are being handled per year. By adding C-TI, the same number of calls could be handled with 45 TSRs. If each TSR costs $20,000 per year in salary and benefits, this yields a yearly cost savings of $300,000. If the cost of adding C-TI capability costs $150,000, it would pay for itself in six months.

## REFERENCE

1. Wiltshire, L. G., "Evaluating Voice Messaging as a Cost-Effective Business Tool," *Online Voice-Processing Conference*, London, May 1985, pp. 107–117.

# Chapter 11
## Voice-Processing Service Providers

Voice-processing service providers are companies that provide voice-processing resources or information in voice form. Companies that own voice-processing hardware and software and provide its use for a fee are known as *service bureaus*. The service bureau manages the operation of the voice-processing system and, in many cases, customizes it to meet the needs of a particular client. It also obtains the telephone lines and pays for them. Service bureaus permit a customer to obtain a service without having to invest money to buy and keep the equipment. Clients pay either a monthly subscriber fee (plus usage) or for a particular project, while service bureaus often program the script and develop the speech recordings. Telemarketing service bureaus provide assistance in developing campaigns for customers in addition to running the campaign. Appendix 11 lists many service bureaus, information providers, and support services companies. Some of the advantages of using a service bureau versus purchasing a voice-processing system are:

- A minimum of financial commitment on the part of a customer is required.
- The customer does not have to deal with managing a voice-processing system.
- Networking capabilities are strong, making a service bureau particularly attractive for multisite organizations.
- The customer does not have to worry about physical aspects such as space, telephone lines, power, and lighting.
- The customer does not have to worry about obsolescence of the voice-processing equipment.
- Leasing is an excellent vehicle for implementing one-time events.

Voice-processing service providers can be segmented into the following categories:

- Service bureaus
  - Voice-mail service bureaus
  - *Telephone-answering service* (TAS) bureaus
  - Telemarketing service bureaus
  - Transaction-processing service bureaus
  - Information-provider service bureaus
- Information service providers
  - 976 service providers
  - 900 service providers
  - Subscription services
  - Sponsor-supported voice information services
  - Advertiser-supported voice information services
  - RCC voice services

## 11.1 VOICE-MAIL SERVICE BUREAUS

The larger voice-mail service bureaus are Tigon, ASYNC, AMVOX, CIBIS, Scherer Communications, and Voicecom Systems. Hundreds of small, regional voice-mail service bureaus also exist, though consolidation of service bureaus is occurring. The Tigon purchase of GTE Telemessager and the Voicecom Systems acquisition of WISC are recent examples of this. Some of the voice-mail service bureaus specialize in providing services to specific market areas, such as doctors or cellular telephone users. Voice-mail service bureaus often sell their services to internal corporate users [1].

The cost of a voice-mail service bureau varies from one service bureau to the next, depending on the features that a client selects. Some voice-mail service bureaus provide toll-free 800 numbers and DID lines at a premium price. With a DID line, each client has a unique voice-mail telephone number, so the entry of a subscriber access code is not required. A major advantage of this is that callers can leave a message for a client without entering any DTMF digits. A premium is frequently charged if a notification capability (automatic paging or dialing out) is required. A one-time installation and setup fee will cost between $15 and $50. A basic monthly fee for the use of a mailbox varies from $10 to $50. In addition, usage charges for the following are common:

- Minutes that the subscriber was connected with the system;
- The number of messages stored;
- The amount of memory storage that was used for storing messages;
- Special features (such as notification) used.

The major advantage of using a voice-mail service bureau is that a customer can quickly obtain the service with a minimal investment. Some of the disadvantages that exist with many of the service bureaus include:

- Access to a live operator is frequently not available or is very limited;
- Message-waiting indicators are frequently unavailable;
- The total cost of the service can be more expensive than an inhouse system;
- Alternative call routing services, such as those provided by an automated attendant, are typically unavailable;
- Message security is a concern, as several companies may use the same system.

## 11.2 TELEPHONE-ANSWERING SERVICE BUREAUS

Over 4,000 TAS operations exist in the United States, and the majority of them are quite small. In most cases, the TAS handles the customer's external calls. These are live-operator services with support equipment for making operators more efficient; the lines are frequently DID. A TAS support system provides the name of the client being called, the client's chosen greeting, and often a message describing how the call should be handled. TAS is the oldest, largest, and most mature type of voice service bureau, and its customer base is primarily small businesses.

## 11.3 TELEMARKETING SERVICE BUREAUS

This is one of the largest and fastest growing service bureau operations, in which revenue is obtained from specific project services. Services typically provided by a telemarketing service bureau include lead generation, credit checking, literature requests, dealer locators, fundraising, and order processing. Some of the leading telemarketing service bureaus are CVTC, American Airlines Direct Marketing, NICE/Appex, Watts Marketing, Teletech, CCI Telemarketing, West Telemarketing, Sitel Telemarketing, *National Data Corporation* (NDC), First Data Resource, AT&T Transtech, May Telemarketing, J.C. Penney Telemarketing, and Advanced Telemarketing Corporation.

The level of automation in telemarketing service bureaus is quite low. Less than 10% have been significantly automated, and over 50% are almost completely manual. The primary automation has been on outbound telemarketing, in which predictive dialers have been used.

Telemarketing service bureaus typically specialize in particular vertical market areas such as publishing, insurance, or travel. Although most provide both inbound and outbound services, most tend to be more strongly oriented toward one method or the other.

The physical location of a telemarketing service bureau is often dictated by the telephone network available in a particular area of the country. During a campaign, the number of calls can become extremely large, and the telephone network must be able to handle this traffic. Many telemarketing centers are located in Omaha, Nebraska, because Omaha is the location of the United States Air Force *Strategic Air Command* (SAC). Massive telephone network capacity was installed by AT&T to accommodate the call traffic that would occur during a war emergency. As long as the United States is not at war, this capacity sits idle and is available for use by telemarketing service bureaus.

A telemarketing service bureau typically enters into an agreement with a customer for a campaign when the campaign has a certain guaranteed-minimum call volume. This minimum is usually between 1,000 and 5,000 hours of call-processing time per month. Rates for inbound call processing are between $0.50 and $1.20 per minute. Rates on outbound call processing are typically tied to the number of calls placed per hour, which depends on the script the customer desires. A typical hourly rate is $30 per agent-hour.

Suppliers of telephone lookup services are available to provide information about the owner of a telephone number. The basic service takes telephone numbers and provides the names and addresses of their owners. Other services available provide lists that are sorted by specific *demographic* parameters, such as age group, income level, gender, geographic location, and time zones. The initial search is a computerized match, which locates about 50% of the numbers supplied for a cost of $0.02 to $0.06 per match. A manual search can then be performed on the remaining telephone numbers. This search usually locates approximately 50% of these telephone numbers, but the cost of finding them is considerably higher than the computer-matched ones—approximately $0.35 to $0.45 per number.

## 11.4 TRANSACTION-PROCESSING SERVICE BUREAUS

Transaction-processing service bureaus provide automatic bill payment, account status inquiry, check-cleared status, and credit card validation and transactions. Some of the leading service bureaus are Citicorp Information Resources, NCR Data Services, Merchant Network, First Corporation, First Data Resources, Mellon Bank, NDC, and credit union leagues. These service bureaus contract with an organization for a relatively long time. A typical customer would be a smaller bank that cannot afford the cost of its own data-processing operation.

Credit card validation and transactions require access to the database of the particular merchant card company. Credit cards are validated at a cost of a few cents per transaction. The cardholder's account is debited by the amount of the transaction, and he or she is able to complete the purchase.

A relatively new segment of the voice transaction processing area is the *operator service provider* (OSP) that is not a telephone company. This group is also known as the *alternate operator services* (AOS) area, although its members prefer the OSP designation. This industry has grown to approximately $800 million since the MFJ in 1984 made its existence possible. The OSP companies go after high call-traffic sites and handle all operator-assisted calls, as described in Chapter 6. They charge for the operator service and the cost of the long-distance line, and contract with the owner of the phones to have all traffic routed to them. In return, they pay a fraction (typically 15%) of their revenues to the phone owners. Target customers have been payphone owners, hotels, and hospitals. The service provided by the OSPs has generally been inferior and more expensive than that provided by the dominant carrier (AT&T). Long call delays, inability to use # for continuation calling, and the inability to process many telephone company credit cards have been typical. Call charges have ranged from 120 to 400% higher than those charged by AT&T. If the OSP determines that they are unable to bill for a call, they will often transfer the call to the LEC, which is known as "splashing." This is done at the OSP operator site, which is usually distant from the call's point of origin. The caller will then receive a bill from the LEC indicating a call that originated at the remote site. Callers are often confused when they see a call originating from a city that they were not in, leading to a high rate of uncollectables.

When a caller uses a calling card, the OSPs depend on the LECs for the actual customer billing and collection for all services they provide. Validation and billing costs are higher, and receivables often run in excess of 90 days. Billing mechanisms for many of the calling cards through the LEC are simply not available. In these cases, the caller is unable to use that calling card.

The cost of using a calling card are significantly higher using a commercial credit card, which is what the OSPs would prefer a customer use. Although OSPs have received a good deal of negative publicity concerning excessive charges, the real cause of the excess is the telephone companies, which charge OSPs high rates for processing and billing and are delinquent in paying the OSPs. The OSPs simply pass these charges on to the caller.

A variety of enhanced services can be provided by the OSPs, which would tend to enhance this business area. OSPs and their support providers are listed and categorized in Appendix 6. Among them are:

- Directory services call completion;
- Automation of collect calls;
- Voice-message delivery on busy or ring/no-answer.

The types of calls and charges AT&T makes for operator-assisted calls include:

- Operator-assisted, station-to-station $1.75;
- Operator-assisted, person-to-person $3.50;
- Automatic credit card call $0.80;
- Collect calls $3.50.

### 11.4.1 OSP Business Model

The OSP receives revenue from the operator charges and the resale of long-distance lines. In addition to the cost of providing the operators, the following costs will also be incurred by the OSP: long-distance line charge, credit card validation charge, call rating charge, and billing and collections charge.

### 11.4.2 OSP Support Providers

A set of services is used by the OSPs and is frequently provided by other companies:

- Long-distance lines;
- Credit card validation;
- Billing;
- Live-operator services.

#### 11.4.2.1 Long-Distance Suppliers

Suppliers of long-distance lines are known as *interexchange carriers* (IXCs). Many exist, and the larger ones are AT&T, U.S. Sprint, MCI, Allnet, and SoutherNet. The reselling of line usage provided by the IXCs is a substantial portion of the OSP revenue stream. Nondiscounted AT&T per minute rates are approximately $0.30 per minute; bulk purchase of telephone line usage ranges from $0.10 to $0.15 per minute. Currently, there is significant line overcapacity in place in the United States, and we anticipate that line-usage charges will decrease in the short term. AT&T rates are tariffed by the FCC.

#### 11.4.2.2 Credit Card Validation

The cost to validate a calling card using one of the available services is approximately $0.13 per validation. The cost to validate a commercial credit card is approximately $0.08 per validation. We assume that a caller makes five calls on a single validation.

#### 11.4.2.3 Billing and Collection

The external cost to bill a calling card call is approximately $0.55 per call. The bulk of that cost is the fee the LEC charges. The cost to bill a commercial credit card call is typically less than $0.10. The collection period from the LEC is typically 90 days, while for a commercial credit card it is usually less than 48 hours. From this, we can see why OSPs prefer that their customers use commercial credit cards. The call must also be rated, and companies such as TeleTech offer subscription services that provide clients with the latest tariffs.

### 11.4.2.4 Live-Operator Services

Companies such as NDC provide operator services at an hourly rate of $35 to $39 per hour; customers are only charged for the actual time the operator is handling calls. This rate is approximately $0.01 per second. Rate variability depends on call volume and length of the contract commitment.

### 11.4.3 OSP Regulatory Issues

There have been numerous newspaper and magazine articles regarding operator service. Unfortunately, from the perspective of the OSPs, almost all of this publicity has been bad. Exorbitant rates charged by the OSPs is the dominant negative point most often expressed. Users of an operator service are often unpleasantly surprised by the bills that they receive. In addition to the higher charges, other complaints have been:

- Callers often cannot use their calling cards.
- Callers are blocked from using another long-distance carrier.
- Callers make short-distance calls and find that they are billed for calls from distant cities they did not make.
- The quality of service is poor.

As a response to these complaints, laws have been passed and the FCC has issued the following rules:

*Branding.* For the next 3 years, all calls must be double branded, and the first brand must come before the bong tone.

*Rate quotes* must be given on request and must be exact.

*Posting.* Identification of the OSP must be posted on or near the telephone.

*Splashing.* The practice of transferring the call to the LEC if the OSP determines that they are unable to bill for the call is barred.

*Unanswered calls* cannot be charged to the caller.

*Access codes* must be permitted to 800 and 950 numbers without charge to the caller.

*Emergency call procedures.* The OSP is required to connect an emergency call immediately to the emergency service provider at the site of the emergency.

*Reporting requirements.* The OSPs must report a compilation of their rates, complaints received, and underlying costs. The FCC specified dates when these reports need to be filed.

OSP companies are not presently regulated, which means that the FCC directive is enforceable in only an indirect fashion (i.e., prohibiting the RBOCs from providing billing services to an offending OSP company). Federal regulations are being proposed that would regulate the OSPs. A key aspect, of course, would be restrictions on pricing. OSP companies are actively lobbying against rate regulation, using the argument that their rates are higher than AT&T's because the "playing field is still not level." They point out that they are required to pay much higher charges than AT&T for validation and billing services. The state PUCs have been responding to complaints against the OSP companies by developing certification requirements. A few states have simply outlawed OSPs.

## 11.5 INFORMATION SERVICE PROVIDERS

Companies that provide voice information are known as *information providers* and offer a service that allows a caller to obtain information over the telephone. The caller either pays for the information directly, or the cost of providing the information is borne by a third party, such as an advertiser.

## 11.6 INFORMATION PROVIDER SUPPORT COMPANIES

A variety of companies exists that provide services to information providers in either setting up or running a service. Service bureaus are available to provide equipment, telephone line and numbers, and scripting and audio recording services.

### 11.6.1 Information Provider Service Bureaus

Service bureaus provide all the services that an information provider requires. They obtain the telephone lines, the equipment, and services to implement the application. The IP has only to provide the program idea and promote it. These service bureaus charge a fixed fee per call in addition to an installation fee and a base monthly charge. Ameritech Audiotex Services is one of the largest information provider service bureaus, and U.S. Sprint provides a service bureau in addition to providing the telephone lines.

### 11.6.1.1 The 976 and 900 Dial-It Services

The 976 and 900 Dial-It services are a medium for providing voice information. The caller pays for accessing the information and the telephone company bills the caller and shares the revenue with the information provider. These services are carried by dedicated switching systems. The 976 services operate within a LATA, while 900 services are either nationwide or cover multiple LATAs. The 976 designation derives from the fact that the NXX is 976; these services use 900 for the NPA.

Until 1983, all voice information services were provided by the telephone company and were usually sponsored by advertisers. Program providers were paid a flat fee by the telephone company, which received all the revenue from the call. Computer Inquiry II, handed down by the FCC, specified the types of businesses in which the telephone companies could participate. The 976 services were classified as information services, so the telephone companies were specifically forbidden from offering them. This created an opportunity for independent organizations that wanted to offer 976 services.

The 976 services have grown dramatically since 1983. Many cities have been added to the five information providers that existed in 1983, and the number of information lines has grown to over 5,000. Although a wide variety of services is in place, the vast majority of revenues has been obtained from six types of information or entertainment:

- Adult (pornographic) entertainment;
- Sports information;
- Financial information;
- Time;
- Weather;
- Gambling and lotteries.

The geographic areas covered by particular 976 services vary quite dramatically from one region of the country to another. They are typically defined by the area covered by a LATA, in some cases covering an entire area code or group of area codes. The areas are defined by a specific telephone company, and there has been no attempt at consistency. In many cases, the television broadcast's reach extends from one LATA to another, so a televised advertisement will generate traffic for a 976 number from outside the LATA. These calls are either blocked, or the caller cannot be billed.

Billing of the calls by the telephone company has been a serious problem for the information provider. We estimate that for approximately 40% of the calls received, no revenue is obtained. There is a variety of reasons for this, including calls from outside the LATA frequently are not billed, and long-distance callers are frequently able to get onto a 976 service without paying anything. If a caller indicates that he or she does not want to pay for a 976 call that is on the bill, the telephone company simply allows a deduction of the amount from the bill. The telephone companies have also been slow to pay the information providers. Ninety-day waits, after the telephone company has billed for service, are common. This has a very negative effect on the cash flow of the information provider business, and its *return on investment* (ROI) suffers. The information providers are, in effect, helping to finance the telephone companies.

The telephone companies require that the information proviers supply a guaranteed number of calls each month. If the quota is not reached, financial penalties are imposed by the telephone company. This tends to penalize the smaller information providers and discourages any sort of experimentation with new information and entertainment programs. Most IPs have found that to generate a reasonable call volume, significant advertising is required. The telephone companies had not advertised the 976 services, not even generically, until the late 1980s. Some of the telephone companies such as Pactel and Ameritech are starting to become aggressive in promoting the 976 area. We estimate that to produce $1 in revenue, an advertising investment of $0.60 is required. Advertising directed at children and pornographic programs are other problem areas of 976 numbers.

The 900 services are nationwide dial-it services. Until 1989, the major service was offered by AT&T and was known as Dial-It 900. It is a noninteractive service. The 900 services have been used for special events and information services and are available on a long-term basis. For Dial-It 900, the two types of service available are *service call count* and *service information*. The service call count is usually associated with a major media event: the audience is asked to vote on an issue by calling a 900 number. AT&T provides a tally of calls to the purchaser of the 900 service. Some of the other options available from AT&T are detailed call reports, call forwarding, minute-by-minute call count data, and caller free service. The cost of the call is $0.50 for the first minute and $0.35 for each additional minute.

During 1987, Telesphere Communications began offering interactive 900 services in Chicago and New York. In 1989, AT&T, U.S. Sprint, and MCI each began offering interactive 900 services. They generally cover the entire country, although at first certain central rural areas (including North and South Dakota) were excluded while billing arrangements with the LEC were being established. A comparison of these services is shown in Table 11.1.

The availability of nationwide 900 services directly competes with the local 976 offerings of the BOCs, causing the BOCs to become more aggressive in providing 976 services. This means that 976 services are focusing on providing information services for a particular region of the country.

The Dial-It 900 service is also a barge-in service. A barge-in service is one in which the caller hears the message from whatever point it has reached, as opposed to hearing it from the beginning. Up to 88 different programs can exist at one time, and the service has the capacity to handle 7,200 calls simultaneously without callers' reaching a busy signal. Dial-It 900 originally operated with a price cap of $2.00 per minute, and 60% of the calls were generated by adult services. In 1988, AT&T took action to clean it up—a price cap of $0.50 per minute was instituted, and Dial-It 900 was converted into primarily a voting-type product for media such as television. Payments to information providers were terminated, and sponsors were permitted to pay for a portion of the call. Dial-It 900 is now primarily a promotional vehicle rather than a source of information provider revenue. The lack of an interactive capability has been a severe limit of Dial-It 900. Even the best known applications, such as simple polling ones, are constrained by the lack of an interactive capability. Two separate 900 numbers are typically used—one to vote yes and the other to vote no—and vote counts are frequently constrained by the network capacity to handle calls. As a result, the number of yes votes and the number of no votes are virtually identical, making the entire poll worthless. With

**Table 11.1**
Characteristics of 900 Services

| Item | AT&T | MCI | Sprint |
|------|------|-----|--------|
| Line installation charge | $250 | $50 | waived |
| Monthly line charge | Volume sensitive | waived | $100 |
| Startup fee | $1,200 | waived | waived |
| Additional program | $125 | waived | waived |
| Monthly fee | $500 | waived | $900 |
| Rate/number change Fee | $175 | $110 | $150 |
| Uncollectable fee | 10% | 10% | 9% |
| Billing and collection fee | | $0.12/call | |
| Preamble fee | | $0.12/call | |
| First minute | $0.30 | $0.28 | $0.30 |
| Additional minutes | $0.30 | $0.28 | $0.30 |
| Billing increments | 1 second | 6 second | 1 second |
| Real time ANI | Yes | Yes | Yes |

an interactive service, this problem would be eliminated, because each caller could vote either yes or no by entering an appropriate digit.

Until recently, 900 services had been available from four national 900 carriers. In mid 1991, Telesphere went out of business. A few months later Sprint announced that they would not provide billing and collection services to information providers that operated romance, credit card, and job lines. A few months later they extended this ban to existing information providers. With these announcements, Sprint has vacated essentially 90% of its 900 business. The ones they continue to support are providers of news, stock quotes, sports information, weather, and other noncontroversial programs. Sprint's decision was based on the negative image that Sprint was acquiring by its association with certain 900 programs. This now leaves AT&T and MCI in command of 900 traffic.

The AT&T MultiQuest service terminates 900 lines at the facility of the information provider. AT&T charges an initial setup fee and then a monthly line rental. AT&T charges the information provider $0.30 for the first minute of each call and $0.25 per minute for each subsequent minute. The information provider can charge the caller between $0.75 and $2.00 per minute for the call. Verbal interim call count data and call detail reports are available. Call counts are available in hourly increments or by geographic area. Call forwarding to another telephone number permits TSR intercept. HICAP service was tariffed in 1989 and allows 5 to 10% discounts for customers spending more that $100,000 per month on MultiQuest.

Now interactive 900 services are offered by the long-distance telephone companies, which bill the caller for each 900 call. The fact that the services are nationwide makes them appropriate for a set of applications that were not possible with the constraints inherent in 976 services.

Many of the businesses that are using and will use 900 services will be previous and current users of 800 services. The 900 services will permit them to eliminate the cost of the 800 service and actually generate a significant revenue stream from the 900 service. Customer service is another significant application area for 900 services. Charging customers fairly for telephone support has always been a difficult proposition. Keeping track of individual telephone calls and then billing them back to a customer is an impossible task for most companies. With 900 service, billing a customer for the actual amount of telephone support time he or she consumed is readily accomplished.

The delivery of expert information is another application of 900 service. Publishers of newsletters and specialized reports can use a 900 service as an alternative delivery mechanism. Fundraising is an excellent application of a 900 service. An individual could make a donation by calling a 900 number, an effective means to provide relief to victims of natural disasters such as hurricanes and earthquakes. Ordering of products and services over a 900 line is another attractive application.

Most problems with 900 services are associated with billing. The telephone companies, which provide the actual billing service, are frequently late (i.e., in excess of 90 days) in paying the information providers. The high rate of chargebacks and uncollectables has been a shock to many. Different tariffs and taxes exist in many states, and each LEC has different criteria as to what they will permit information providers to bill. Because the charge for the service will be billed to the telephone from which the call was made, a potential for abuse does exist. The problem is that LECs are reluctant to force collection for information provider services, and many of the uncollectables are caused by an awareness that the telephone company will not pursue it. The amount limits, set by the IXCs, would constrain some of the applications. In particular, fundraisers and shopping-by-telephone are a couple of the applications that are limited by a price cap.

Blocking of 900 calls is another problem that will limit the applicability of 900 services. Presently the RBOCs require that a customer request that 900 calls be blocked. The possibility that the RBOCs will make blocking the default situation and require that a customer request nonblocking of 900 calls is real and could be devastating to the 900 services. Many potential 900 services require widespread access. If users find that many phones cannot be used for 900 calls, the popularity of the service will diminish considerably. Many businesses already block all 900 and 976 calls because of employee abuse of company telephones.

We estimate that approximately 70% of calls to 900 services are being made by individuals that are under 18 years old. This is not a good sign and explains why the uncollectables rate is so high. Clearly, 900 applications need to be those that would attract a larger percentage of mature and responsible customers. The 900 service providers have put a lot of effort into restricting the use of 900 services for adult entertainment and advertisements directed at children. This has helped to improve the image of 900 and establish it as a legitimate business service. The promotion of 900 services by organizations such as AT&T, U.S. Sprint, and MCI will provide a significant stimulus to this market area.

The availability of interactive 900 services makes it possible to offer nationwide audiotex and has been a catalyst for the entry of large nationwide information providers. The 976 service will become an information service used strictly to reach a regional market. If large companies already in publishing and broadcasting become information providers, they will help accelerate growth in this market area. These organizations are well positioned to address the promotion requirements of audiotex services.

There are 800 numbers presently assigned to specific IXCs that cannot be transferred. This makes it difficult for a company to change their long-distance carrier, since they typically have invested in promoting a particular 800 number. The FCC has mandated that the telephone companies provide 800-number portability. This is presently scheduled to be in place by mid 1993. The current 800 service exchange number assignments are shown in Table 11.2. The 900 exchange numbers are listed in Table 11.3 (page 254).

*11.6.1.2 A Comparison: 900 Versus 976 Services*

The 900 services are the best approach for programs that have a nationwide market. The reality, though, is that the majority of products are marketed on a local basis. Reaching people in California is of no benefit to an organization that is selling in Boston. The use of 976 tends to be much more appealing for products that have a regional market. One of the clear advantages of 976 is that the telephone company fees are considerably lower. A 976 charge is typically less than $0.10 for the first

**Table 11.2**

800 Service Exchange Number Assignment

| Interexchange carrier | NXX |
|---|---|
| Access Long Distance | 574 |
| ACC Long Distance Corporation | 295 |
| Action Telecom Company | 586 588 |
| Afford A Call | 294 |
| Alascom | 478 764 |
| Allnet Communication Services | 454 466 471 536 557 566 783 863 875 878 886 923 |
| Alternate Communications Technology | 761 |
| Americall Corporation | 399 |
| Americall Systems LA | 928 |
| American Express TRS | 297 |
| American Long Lines | 784 |
| American Teleco | 856 |
| Amerigon | 434 |
| Ameritech Audiotex Services | 808 908 |
| Amvox | 656 |
| Arvig Telephone Company | 620 |

minute and close to $0.05 for subsequent minutes. Typically, 900 services are three times higher. Billing and collection charges are typically $0.10 per call. Compare this to the 900 services that typically consume 10% of the total price of the service. On an uncollectable, 900 services will still bill the information provider for the transport cost. Most of the telephone companies that provide 976 services bill the caller for the transport costs, even if they refuse to pay the IP service charge. Although 900 services have received much larger visibility because of their national scope, 976 remains a very viable set of services. Table 11.4 (page 259) is a summary comparison of 900 versus 976 services.

*11.6.1.3 Regulatory Status of 900 and 976 Services*

Complaints from businesses and consumers have caused legislation to be enacted to address the problem areas. The legislation in this area is directed at fraudulent

**Table 11.2 (continued)**

| Interexchange carrier | NXX |
|---|---|
| AT&T | 050 141 221 222 223 225 227 228 231 232 233 235 237 238 241 242 245 247 248 251 252 253 255 272 262 282 292 321 322 323 325 327 328 331 332 334 336 338 341 342 343 344 345 346 348 351 352 354 356 362 367 368 372 382 392 421 422 423 424 426 428 431 432 433 435 437 438 441 442 443 445 446 447 448 451 452 453 457 458 462 468 472 482 492 521 522 523 524 525 526 527 528 531 532 533 535 537 538 541 542 543 544 545 547 548 551 552 553 554 555 556 558 562 572 582 592 621 622 624 626 628 631 632 633 634 635 637 638 641 642 643 645 647 648 652 654 662 672 682 692 722 732 742 752 762 772 782 792 821 822 824 826 828 831 832 833 835 841 842 843 845 847 848 851 852 854 855 858 872 874 882 892 922 932 942 952 962 972 982 992 |
| ATC | 226 375 741 |
| ATX Telecom Services | 220 355 890 |
| AUS Inc. | 942 |
| Beehive Telephone Company | 629 |
| Bittle Telecom | 987 |
| Bridgewater Telephone Company | 650 |
| Burlington Telephone | 639 |
| Business Telecom, Inc. | 849 |

or objectionable services that have sprung up in the 900 and 976 area. The legislation would require:

1. A price and product identification preamble before the imposition of a charge. For services that would be of interest to children, the preamble would need to include a warning that parental permission is required before service use.
2. LECs would have to provide a call blocking option. This would be on all interstate 900 calls where technically feasible.
3. Carriers would be prohibited from canceling basic telephone service for failure to pay interstate 900 service charges.

**Table 11.2 (continued)**

| Interexchange carrier | NXX |
|---|---|
| Cable & Wireless | 229 394 486 883 899 966 969 989 |
| Call America | 549 550 644 |
| Call USA, Inc. | 278 |
| Cam-Net Systems | 357 |
| Chadwick Telephone | 360 |
| Chernow Communications | 935 |
| Cincinnati Bell | 213 |
| Claydesta | 299 |
| Communications Group of Jackson | 898 |
| Com Systems | 266 350 |
| Comm. Cbl. Laying Hedges | 385 |
| Conquest Communications Corp. | 645 |
| Conquest Long Distance | 320 |
| Consolidated Network | 500 |
| Cleartel Communications | 270 |
| Delta Communications | 239 |
| Deluxe Data Systems | 997 |
| Digital Network, Inc | 871 |
| Digitel | 850 |
| Eastern Microwave | 379 |

4. The use of 800 numbers that automatically connect the caller with a pay-per-call service would be prohibited.

In addition, a variety of voluntary standards of practice has been proposed and instituted by industry participants, including the IXCs, NAIS, and IIA. These include hotlines and other monitoring systems for consumers to report fraudulent or otherwise illegal 900 service programs, refusal to bill for certain types of programs (e.g., adult), price caps, prescreening of programs and advertising that supports them, and general control of the quality of 900 programs.

**Table 11.2 (continued)**

| Interexchange carrier | NXX |
|---|---|
| Eastern Telephone Systems | 887 |
| Econo Call Long Distance | 376 |
| Electronic Data Systems | 778 |
| Entre Telecom Corporation | 796 |
| Execuline Sacramento | 655 |
| FEB Corporation | 990 |
| First Digital Network | 269 |
| First Data Resources | 337 |
| First Financial Management | 884 |
| First Phone | 539 |
| Flex Communications | 721 |
| Fox Communications | 664 |
| FTC Communications | 746 |
| General Communications | 770 |
| GTE North | 481 |
| GTE Florida | 483 |
| GTE Hawaiian Telephone Co. | 865 |
| Indiana Switch, Inc | 436 |
| International Pacific | 493 |
| Lakes States Communications | 993 |

## 11.6.1.4 Gateway Services

Gateway services provide a single point of access to a variety of audiotex services. The caller dials a single number and is presented a menu from which to choose. After he or she selects, the caller is switched to that particular service. Gateway services are being provided by some of the RBOCs, though many information providers have found that the gateway services have some pitfalls. The basic concept is in direct violation of some basic marketing concepts. In a shopping mall, customers do not locate shops that offer identical services, yet this is what a gateway

**Table 11.2 (continued)**

| Interexchange Carrier | NXX |
|---|---|
| Lassman Weber Communications | 249 |
| LDD, Inc. | 455 |
| LDDS | 260 298 264 279 280 467 489 737 738 844 880 946 951 960 |
| Link USA Corporation | 978 |
| Lintel Systems | 579 |
| Litel | 589 686 |
| Long Distance Communications | 975 |
| Long Distance For Less | 224 |
| Long Distance Management | 599 |
| Long Distance of Michigan | 381 |
| Long Distance Savers | 256 259 |
| Long Distance Services | 296 |
| LTS, Inc. | 587 |
| MCI Communications | 234 274 283 284 285 288 289 333 365 374 388 395 444 456 477 627 666 677 678 685 688 695 723 727 753 756 759 765 766 777 825 846 866 873 876 879 888 925 926 928 933 934 937 944 945 947 950 955 964 967 999 |
| Metromedia Communications Corp. | 275 929 935 938 |
| Metromedia Long Distance | 683 |
| Mid-Atlantic Telephone | 787 |
| Midco Communications | 529 |

service does. The information providers are not motivated to advertise a phone number that also belongs to their competition.

## 11.6.1.5 Bridging and Conferencing

"Gab" services became popular in the mid 1980s, but growth has leveled off since then. The biggest problem was the uncollectables rate, which ran as high as 70%. The negative image of the gab lines is similar to the image of adult lines.

**Table 11.2 (continued)**

| Interexchange carrier | NXX |
|---|---|
| Napa Valley Telephone Services | 799 |
| National Data Corporation | 625 |
| National Telecom | 881 |
| National Telecom Florida | 895 |
| National Telephone Company | 378 |
| National Telephone Exchange | 460 |
| Network Long Distance | 349 |
| Network Telemanagement Systems | 230 |
| Network Telephone Services | 494 |
| Northern Arizona Communications | 897 |
| Northern Telecom, Inc. | 684 |
| Northwestern Bell | 459 |
| Northwest Telco | 689 |
| NTS Communications | 687 |
| One-2-One | 293 |
| One Call Communications, Inc. | 276 |
| Pentagon Computer | 520 |
| Phoenix Communications Group | 217 |
| Pilgrim Telephone Company | 699 |
| Phoenix Network | 948 |

## 11.6.1.6 Voice Information Sources

Telecom*USA Information Resources (now a subsidiary of MCI) is the producer of *Voice News Network* (VNN), an information service syndicated to the talking yellow pages and newspaper industry. VNN produces news, sports, financial, and weather reports for private-label distribution. VNN also offers soap opera updates, horoscopes, top movie hits and reviews, top video hits and reviews, weekly music top 10 hits, and ski reports. Other providers of information include Dow Jones and The Associated Press. SportsTicker provides a sports information service.

**Table 11.2 (continued)**

| Interexchange carrier | NXX |
|---|---|
| Phone one | 393 |
| Puerto Rico Telephone Company | 595 981 |
| RCC Paging Systems | 202 212 302 312 402 412 502 512 602 612 702 712 802 812 902 912 |
| RCI Corporation | 724 |
| R-Comm Long Distance Telephone | 936 |
| Satelco | 725 |
| Schneider Communications | 236 261 335 353 |
| SM Long Distance | 700 |
| Southern Interexchange | 240 |
| SouthernNet | 277 768 771 868 |
| Southern NE Telephone | 286 |
| South Tel | 940 |
| Southwest Long Distance | 495 |
| Southwestern Bell | 246 |
| Star-line | 839 |
| State of California | 963 |
| Sunshine Telephone, Inc. | 785 |
| Superior Telecom | 200 |
| Tel America | 789 |
| Telco | 581 |
| Telecable Corporation | 386 |

Telephone number lookup services that provide the name and address associated with the telephone number are available from a variety of sources.

### 11.6.1.7 Talking Yellow Pages

The *talking yellow pages* (TYPs) area was created in the last few years. The TYPs provide the functionality of printed yellow pages but also audio information. They derive their revenue from listed advertisers. In some cases, the suppliers actually

**Table 11.2 (continued)**

| Interexchange Carrier | NXX |
|---|---|
| Telecom Canada | 263 265 268 361 363 387 461 463 465 561 563 565 567 661 663 665 667 668 |
| Telecom Options Plus | 596 |
| Teleconnect Company | 369 370 373 383 397 475 476 484 485 583 584 593 594 657 658 673 674 729 747 748 749 779 780 798 836 837 857 988 |
| Teledial America | 968 |
| Telephone Utilities of Washington | 680 889 |
| Telemanagement Cons | 720 |
| Telnational Communications | 939 |
| Telenet Communications Company | 377 577 |
| Telescan | 694 |
| Telesphere Network | 864 |
| Tel Share | 754 |
| Tel Tech, Inc. | 425 |
| Telus Communication | 329 330 |
| Telvue Corporation | 885 |
| Tex-Net, Inc. | 440 896 |
| TDMT Ltd Inc. | 651 |
| TMC Communications | 891 |
| TMC Long Distance | 781 |
| TMC of Lexington | 965 |
| TMC Southwest FL | 429 |

publish a complete phonebook, and the talking aspect is used to complement the book and sell the service to advertisers. TYPs typically include a variety of other free voice information services, such as sports, horoscopes, weather, news, and financial information. An advertiser will have a number in the advertisement that will provide voice information about the advertiser.

TYPs were introduced in 1986 by the independent publishers of classified telephone books. The motivation for adding the talking capability was to differ-

**Table 11.2 (continued)**

| Interexchange Carrier | NXX |
|---|---|
| TMC South Central Indiana | 757 797 |
| Total Telephone USA | 254 |
| Touch America | 823 |
| Touch & Save | 762 |
| Trans Net Inc. | 679 |
| Tri J | 693 |
| T Tel | 429 |
| TTE of Charleston | 774 |
| United Inter-Mtn. Telephone | 838 |
| Union Telephone Company | 646 |
| United Telephone Co. of Florida | 786 |
| United DBA Telemar | 449 |
| Unitel Communications Canada | 575 |
| Universal Communications, Inc. | 853 |
| US Link Long Distance | 450 |
| U.S. Sprint | 326 340 347 359 366 398 487 488 497 546 578 597 598 653 659 669 676 697 726 729 733 735 736 743 745 755 758 767 769 775 776 788 793 795 800 827 829 859 869 927 949 959 998 |
| U S Telecom | 396 |
| Valu-Line | 996 |
| Vartec National, Inc | 530 |
| Virtual Network | 860 |

entiate them from their competitors' books by providing a variety of local community information or current topics, such as community activity calendars, concert information, movie information, ski conditions, and lottery numbers. Another motivation for providing TYPs is to increase directory usage. Four-digit codes are listed in the printed directory with each advertisement. By calling and entering the

**Table 11.2 (continued)**

| *Interexchange Carrier* | *NXX* |
| --- | --- |
| Voicecom Systems | 384 |
| Vortel | 867 |
| VYVX Telecom, Inc. | 324 364 |
| West Coast Telecom | 576 |
| Western Union Telegraph | 983 986 |
| Westel | 580 |
| Westinghouse Communications | 941 |

code, the consumer is able to hear a current special offer or announcement from the advertiser. The major advantage is that the information being provided by the advertiser can be updated frequently. This is in contrast to the printed information in the yellow pages, which is only updated once each year.

The market for TYPs is tied to the economic health of the independent directory suppliers. During the last few years, cutbacks, bankruptcies, and red ink have been a dominant characteristic of companies in this area. Books that simply duplicate what is already done by another book are not an attractive venture. The independents are going after niche markets and providing capabilities that differentiate them from the telephone company books. Printing TYPs is one of the ways by which the independents have attempted to differentiate themselves.

The biggest problem with TYPs is the massive advertising needed to remind consumers to use the talking feature. Convincing advertisers that the TYPs are an effective way to help sell a product is another challenge. Although the telephone companies had been forbidden from providing information services themselves, they have set up TYPs by going to third-party audiotex service bureaus.

We estimate that approximately 200 TYPs sites exist in the United States and Canada. The RBOCs' role in this industry will determine future growth. As RBOCs enter this arena, the market for TYPs should grow and prosper. The TYPs will grow slowly during the next couple of years, while advertisers become convinced that this area is a worthwhile investment of their advertising dollars. The independent publishers of yellow pages directories will be the prime drivers.

### 11.6.2 Other Information Provider Support

In addition to the full-line service bureaus, other companies are available to provide specialized support to the information provider. Companies that specialize in audio

**Table 11.3**
900 Service Exchange Number Assignments

| Interexchange Carrier | NXX |
|---|---|
| ACC Long Distance Corporation | 356 |
| Advantage Network | 264 |
| Alascom | 478 866 |
| Allnet Communication Services | 224 227 345 422 540 543 550 567 665 753 765 974 975 977 978 979 |
| Americall Corporation | 399 477 948 |
| American Information Network | 330 440 638 782 890 |
| American Long Lines | 991 |
| Ameritech Audiotex Services | 235 248 280 301 302 338 340 347 367 428 432 441 450 551 620 627 628 640 778 780 874 924 946 |
| Arvig Telephone Company | 610 |
| AT&T | 200 210 220 225 250 260 268 288 300 328 339 342 344 350 370 400 407 410 420 436 454 460 480 490 500 520 527 555 590 600 650 660 680 720 730 737 738 740 773 786 820 840 850 860 884 896 903 909 920 932 933 976 |
| ATC | 949 970 971 972 973 |
| AUS Inc. | 569 657 729 871 925 |
| Bittle Telecom | 421 544 653 763 877 |
| Bridgewater Telephone Company | 644 |
| Bell Atlantic | 272 335 701 801 901 |
| Burlington Telephone | 536 |

recording are available. They work with the information provider to design audio messages, supply the talent for the recordings, and then implement the messages. Advertising companies that specialize in the 900 and 976 area are available to develop advertising campaigns for an information provider product.

## Table 11.3 (continued)

| Interexchange Carrier | NXX |
|---|---|
| Cable & Wireless | 221 223 233 322 888 900 |
| Call America | 549 |
| Call USA, Inc. | 493 |
| Capital Network Systems | 425 |
| Cincinnati Bell | 253 |
| Com Systems | 266 626 739 |
| Comm. Cbl. Laying Hedges | 625 |
| Conquest Operator Services Corp. | 875 |
| Delta Communications | 239 |
| Digital Network, Inc. | 771 |
| Digitel | 851 |
| Eastern Telephone Systems, Inc. | 327 887 |
| Execuline Sacramento | 395 |
| FEB Corporation | 990 |
| First Digital Network | 269 |
| First Phone | 357 412 632 852 951 |
| Flex Communications | 721 |
| GTE California | 343 545 727 848 |
| GTE North | 483 |
| H&M Telecomm Services | 464 467 566 588 735 |
| Integretel, Inc. | 244 487 879 937 968 |
| International Telecharge | 465 |

## 11.7 INFORMATION PROVIDER SUBSCRIPTION SERVICES

Subscription services are provided to clients who pay a monthly charge. Subscribers call in and obtain financial information on a variety of topics. Many of these are

## Table 11.3 (continued)

| Interexchange Carrier | NXX |
|---|---|
| Iowa Network Services, Inc. | 856 |
| LDDS | 229 355 533 636 960 |
| Litel Telecomm Corporation | 282 686 |
| Long Distance Savers | 259 296 |
| Long Distance Services | 361 |
| Long Distance of Michigan | 564 |
| Long Distance USA | 365 563 |
| MCI Communications | 226 255 263 285 287 289 329 388 389 435 438 443 446 448 476 484 486 526 562 622 656 659 674 678 725 733 726 745 722 776 787 825 835 868 876 950 964 988 990 993 |
| Meade Associates | 663 |
| Metromedia Communications Corporation | 275 575 683 746 |
| Mid Atlantic Telecom | 696 |
| Midco Communications | 529 633 |
| National Telecom | 747 992 994 995 996 |
| National Telephone Exchange | 689 |
| Network Long Distance | 349 |
| Network Operator Services | 667 |
| Network Telecom | 359 669 752 754 762 |
| Network Telephone Services, Inc | 404 528 707 808 989 |
| New York Telephone | 698 |
| Northern Arizona Communications | 337 |
| NYCOM, Inc. | 424 828 |

Table 11.3 (continued)

| Interexchange Carrier | NXX |
|---|---|
| NYNEX Services | 770 880 |
| Omnicall | 222 366 444 488 666 |
| Pacific Bell Region | 303 505 777 843 844 |
| Parker Communications | 309 353 397 532 736 |
| Pentagon Computer | 522 |
| Phoenix Communications Group | 247 |
| Phone America | 742 |
| Phone Mail, Inc. | 445 |
| Pilgrim Telephone Company | 332 426 639 699 |
| Puerto Rico Telephone Company | 475 |
| RCI Corporation | 724 |
| Schneider Communications | 236 |
| Southern Interexchange | 238 |
| Southern NE Telephone | 306 606 |
| Southwest Long Distance | 755 |
| Sunshine Telephone, Inc. | 784 |
| Superior Telecom | 232 242 |
| Telecom Canada | 273 297 451 595 630 643 645 670 677 690 750 790 792 830 870 |
| Telecom Options Plus | 231 |
| Teledial America | 326 |
| Telefonica Larga Dis | 853 |
| Telemanagement Cons | 710 |

## Table 11.3 (continued)

| Interexchange Carrier | NXX |
|---|---|
| Telenational Communications | 423 459 621 |
| Telenet Communications Company | 377 |
| Telescan | 998 |
| Telesphere Network | 228 234 258 269 321 369 394 456 462 654 687 741 838 872 963 999 |
| Telus Communication | 331 |
| Telvue Corporation | 789 885 987 |
| TMC Communications | 655 |
| Total Telephone USA | 254 |
| Trans Net Inc. | 679 |
| United Telephone Long Distance | 408 508 |
| U.S. Sprint | 230 246 262 346 386 463 468 535 568 642 646 700 800 847 929 |
| US Link Long Distance | 252 858 |
| U.S. West Communications | 240 333 341 430 580 |
| Vartec National, Inc | 583 748 |
| Vortel | 867 |
| VYVX Telecom, Inc. | 324 534 546 662 676 822 826 857 898 997 |
| West Coast Telecom | 635 |
| Westel | 469 629 839 942 943 |

financial services that provide information about stocks, bonds, and other securities. A service provided by a company called Zephyr Weather Information Services, Inc. provides weather information to pilots on a subscription basis. The information provided is a facsimile and is typically a weather map. A client signs up for the service and pays a fee for one year. Each time that the caller requests a report, a fee is charged. Figure 11.1 is an example of a facsimile that a subscriber would obtain.

## Table 11.4
### 900 and 976 Cost Structure

|  | *Per minute charge* | *Per call charge* | *1991 Revenue* | |
|---|---|---|---|---|
|  |  |  | *Millions* | *%* |
| *Nationwide 900 services* | | | | |
| Service bureau | $0.14 | $0.38 | $116.7 | 11.1 |
| IXC | $0.44 | $1.25 | $383.9 | 36.6 |
| Information provider | $0.67 | $1.88 | $577.4 | 55.0 |
| Total | $1.25 | $3.51 | $1,050.4 | 100.0 |
| *976 services* | | | | |
| Service bureau | $0.14 | $0.24 | $70.3 | 16.0 |
| IXC | $0.09 | $0.16 | $46.9 | 10.7 |
| Information provider | $0.72 | $1.10 | $322.4 | 73.3 |
| Total | $0.95 | $1.50 | $439.6 | 100.0 |

## REFERENCE

1. Jadhav, A. G., "Voice Store-and-Forward Services," *Electro/84 convention* record, Boston, May 1984, pp. 1–5.

**Figure 11.1** Facsimile of a weather map for pilots. Photograph courtesy of Zephyr Weather Information Services, Inc.

# Chapter 12

## Sizing a Voice-Processing System

The throughput capacity of a voice-processing system is determined by a variety of factors. The ability of the computer hardware and software to accommodate the call traffic is of fundamental importance in a voice-processing system. Whether the system can handle the required call traffic depends upon the particular product and how the application is implemented. In the following analysis, we assume that the voice processing hardware and software is capable of handling the load and focus on the ports and speech storage required for specific telephone traffic.

### 12.1 DETERMINING THE NUMBER OF LINES REQUIRED

To provide quality service, system designers must make a careful effort to determine the number of telephone lines required for the voice-processing application. The factors that determine the number of lines that are required are

- The number of calls expected during the busiest hour of the day;
- The average length of time that each call takes (average call-hold time);
- The acceptable percentage of callers that would receive a busy signal during the busiest hour.

The number of calls during the busy hour and the average call-hold time are used to calculate the telephone traffic in units called *erlangs*:

busy-hour calls x call-hold time in seconds/3,600 (sec/hr) = traffic (erlangs)

After obtaining this traffic information, telephony traffic tables are used to determine the number of telephone lines required to achieve a particular grade of service. Table 12.1 is based on the Erlang B formula, and Table 12.2 is based on

**Table 12.1**
Erlang B Telephone Traffic Capacity

| Number of ports | Blockage Levels | | | | | | Number of ports |
|---|---|---|---|---|---|---|---|
| | 10 % | 5 % | 3 % | 2 % | 1 % | 0.1 % | |
| 1 | 0.01 | 0.05 | 0.02 | 0.01 | 0.01 | 0.00 | 1 |
| 2 | 0.54 | 0.36 | 0.22 | 0.15 | 0.10 | 0.10 | 2 |
| 3 | 1.14 | 0.85 | 0.59 | 0.45 | 0.35 | 0.19 | 3 |
| 4 | 1.84 | 1.45 | 1.07 | 0.86 | 0.70 | 0.44 | 4 |
| 5 | 2.59 | 2.11 | 1.62 | 1.35 | 1.13 | 0.76 | 5 |
| 6 | 3.38 | 2.81 | 2.23 | 1.89 | 1.61 | 1.14 | 6 |
| 7 | 4.20 | 3.55 | 2.88 | 2.48 | 2.15 | 1.58 | 7 |
| 8 | 5.04 | 4.32 | 3.55 | 3.10 | 2.72 | 2.05 | 8 |
| 9 | 5.89 | 5.10 | 4.26 | 3.74 | 3.32 | 2.55 | 9 |
| 10 | 6.76 | 5.91 | 4.98 | 4.42 | 3.94 | 3.09 | 10 |
| 11 | 7.64 | 6.72 | 5.72 | 5.11 | 4.59 | 3.65 | 11 |
| 12 | 8.53 | 7.55 | 6.48 | 5.82 | 5.25 | 4.23 | 12 |
| 13 | 9.42 | 8.39 | 7.25 | 6.54 | 5.93 | 4.83 | 13 |
| 14 | 10.33 | 9.24 | 8.04 | 7.28 | 6.63 | 5.44 | 14 |
| 15 | 11.24 | 10.10 | 8.83 | 8.03 | 7.34 | 6.07 | 15 |
| 16 | 12.15 | 10.97 | 9.63 | 8.79 | 8.06 | 6.71 | 16 |
| 17 | 13.07 | 11.84 | 10.44 | 9.56 | 8.79 | 7.37 | 17 |
| 18 | 13.99 | 12.72 | 11.26 | 10.33 | 9.53 | 8.04 | 18 |
| 19 | 14.92 | 13.60 | 12.09 | 11.12 | 10.28 | 8.72 | 19 |
| 20 | 15.86 | 14.49 | 12.92 | 11.91 | 11.04 | 9.40 | 20 |
| 21 | 16.79 | 15.38 | 13.76 | 12.71 | 11.80 | 10.10 | 21 |
| 22 | 17.72 | 16.28 | 14.60 | 13.51 | 12.57 | 10.80 | 22 |
| 23 | 18.66 | 17.18 | 15.45 | 14.32 | 13.35 | 11.51 | 23 |
| 24 | 19.61 | 18.08 | 16.30 | 15.14 | 14.13 | 12.23 | 24 |
| 25 | 20.55 | 18.99 | 17.15 | 15.96 | 14.92 | 12.96 | 25 |
| 26 | 21.50 | 19.90 | 18.02 | 16.79 | 15.72 | 13.69 | 26 |
| 27 | 22.45 | 20.81 | 18.88 | 17.62 | 16.52 | 14.42 | 27 |
| 28 | 23.40 | 21.72 | 19.75 | 18.45 | 17.32 | 15.17 | 28 |
| 29 | 24.35 | 22.64 | 20.62 | 19.29 | 18.13 | 15.91 | 29 |
| 30 | 25.30 | 23.56 | 21.49 | 20.13 | 18.94 | 16.67 | 30 |
| 31 | 26.26 | 24.48 | 22.37 | 20.98 | 19.75 | 17.42 | 31 |
| 32 | 27.21 | 25.41 | 23.25 | 21.83 | 20.57 | 18.19 | 32 |
| 33 | 28.17 | 26.33 | 24.13 | 22.68 | 21.40 | 18.95 | 33 |
| 34 | 29.13 | 27.26 | 25.02 | 23.54 | 22.22 | 19.72 | 34 |
| 35 | 30.09 | 28.19 | 25.91 | 24.39 | 23.05 | 20.50 | 35 |
| 36 | 31.05 | 29.12 | 26.80 | 25.25 | 23.89 | 21.27 | 36 |
| 37 | 32.02 | 30.06 | 27.69 | 26.12 | 24.72 | 22.06 | 37 |
| 38 | 32.98 | 30.99 | 28.58 | 26.98 | 25.56 | 22.84 | 38 |
| 39 | 33.94 | 31.93 | 29.48 | 27.85 | 26.40 | 23.63 | 39 |
| 40 | 34.91 | 32.86 | 30.38 | 28.72 | 27.24 | 24.42 | 40 |

## Table 12.2
### Poisson Telephone Traffic Capacity

| Number of ports | Blockage Levels | | | | | | Number of ports |
|---|---|---|---|---|---|---|---|
| | 10 % | 5% | 3% | 2% | 1% | 0.1% | |
| 1 | 0.11 | 0.05 | 0.03 | 0.02 | 0.01 | 0.00 | 1 |
| 2 | 0.53 | 0.36 | 0.27 | 0.21 | 0.15 | 0.04 | 2 |
| 3 | 1.10 | 0.82 | 0.67 | 0.57 | 0.44 | 0.19 | 3 |
| 4 | 1.75 | 1.37 | 1.16 | 1.02 | 0.82 | 0.43 | 4 |
| 5 | 2.44 | 1.97 | 1.71 | 1.55 | 1.28 | 0.74 | 5 |
| 6 | 3.14 | 2.61 | 2.30 | 2.11 | 1.79 | 1.11 | 6 |
| 7 | 3.89 | 3.28 | 2.92 | 2.69 | 2.33 | 1.52 | 7 |
| 8 | 4.67 | 3.97 | 3.58 | 3.31 | 2.91 | 1.97 | 8 |
| 9 | 5.42 | 4.69 | 4.25 | 3.94 | 3.50 | 2.45 | 9 |
| 10 | 6.22 | 5.42 | 4.94 | 4.61 | 4.14 | 2.97 | 10 |
| 11 | 7.03 | 6.17 | 5.67 | 5.31 | 4.78 | 3.50 | 11 |
| 12 | 7.83 | 6.92 | 6.39 | 6.00 | 5.42 | 4.03 | 12 |
| 13 | 8.64 | 7.69 | 7.11 | 6.69 | 6.11 | 4.61 | 13 |
| 14 | 9.47 | 8.47 | 7.83 | 7.42 | 6.78 | 5.19 | 14 |
| 15 | 10.28 | 9.25 | 8.61 | 8.14 | 7.74 | 5.78 | 15 |
| 16 | 11.14 | 10.06 | 9.36 | 8.89 | 8.18 | 6.42 | 16 |
| 17 | 11.97 | 10.83 | 10.14 | 9.64 | 8.89 | 7.03 | 17 |
| 18 | 12.83 | 11.64 | 10.89 | 10.39 | 9.61 | 7.67 | 18 |
| 19 | 13.67 | 12.44 | 11.67 | 11.14 | 10.36 | 8.31 | 19 |
| 20 | 14.53 | 13.25 | 12.47 | 11.92 | 11.08 | 8.97 | 20 |
| 21 | 15.39 | 14.08 | 13.28 | 12.72 | 11.83 | 9.61 | 21 |
| 22 | 16.25 | 14.89 | 14.08 | 13.50 | 12.58 | 10.28 | 22 |
| 23 | 17.11 | 15.72 | 14.89 | 14.28 | 13.33 | 10.97 | 23 |
| 24 | 17.97 | 16.56 | 15.67 | 15.06 | 14.08 | 11.64 | 24 |
| 25 | 18.83 | 17.39 | 16.47 | 15.86 | 14.86 | 12.33 | 25 |
| 26 | 19.72 | 18.22 | 17.31 | 16.64 | 15.61 | 13.03 | 26 |
| 27 | 20.58 | 19.06 | 18.11 | 17.42 | 16.39 | 13.75 | 27 |
| 28 | 21.47 | 19.92 | 18.94 | 18.22 | 17.17 | 14.44 | 28 |
| 29 | 22.36 | 20.75 | 19.75 | 19.03 | 17.97 | 15.14 | 29 |
| 30 | 23.22 | 21.61 | 20.59 | 19.86 | 18.75 | 15.86 | 30 |
| 31 | 24.11 | 22.47 | 21.42 | 20.67 | 19.53 | 16.58 | 31 |
| 32 | 25.00 | 23.33 | 22.25 | 21.47 | 20.33 | 17.33 | 32 |
| 33 | 25.89 | 24.19 | 23.08 | 22.31 | 21.11 | 18.06 | 33 |
| 34 | 26.78 | 25.06 | 23.92 | 23.11 | 21.92 | 18.78 | 34 |
| 35 | 27.67 | 25.92 | 24.75 | 23.94 | 22.72 | 19.53 | 35 |
| 36 | 28.56 | 26.78 | 25.61 | 24.78 | 23.53 | 20.25 | 36 |
| 37 | 29.44 | 27.54 | 26.44 | 25.61 | 24.33 | 21.00 | 37 |
| 38 | 30.33 | 28.50 | 27.28 | 26.44 | 25.14 | 21.75 | 38 |
| 39 | 31.25 | 29.36 | 28.14 | 27.28 | 25.97 | 22.50 | 39 |
| 40 | 32.14 | 30.22 | 28.97 | 28.11 | 26.78 | 23.25 | 40 |

the Poisson formula. The Erlang B formula is used when traffic is random and there is no queuing. Calls that cannot get through disappear and do not return. The Poisson formula describes what happens to traffic when calls are temporarily blocked. The Poisson model assumes that blocked calls do not disappear; the caller simply continues to redial until the call is completed. More ports are required under the Poisson model than using the Erlang B. However, neither of these formulas exactly describes the traffic profile of a particular application. They should, however, provide adequate results if care is taken in determining the busy-hour calls and the call-hold time.

As an example, if an application receives 640 calls during the busy hour and each call lasts for 80 seconds, the traffic is

$$640 \times 80/3,600 = 14.22 \text{ erlangs}$$

If the acceptable blockage level is 1%, the Erlang B traffic table (Table 12.1) indicates that the application requires 23 telephone lines. Figure 12.1 shows an example of telephonic traffic capacity.

## 12.2 DETERMINING THE AMOUNT OF SPEECH STORAGE REQUIRED

The amount of speech storage required depends on the type of application. The basic parameter that establishes the speech memory requirement is the system sampling rate. Most systems use either 24- or 32-kb/s algorithms. Lower sampling rates are often available, but the voice quality is usually unacceptable for most applications at sampling rates below 24 kb/s. At 32 kb/s, 1 Mbyte of memory can store approximately 250 seconds of speech, and at 24 kb/s, 1 Mbyte of memory can store approximately 333 seconds of speech. A normal speaking rate is 180 words per minute. Speech storage requirements are shown in Table 12.3 and Figure 12.2.

For example, a locator service is desired for a nationwide organization that has 10,000 different locations. The average number of words in an address of this sort is 10, indicating that storage for 100,000 words is required. At 32 kb/s, this would indicate that 133 Mbytes of storage are required for the speech.

The storage requirement of a voice-mail system is dominated by the number of subscribers and their call profiles. We assume a system with 200 subscribers who each receive an average of five messages per day; the average message length is 30 seconds, and the average retention time of a message is 1 day. The calculation then would be: $200 \times 5 \times 30 \times 1 = 30,000$ seconds $= 8.33$ hours

System prompts, personal greeting, and name-prompt storage must be added to this figure. Typically, this would add another 0.5 hour of speech storage to the requirement.

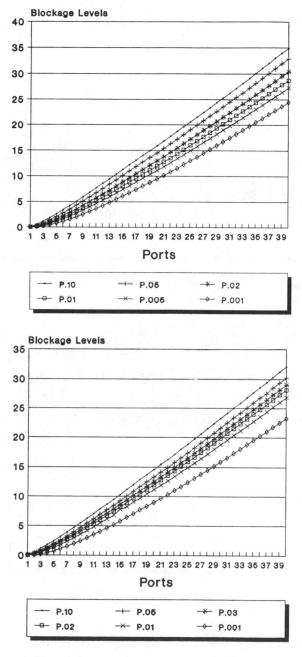

igure 12.1 Telephone traffic capacity.

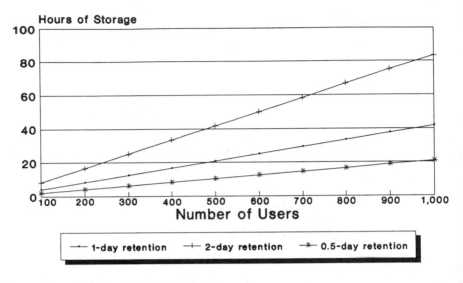

30-second message length, 5 messages/day

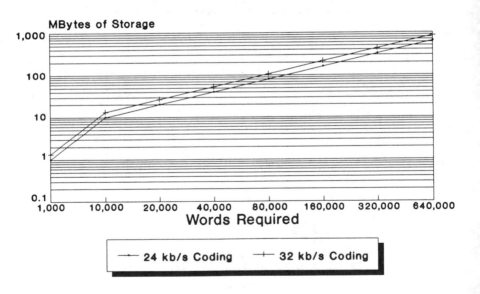

**Figure 12.2** Voice-processing speech storage requirement.

Because we are dealing with estimates of averages, the potential for being off on the calculation is high. The retention time is one of the biggest manageable factors. The retention time allowed by the voice-mail system can be reduced, and

**Table 12.3**
Speech Storage requirements

| Sampling rate | Seconds of speech (1 Mbyte) | Words of speech (1 Mbyte) |
|---|---|---|
| 16 kb/s | 500 | 1,500 |
| 24 kb/s | 333 | 1,000 |
| 32 kb/s | 250 | 750 |
| 64 kb/s | 125 | 375 |

subscribers can be encouraged to discard messages once they have heard them and acted on them. The storage requirement can also be reduced by decreasing the maximum permitted message length and the number of messages that a subscriber can retain.

# Chapter 13
## Voice-Processing Marketplace

The voice-processing market consists of CPE suppliers and service suppliers and includes a variety of market segments and distribution channels.

### 13.1 TOTAL VOICE-PROCESSING MARKET SIZE

The total voice-processing market can be broken into two segments: CPE and services, as indicated in Table 13.1 and Figure 13.1. The CPE segment is broken down further in Table 13.2 and Figures 13.2 and 13.3.

CPE includes all equipment that is sold, including that sold to service bureaus. The growth in the CPE area is deceasing while the growth in the services area is fairly constant and in excess of 40% per year. The service bureau revenue shown in Table 13.1 is the amount that end users paid for services. The growth in the large system and small systems areas will continue in excess of 20% per year through the mid 1990s. The *telephone answering machine* (TAM) area is starting

**Table 13.1**
Total Voice Processing Market Revenue

|                | 1989        | 1990        | 1991        |
|----------------|-------------|-------------|-------------|
| CPE            | $2,278.6M   | $2,821.9M   | $3,445.1M   |
| Service bureau | $2,264.7M   | $3,038.9M   | $4,136.3M   |
| Total          | $4,543.3M   | $5,860.8M   | $7,581.4M   |

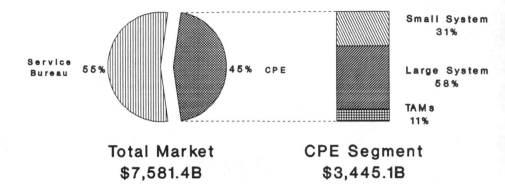

## Total Market
## $7,581.4B

## CPE Segment
## $3,445.1B

**Figure 13.1** Total voice-processing market.

### Table 13.2
Voice Processing CPE Market Revenue

|  | *1989* | *1990* | *1991* |
|---|---|---|---|
| Small system | $ 781.4M | $ 976.2M | $1,221.1M |
| Large system | $1,497.2M | $1,845.7M | $2,224.0M |
| Telephone answering machines (TAMs) | $ 346.8M | $ 385.9M | $ 425.0M |
| Total | $2,625.4M | $3,207.8M | $3,870.1M |

to flatten out and will start to decline rapidly as the central-office-based voice-mail services become widely available.

### 13.2 SMALL AND LARGE COMPUTER-BASED VOICE-PROCESSING PRODUCTS

The voice-processing market consists of small computer-based and large computer-based products. Small computer-based products are defined as products with a minimum configuration, the list price of which is $30,000 or less. These tend to have port counts between one and eight and are not readily expanded to larger configurations. Table 13.3 shows the total revenue and units for this area as compared with large computer-based revenue and units. Table 13.4 shows the same comparison, but with the amounts from the market segments in which the large computer products do not compete (passive intercept and subsystem components) removed.

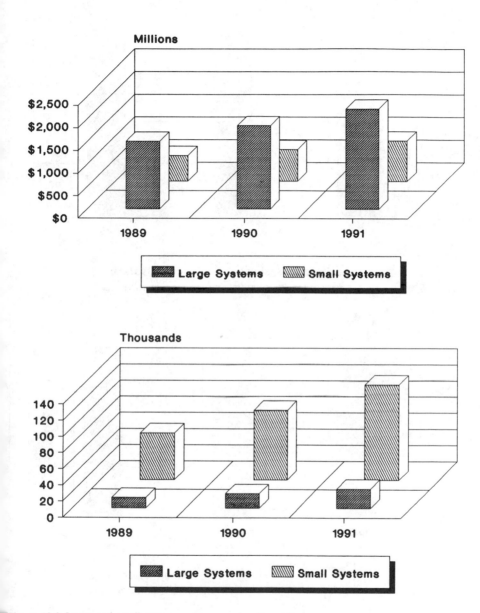

**Figure 13.2** Large and small systems revenue and units profile.

In the past few years, the growth of the small system area has been higher than that in the large system area. This is tending to change as deployment of large-scale nationwide applications occurs. The early systems were proprietary architectures and were in the large system class. Products based on the PC architecture have fueled the growth of the small system area, offering significantly lower end-user prices and more flexibility in user customization.

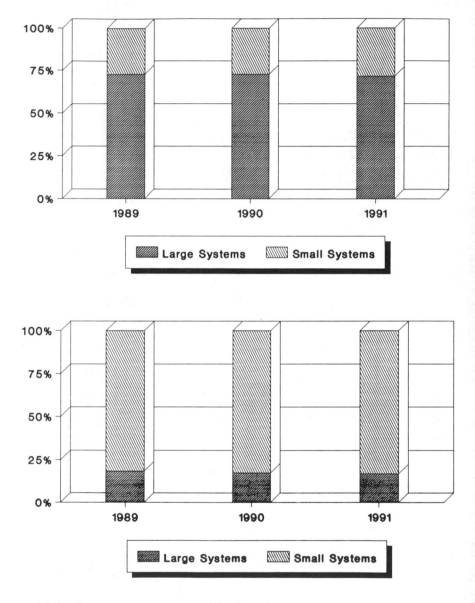

**Figure 13.3** Small and large systems percentage split.

Growth from 1988 to 1989 was 29.5%; from 1989 to 1990 it was 23.6%. Much of this expansion is attributed to the lower product cost. Although there are many suppliers that tend to specialize in either small or large systems, many supply both. The reduction in the growth rate is partially due to the recession that began in mid 1990. Figures 13.3 to 13.5 show voice-processing market profiles.

**Table 13.3**

Total Small/Large Voice Processing Revenue and Units Profile

| Year | Small system | | Large system | |
|------|------|------|------|------|
| | *Revenue* | *Units* | *Revenue* | *Units* |
| 1989 | $ 781.4M | 172,400 | $1,497.2M | 13,000 |
| 1990 | $ 976.2M | 244,200 | $1,845.7M | 18,000 |
| 1991 | $1,221.1M | 325,600 | $2,224.0M | 24,000 |

**Table 13.4**

Subset Small/Large Voice Processing Systems Revenue and Units Profile

| *Year* | *Small system* | | *Large system* | |
|------|------|------|------|------|
| | *Revenue* | *Units* | *Revenue* | *Units* |
| 1989 | $565.8M | 57,900 | $1,497.2M | 13,000 |
| 1990 | $699.2M | 86,400 | $1,845.7M | 18,000 |
| 1991 | $888.1M | 118,300 | $2,224.0M | 24,000 |

It is projected that the voice- and call-processing areas will continue to grow at an annual rate in excess of 20% through 1996 (see Table 13.5).

### 13.3 CPE SUPPLIER GROUPINGS

Table 13.6 groups CPE suppliers by revenue. Of the over 350 suppliers, the top ten percent accounts for over 50% of the revenue. This percentage of revenue will continue to grow as the voice-processing industry moves through a consolidation stage.

### 13.4 VOICE-PROCESSING MARKET SEGMENTS

Voice-processing markets can be separated into the following categories:
- Interactive voice response;
- Voice mail and auto attendant;
- Information providing;

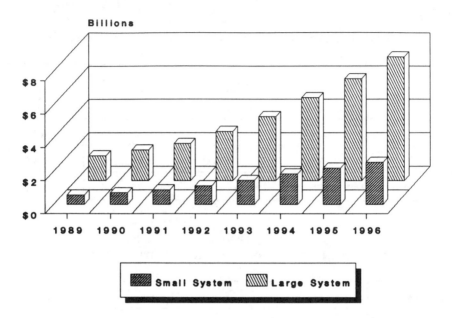

**Figure 13.4** Voice-processing CPE market growth.

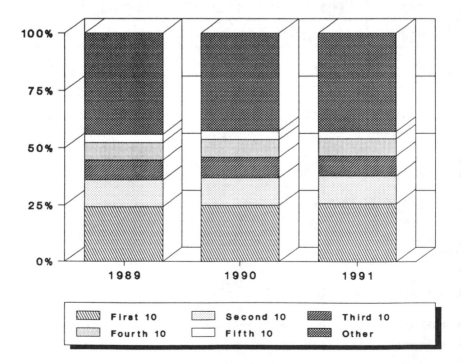

**Figure 13.5** Supplier size grouping.

**Table 13.5**

Small/Large Voice Processing Systems Revenue Growth Rate

| Year | Small systems | | Large systems | |
|------|------|------|------|------|
| | Revenue | % Growth | Revenue | % Growth |
| 1989 | $ 565.8M | 29.5 | $1,497.2M | 22.0 |
| 1990 | $ 699.2M | 23.6 | $1,845.7M | 23.3 |
| 1991 | $ 888.1M | 27.0 | $2,224.0M | 20.5 |
| 1992 | $1,144.2M | 28.8 | $2,951.0M | 32.7 |
| 1993 | $1,451.1M | 26.8 | $3,838.0M | 30.1 |
| 1994 | $1,842.5M | 27.0 | $4,973.0M | 29.6 |
| 1995 | $2,191.1M | 18.9 | $6,127.0M | 23.2 |
| 1996 | $2,549.5M | 16.4 | $7,416.0M | 21.0 |

- Outbound;
- Subsystem components;
- Passive intercept;
- Automatic call distributor;
- Computer-telephone integration.

These markets generally do not overlap or compete with one another. The end users are usually different and have a different set of needs. The distribution channels are common in that the interconnect dealers, system integrators, and wholesale distributors will often handle products for multiple market segments. The companies that participate in the voice-processing market often sell products in more than one category. Table 13.7 shows the number of companies in each market segment and the percentage of revenue for each market segment.

## 13.5 REVENUE AND UNIT PROFILES BY MARKET SEGMENT

The *voice mail and auto attendant* (VMAA) market segment displays the strongest growth profile. Because vendors in the market segments do not compete against one another, the growth in the VM area is not at the expense of the other market segments. Growth in any area tends to have a positive effect on other segments. Each market segment shows growth rates of more than 30% per year. Table 13.8 identifies each voice-processing product supplier and the market segment that they address. Note that many of the suppliers are in multiple market segments.

## Table 13.6
Supplier Size Grouping

| 1989 | | | | |
|---|---|---|---|---|
| | *Revenue* | *% of Total* | *Units* | *% of Total* |
| First 10 suppliers | $ 551,900,000 | 24.2 | 7,600 | 4.1 |
| Second 10 suppliers | $ 267,100,000 | 11.7 | 3,700 | 2.0 |
| Third 10 suppliers | $ 198,900,000 | 8.7 | 12,900 | 7.0 |
| Fourth 10 suppliers | $ 173,600,000 | 7.6 | 16,600 | 9.0 |
| Fifth 10 suppliers | $ 84,500,000 | 3.7 | 18,200 | 9.8 |
| Other suppliers (365) | $1,002,600,000 | 44.0 | 126,400 | 68.2 |
| Total | $2,278,600,000 | | 185,400 | |
| **1990** | | | | |
| First 10 suppliers | $ 704,400,000 | 25.0 | 10,000 | 3.8 |
| Second 10 suppliers | $ 337,100,000 | 11.9 | 4,200 | 1.6 |
| Third 10 suppliers | $ 255,300,000 | 9.0 | 17,400 | 6.6 |
| Fourth 10 suppliers | $ 217,100,000 | 7.7 | 25,000 | 9.5 |
| Fifth 10 suppliers | $ 107,400,000 | 3.8 | 26,000 | 9.9 |
| Other suppliers (366) | $1,200,600,000 | 42.5 | 179,600 | 68.5 |
| Total | $2,821,900,000 | | 262,200 | |
| **1991** | | | | |
| First 10 suppliers | $ 883,700,000 | 25.7 | 12,600 | 3.6 |
| Second 10 suppliers | $ 418,000,000 | 12.1 | 6,500 | 1.9 |
| Third 10 suppliers | $ 300,500,000 | 8.7 | 22,600 | 6.5 |
| Fourth 10 suppliers | $ 254,700,000 | 7.4 | 32,000 | 9.1 |
| Fifth 10 suppliers | $ 116,000,000 | 3.4 | 35,000 | 10.0 |
| Other suppliers (370) | $1,472,200,000 | 42.7 | 240,900 | 68.8 |
| Total | $3,445,100,000 | | 349,600 | |

**Table 13.7**
Voice/Facsimile Processing Market Segment Breakdown

| Market segment | Number of suppliers | 1991 revenue | % of total revenue (1991) |
|---|---|---|---|
| Voice mail/Auto attendant | 75 | $1,169.2M | 33.9 |
| Interactive voice response | 64 | $ 350.2M | 10.2 |
| Information provider | 42 | $ 115.5M | 3.4 |
| Outbound | 49 | $ 298.7M | 8.7 |
| Passive intercept | 14 | $ 119.3M | 3.5 |
| Sub-system components | 68 | $ 213.7M | 6.2 |
| Facsimile processing | 126 | $ 113.0M | 3.3 |
| ACD | 32 | $ 812.0M | 23.6 |
| C-TI | 125 | $ 253.5M | 7.4 |
| Total | | $3,445.1M | |

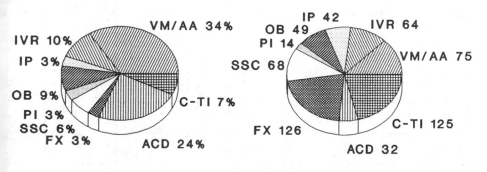

Figure 13.6 Market segment summary.

**Table 13.8**
Voice and Facsimile Processing Product Suppliers

| Supplier | IVR | VMAA | IP | OB | SSC | PI | FP |
|---|---|---|---|---|---|---|---|
| Abaton | | | | | | | * |
| Accelerated Voice | | | | | | | * |
| Access Radio | | | * | | | | |
| Access International | * | | | | | | |
| Active Voice | | * | | | | | |
| ACS Communications | | * | | | | | |
| AcuVoice | | | | | * | | |
| Adaptive Solutions, Inc. | | | | | * | | |
| Adtech | | | | | | | * |
| Advanced Compression Techniques | | | | | * | | |
| Advanced Interactive Systems | | * | | | | | |
| Advanced Microcomputer Systems | | | | | | | * |
| Advanced Voice Technology | | * | | | | | |
| AGT International, Inc. | * | | | | | | |
| Aicom | | | | | * | | |
| Alcom | | | | | | | * |

## 13.6 DISTRIBUTION OF VOICE-PROCESSING PRODUCTS

Voice-processing systems are sold through a variety of channels. These distribution channels vary considerably from one market segment to the next. The marketing channels being used are: direct sales; telephone equipment manufacturers; tele-

Table 13.8 (continued)

| Supplier | IVR | VMAA | IP | OB | SSC | PI | FP |
|---|---|---|---|---|---|---|---|
| All The Fax | | | | | | | * |
| Alston | | * | | | | | |
| Amcat | | | * | | | | |
| Amarex Technology | * | | | | | | |
| American Communications & Engineering | * | | * | | | | |
| American Data Technology | | | | | | | * |
| American Telesystems | | * | | | | | |
| Amtelco | | * | | | | | |
| Antex Electronics | | | | | * | | |
| Apex Voice Communications | * | * | * | | | | |
| Apple Computer | | | | | | | * |
| Applied Voice Technology | * | * | * | | | | |
| Argos Computer Systems | * | | | | | | |
| Arkansas Systems | * | | | | | | |
| Arctic Technologies | | | | | * | | |

phone interconnect companies; telephone equipment wholesale supply houses; Computer manufacturers; VARs and OEMs; and office equipment suppliers.

### 13.6.1 Telephone Interconnect Companies

Telephone interconnect dealers are a significant distribution channel for the voice mail, auto attendant, and passive interception products, but they are not a significant channel for any other market segments.

Table 13.8 (continued)

| Supplier | IVR | VMAA | IP | OB | SSC | PI | FP |
|----------|-----|------|-----|-----|-----|-----|-----|
| Atlanta Signal Processing, Inc. | | | | | | | |
| AT&S | | | | | * | | |
| AT&T BCS | * | * | * | * | | | * |
| ATC | | | | | | | * |
| ATIS | | | | | | * | |
| ATM Systems | | | | * | | | |
| Audiocom | | | | * | | * | |
| Audiofax | | | | | | | * |
| BCB Electronics | | | * | | * | | |
| Bell South IS | | | | | | | * |
| Berkeley Speech Technologies | | | | | * | | |
| Best Data Products | | | | | | | * |
| BI, Inc. | * | | | | | | |
| Bicom | | | | | * | | |
| Biscom | | | | | | | * |

## 13.6.2 Telephone Equipment Manufacturers

The telephone equipment manufacturers include suppliers of PBXs, keysets ACDs, and telephone system switches. Many of these manufacturers have inte grated a VM product into their keyphone systems.

## 13.6.3 Distribution Trends

The percentage of products distributed through indirect channels is increasing while the percentage sold through direct sales is decreasing. Suppliers want t

## Table 13.8 (continued)

| Supplier | IVR | VMAA | IP | OB | SSC | PI | FP |
|---|---|---|---|---|---|---|---|
| Black Box Corporation | | | | | | | * |
| BMC Group | | * | | | | | |
| Boston Technology | | * | | | | | |
| Brite Voice Systems | * | * | * | | | | |
| Brock Control Systems | | | | | * | | |
| Brooktrout Technology | | * | | | | | * |
| Brother International Corporation | | | | | | | * |
| C-AT | | | | | * | | |
| Calculaus, Inc. | | | | | | | * |
| Call Management Products | | | | * | | | |
| Cascade Technologies | | | | | * | | |
| Castelle | | | | | | | * |
| Cardinal Technologies | | | | | | | * |
| CC:Mail | | | | | | | * |
| CE Corporation | * | | | | | | |
| Centigram Communications | * | * | | | * | | * |
| Ceredata | | | | | * | | |
| CDT | | * | | | | | |

obtain broader and more extensive distribution with a minimal investment. The interconnect dealers are interested in and capable of supporting products that are standardized, easy to install, require little customizing, and can be sold in a short time with a minimum of effort. Voice-mail, auto attendant, and passive intercept

**Table 13.8 (continued)**

| Supplier | IVR | VMAA | IP | OB | SSC | PI | FP |
|---|---|---|---|---|---|---|---|
| Chelsea Software | | | | | * | | |
| Cherry Electric | | | | | * | | |
| Chinon America | | | | | | | * |
| Choice Technology Group | | | | | | | * |
| Circuit Research Corporation | | | | | | | * |
| CISCORP | | | * | | | | |
| Cobotyx Corporation | | * | | | | | * |
| Code-A-Phone | | * | | | | | |
| Coffman Systems | | | | * | | | |
| Cognitronics | * | | | | | * | |
| Communicator Asystance Systems | | | | * | | | |
| Community Alert Network | | | | * | | | |
| Compass Computer Systems | | * | | | | | |
| Complete PC, The | | * | | | | | * |
| CompLink, Ltd | | | | | | | * |
| Computer Automation, Inc. | | | | | | | * |

Table 13.8 (continued)

| Supplier | IVR | VMAA | IP | OB | SSC | PI | FP |
|---|---|---|---|---|---|---|---|
| Computer Consoles, Inc. (Northern Telecom) | * | | | | | | |
| Computer Communications Specialists | * | | | | | | |
| Computer Friends | | | | | | | * |
| Computer Peripherals, Inc. | | | | | | | * |
| Computer System Integration | | | | | | | * |
| Computer Talk Technology | * | * | | | | | |
| Computer Voice Systems, Inc. | * | | | | | | |
| Comtel Broadcasting | | | | * | | | |
| Comverse Technology | | * | | | | | * |
| Connex Systems | | | | | | | * |
| Consumers Software | | | | | | | * |
| Cook Electric | | | | | | * | |
| Copia International | | | | | | | * |
| COS, Inc. | | | | | | | * |
| Covox | | | | | * | | |

products meet these requirements, while IVR, ACD, C-TI, and outbound products generally do not. We anticipate that all of the product areas will drive toward these requirements.

**Table 13.8 (continued)**

| Supplier | IVR | VMAA | IP | OB | SSC | PI | FP |
|----------|-----|------|----|----|-----|----|----|
| Cracchiolo & Feder | | | | | | | * |
| CRC | | | | * | | | |
| Cybercorp | | | | | * | | |
| Cypress Research Corporation | | | | | | | * |
| Dacon | | * | | | | | |
| Dalanco Spry | | | | | * | | |
| Danyl | | | | | | | * |
| Database Systems Corporation | | | | * | | | |
| DataVoice | | | | | * | | |
| Dataway Systems | * | | | | | | |
| Datap | * | | | | | | |
| Data Processing Design | | | | | | | * |
| Data Race | | | | | | | * |
| Davox | | | | * | | | |
| DCE | | | | | | | * |
| DCS | | | | | | | * |
| DemoSource | | | | | | | * |

## 13.7 INDUSTRY SEGMENT BY VOICE-PROCESSING MARKET SEGMENT

The revenue projections for each of the voice-processing market segments are shown in Table 13.9. Table 13.10 (page 301) and Figure 13.7 (page 298) show the revenue that each of the industry segments spent in each of the voice-processing market segments during 1991.

Table 13.8 (continued)

| Supplier | IVR | VMAA | IP | OB | SSC | PI | FP |
|---|---|---|---|---|---|---|---|
| Denniston & Denniston | * | | | | | | |
| Dialogic Communications Corporation | | | | * | | | |
| Dialogic Corporation | | | | | * | | |
| Dial Tech International | * | * | * | * | | | |
| Dianatel | | | | | * | | |
| Diatek | * | | | | | | |
| Dictaphone Corporation | | * | | | | | |
| Digital Data Systems | | | | | | | * |
| Digital Equipment Corporation | | | | | * | | |
| Digital Products Corporation | | | | * | | | |
| Digital Recorders | | | | | | * | |
| Digital Sound Corporation | * | * | | | | | |
| Digital Speech Systems | | * | | | | | |
| Digital Systems International | | | | * | | | |
| Digitcom Communications Corporation | * | * | * | * | | | |
| Digitran Communications | | | | | | | |
| DIRAD Technologies | | | * | | | | |
| DMG, Inc. | | | | | | | * |

Table 13.8 (continued)

| Supplier | IVR | VMAA | IP | OB | SSC | PI | FP |
|---|---|---|---|---|---|---|---|
| Dove Computer Corporation | | | | | | | * |
| Dragon Systems | | | | | * | | |
| Draxus | * | | | | | | |
| DRW | | | | * | | | |
| DSP Group, The | | | | | * | | |
| Dytel | | * | | | | | |
| Early, Cloud and Company | | | | * | | | |
| Electronic Information Systems | | | | * | | | |
| ECAP Systems | | | | | | | * |
| EEC Systems, Inc. | | | | | | | * |
| Electronic Modules, Inc. | | | | | | | * |
| Electronic Telecommunications Corp. | * | | * | | | * | |
| Electronic Warfare Associates | | | | | * | | |
| Eltrex International | | | | | | * | |
| Enable Software/Higgins | | | | | | | * |
| Enhanced Systems | | * | * | | | | |
| Entropic Processing | | | | | * | | |
| EPG America | | | | | | | * |

## Table 13.8 (continued)

| Supplier | IVR | VMAA | IP | OB | SSC | PI | FP |
|---|---|---|---|---|---|---|---|
| EPOS | * | | | | | | |
| ESCO Systems, Inc. | | | | | | | * |
| Everex Systems | | | | | | | * |
| Expert Systems | | | | | * | | |
| Farallon Computing | | * | | | | | |
| Faxbank Systems | | | | | | | * |
| Faximum Software | | | | | | | * |
| First Byte | | | | | * | | |
| Fremont Communications | | | | | | | * |
| Fujitsu Business Communications | | * | | | | | |
| Fujitsu Imaging | | | | | | | * |
| Gammalink | | | | | | | * |
| Glenayre Electronics | | * | | | | | |
| Granite Telecom | | | * | * | | | |
| GW Instruments | | | | | * | | |
| GUIS America | | | | | | | * |
| HTI Voice Solutions | * | | | | | | |
| Hays Microsystems | | | | | | | * |

## Table 13.8 (continued)

| Supplier | IVR | VMAA | IP | OB | SSC | PI | FP |
|---|---|---|---|---|---|---|---|
| Heliotrope General | | | | | * | | |
| Hitachi | | | | | | | * |
| Holmes Microsystems | | | | | | | * |
| Hybrid Fax | | | | | | | * |
| Hyperception | | | | | * | | |
| Hypercom | * | | | | | | |
| Ibex | | | | | | | * |
| IBM Corporation | * | | | | * | | |
| IdealDial | | | | | | | * |
| Imavox Corporation | | | | | | | * |
| Information Access | | | | * | | | |
| Information Associates | * | | | | | | |
| Information Management Associates | | | | * | | | |
| Infotel | | | | | | | * |
| In.Gate | | * | | | | | |
| Innovative Technology | | * | | | | | |
| Intel Corporation | | | | | | | * |
| Intellisystems | * | * | | | | | |

## Table 13.8 (continued)

| Supplier | IVR | VMAA | IP | OB | SSC | PI | FP |
|---|---|---|---|---|---|---|---|
| Intellivoice Communications | * | | * | * | | | |
| Interfax | | | | | | | * |
| Interalia Communications | | | * | | | * | |
| International Telesystems Corporation | | | | * | | | |
| Intervoice | * | | | * | | | * |
| IOCS | * | | | | | | * |
| IT Research | | | | * | | | |
| ITT | * | | | | * | | |
| IVM Systems | | * | | | | | * |
| InTouch Software | | | | | | | * |
| Kay Elemetric | | | | | * | | |
| Kerygma Technologies | | * | | | | | * |
| Kurzweil AI | | * | | | * | | |
| Lanier Voice Products | | * | | | | | |
| LEADtrack | | * | | | | | * |
| Linker Systems | * | | | | | | |
| Linkon Corporation | | | | | * | | |
| Livewire Voice Systems | | | * | | | | |
| Logicraft | | | | | | | * |

Table 13.8 (continued)

| Supplier | IVR | VMAA | IP | OB | SSC | PI | FP |
|---|---|---|---|---|---|---|---|
| Macronics | | | | | | | * |
| Macrotel | | * | | | | | |
| MAMS | | | | * | | | |
| MEC | | | | | | | * |
| Melita International | | | | * | | | |
| Mer Communications | | | | * | | | |
| Metafile Information Systems | | | | | | | * |
| Micro Electronic Technology | | | | | | | * |
| Micro Delta | | | | * | | | |
| Miami Voice | | * | | | | | |
| Microlink International | | | | | | | * |
| Microlog Corporation | * | * | * | | | | * |
| MPSI | | * | | * | | | |
| Missing Link | * | | | * | | | |
| MTU | | | | | * | | |
| Multilink | | | * | | | | |

## 13.8 VOICE-PROCESSING SERVICE PROVIDERS

The revenue profile of voice-processing service providers is shown in Table 13.11 (page 302) and Figure 13.8 (page 303). The revenue growth rate has been more than 25% per year, and it is anticipated that this will continue through the 1990s.

## Table 13.8 (continued)

| Supplier | IVR | VMAA | IP | OB | SSC | PI | FP |
|---|---|---|---|---|---|---|---|
| Multi-Tech Systems | | | | | | | * |
| Multiverse Communications | | * | * | | | | * |
| Murata | | | | | | | * |
| Natural Microsystems | | * | | * | * | | |
| NBS Systems | | | | | | | * |
| NCD | | | | | | | * |
| NEC | | * | | | * | | |
| Neltech Labs | | | | | | * | |
| Networking Dynamics | | | | | | | * |
| Noble Systems | | | | * | | | |
| Northern Telecom | | * | | | | | |
| NPRI | | | | * | | | |
| Nuntius | | | | | | | * |
| OAZ Communications | | | | | | | * |
| Octel Communications | * | * | * | | | | * |
| Omnium Corporation | | | | | | | * |

## 13.9 VOICE-PROCESSING MARKET TRENDS

Products will become significantly easier to use. The ability to permit the end user
to customize the product to meet specific requirements will become universal. This
is one of the signs of a market maturing. The customer's needs (and how these

**Table 13.8 (continued)**

| Supplier | IVR | VMAA | IP | OB | SSC | PI | FP |
|---|---|---|---|---|---|---|---|
| Optus Software | | | | | | | * |
| Orchid Technology | | | | | | | * |
| Orion Network Communications | | | | | | | * |
| Panasonic Corporation | | | | | | | * |
| Paradox Development Corporation | | | | | | | * |
| Parity Software Development Corporation | | | | | * | | |
| Parwan Electronics | | * | | | | | |
| Pelton Systems | * | | * | | * | | |
| Perception Technology | * | | * | | | | * |
| Periphonics | * | | * | | | | * |
| Pertek | * | | | | | | |
| Plantronics | | | | | * | | |
| Prairie Systems | | | | | | | * |
| Princeton Telecom | * | | | | | | |
| Processing Innovations | * | | | | | | |

tend to vary) are well understood by the suppliers, so the products are designed with flexibility to meet these needs [1]. The passive intercept area is presently at this stage of maturity. The IVR area, however, is currently the furthest removed from this maturity. Product trends will initially be to decrease the price while maintaining constant functionality, and then reach a stage of constant cost with an

**Table 13.8** (continued)

| Supplier | IVR | VMAA | IP | OB | SSC | PI | FP |
|---|---|---|---|---|---|---|---|
| Product R&D | | | | | | | * |
| Prometheus Products, Inc | | | | | | | * |
| Protocall | * | | | | | | |
| Racom | | | | | | * | |
| Republic Telecom | | | | | * | | |
| Rhetorex | | | | | * | | |
| Ricoh Corporation | | | | | | | * |
| Rolm | | * | | | | | |
| Science Dynamics | * | | | | | * | |
| Scott Instruments | | | | | * | | |
| Share Communications | | | | | | | * |
| Shure Brothers | | | | | * | | |
| Skutch Electronics | | | | | | * | |
| Signal Technology | | | | | * | | |
| Simpact Voice Products | * | | * | | * | | |
| Soft-Com | | * | | | | | |
| SoftNet Systems | | | | | | | * |
| Sonic Systems | | | | | * | | |
| Spectrafax | | | | | | | * |

**Table 13.8 (continued)**

| Supplier | IVR | VMAA | IP | OB | SSC | PI | FP |
|---|---|---|---|---|---|---|---|
| Spectrum Communications | | | | | * | | |
| SpeechSoft | | | | | * | | |
| Speech Solutions | * | * | * | | | | |
| Speech Systems, Inc. | | | | | * | | |
| Startel | | * | | | | | |
| STF Technologies, Inc. | | | | | | | * |
| Stok Software | | * | * | * | * | | |
| Strategic Dimensions, Inc. | | * | | | | | |
| Street Electronics | | | | | * | | |
| Sudbury Systems, Inc. | | * | | | | | |
| Support Net, Inc. | | | | | | | * |
| SwitchLink Systems | | | | | | | |
| T1 Systems | * | | * | | | | |
| T-4 Systems | | | | | | | * |
| Takachino | | | | | | * | |
| TEC-Advice S.A. | | | | | | | * |
| Technologic Systems | | | | | * | | |
| TEO Technologies, Inc. | | | | | | | * |
| Teknekron Infoswitch | | | | * | | | |

## Table 13.8 (continued)

| Supplier | IVR | VMAA | IP | OB | SSC | PI | FP |
|---|---|---|---|---|---|---|---|
| Telcom Design | | | * | | | | |
| Telecorp Systems | * | * | * | * | | | |
| Telephonic Equipment Corporation | | * | | | | | |
| Teledate | | | * | | | | |
| Teledirect International | | | | * | | | |
| TeleSystems Marketing, Inc. | | | | * | | | |
| Televation | | | * | | | * | |
| Telxon | * | | | | | | |
| Texas Instruments | | | | | * | | |
| Teubner Associates | | | | | | | * |
| Time & Space Processing | | | | | * | | |
| TKM | | | | * | | | |
| Toshiba | | * | | | | | |
| Touchbase Systems | | | | | | | * |
| Touch Talk | * | * | | | * | | |
| TRT | | | | | * | | * |
| Turbo Group, The | | | | | | | * |
| TWT International | | | | * | | | |
| Unidata | | | | | * | | |

**Table 13.8 (continued)**

| Supplier | IVR | VMAA | IP | OB | SSC | PI | FP |
|---|---|---|---|---|---|---|---|
| UNISYS | * | * | | | | | |
| UniVoice | * | | | | | | |
| UniVoice Products | | | | | * | | |
| UREX | | | | | * | | |
| URIX Corporation | | | | | | | |
| U.S. Audiotex | | | * | | | | |
| U.S. Telecom | | | | * | * | | |
| Verbex Voice Systems | * | | | | * | | |
| Viking Electronics | | * | | | * | | |
| VMI | * | * | * | | | | |
| VMX | * | * | * | | | | |
| Voad Systems | | | | * | | | |
| Voicecom | | * | | | | | |
| Voice Control Products | | | | | * | | |
| Voice Control Systems | | | | | * | | |
| Voice Plus, Inc. | | | | * | | | |
| Voice Processing Corporation | | | | | * | | |
| Voice Response, Inc. | * | | | | | | |
| VoiceSmart Corporation | | * | * | | * | | |

## Table 13.8 (continued)

| Supplier | IVR | VMAA | IP | OB | SSC | PI | FP |
|---|---|---|---|---|---|---|---|
| VoiceSoft | | | | | | | |
| Voice Systems & Services | | | | * | | | |
| Voicetek Corporation | * | * | * | | * | | |
| Volt Delta Resources | * | | | | | | |
| Votan | * | * | * | | * | | |
| Votrax | * | | * | | | | |
| Voxem | | | | | | | * |
| VoxLink Corporation | | | | | | | * |
| Voysys Corporation | | | | | * | | |
| V-Pec | * | | | | | | |
| VSSI | | * | * | | | | |
| V-Systems | | | | | | | * |
| Wang | * | * | * | | * | | |
| Wespercorp | | | | | * | | |
| Wilco International | | | | | | | * |
| Wygant Scientific | * | | * | * | | | |
| Xecom | | | | | | | * |
| Xerox | | | | | | | * |
| Xiox | | * | | | | | |

**Table 13.8 (continued)**

| Supplier | IVR | VMAA | IP | OB | SSC | PI | FP |
|---|---|---|---|---|---|---|---|
| Zaison | | | | | * | | |
| Zoltrix | | | | | | | * |
| Zoom Telephonics | | | | | | | * |

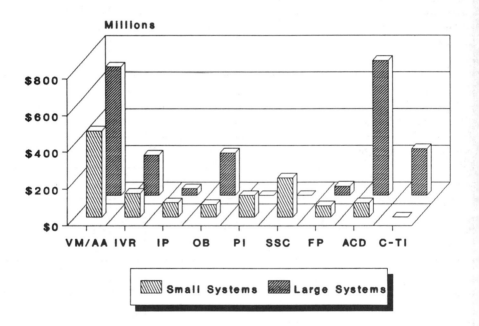

**Figure 13.7** Market segment revenue.

increase in functionality. This increase will include the incorporation of multiple voice-processing functions within a single, integrated architecture and the use of multiple voice-processing technologies within a single architecture [2].

## 13.10 VOICE-MAIL OVERALL TRENDS AND FUTURE DIRECTIONS

The areas in which the small and large computer suppliers differ will tend to disappear. As international standards such as X.400 become generally accepted, all systems will have an ability to be integrated with large text-mail systems, and

Table 13.9
Small and Large Systems Breakdown

| | | Small system | | Large system | | Total | |
|---|---|---|---|---|---|---|---|
| | | Revenue | Units | Revenue | Units | Revenue | Units |
| VM/AA | 1989 | $ 295.2M | 38.0K | $ 394.7M | 6.4K | $ 689.9M | 44.4K |
| | 1990 | $ 355.3M | 60.3K | $ 528.7M | 9.0K | $ 884.0M | 69.3K |
| | 1991 | $ 469.2M | 82.3K | $ 700.0M | 12.3K | $1,169.2M | 94.6K |
| IVR | 1989 | $ 80.2M | 2.3K | $ 148.0M | 1.9K | $ 228.2M | 4.2K |
| | 1990 | $ 114.1M | 3.2K | $ 191.8M | 2.6K | $ 305.9M | 5.8K |
| | 1991 | $ 130.9M | 3.7K | $ 219.3M | 3.0K | $ 350.2M | 6.7K |
| IP | 1989 | $ 54.5M | 2.0K | $ 18.2M | 0.2K | $ 72.7M | 2.2K |
| | 1990 | $ 66.7M | 2.5K | $ 28.9M | 0.4K | $ 95.6M | 2.9K |
| | 1991 | $ 78.7M | 3.3K | $ 36.8M | 0.6K | $ 115.5M | 3.9K |
| OB | 1989 | $ 45.3M | 6.1K | $ 115.0M | 0.8K | $ 160.3M | 6.9K |
| | 1990 | $ 52.9M | 7.7K | $ 173.2M | 1.2K | $ 226.1M | 8.9K |
| | 1991 | $ 68.9M | 10.6K | $ 229.8M | 1.6K | $ 298.7M | 12.2K |
| PI | 1989 | $ 97.6M | 11.0K | NA | NA | $ 97.6M | 11.0K |
| | 1990 | $ 108.6M | 12.0K | NA | NA | $ 108.6M | 12.0K |
| | 1991 | $ 119.3M | 13.0K | NA | NA | $ 119.3M | 13.0K |

Table 13.9 (continued)

| | | | | | | | |
|---|---|---|---|---|---|---|---|
| SSC | 1989 | $ 118.0M | 103.5K | NA | NA | $ 118.0M | 103.5K |
| | 1990 | $ 168.4M | 145.8K | NA | NA | $ 168.4M | 145.8K |
| | 1991 | $ 213.7M | 194.3K | NA | NA | $ 213.7M | 194.3K |
| FP | 1989 | $ 30.6M | 7.5K | $ 8.3M | 0.1K | $ 38.9M | 7.6K |
| | 1990 | $ 41.2M | 10.4K | $ 19.9M | 0.3K | $ 61.1M | 10.7K |
| | 1991 | $ 62.4M | 15.8K | $ 50.6M | 0.8K | $ 113.0M | 16.6K |
| ACD | 1989 | $ 60.0M | 2.0K | $ 620.0M | 2.9K | $ 680.0 | 4.9 |
| | 1990 | $ 69.0M | 2.3K | $ 681.0M | 3.6K | $ 750.0 | 5.9 |
| | 1991 | $ 78.0M | 2.6K | $ 734.0M | 4.2K | $ 812.0 | 6.8 |
| CTI | 1989 | NA | NA | $ 193.0M | 0.7K | $ 193.0 | 0.7 |
| | 1990 | NA | NA | $ 222.2M | 0.9K | $ 222.2 | 0.9 |
| | 1991 | NA | NA | $ 253.5M | 1.5K | $ 253.5 | 1.5 |
| Total | 1989 | $ 781.4M | 172.4K | $ 1,497.2M | 13.0K | $2,278.6M | 185.4K |
| | 1990 | $ 976.2M | 244.2K | $ 1,845.7M | 18.0K | $2,821.9M | 262.2K |
| | 1991 | $1,221.1M | 325.6K | $2,224.0M | 24.0K | $3,445.1M | 349.6K |

**Table 13.10**

Voice/Facsimile Processing Market Segment Revenue Projections

| Market Segment | | 1990 | 1991 | 1992 | 1993 | 1994 | 1995 | 1996 |
|---|---|---|---|---|---|---|---|---|
| VM/AA | $Ms | 884.0 | 1169.2 | 1534.0 | 1922.8 | 2403.4 | 2930.0 | 3,457.4 |
| | % | 28.1 | 32.3 | 31.2 | 25.3 | 25.0 | 21.9 | 18.0 |
| IVR | $Ms | 305.9 | 350.2 | 534.0 | 681.0 | 872.0 | 1,030.0 | 1,205.0 |
| | % | 34.0 | 14.5 | 52.5 | 27.5 | 28.0 | 18.1 | 17.0 |
| IP | $Ms | 95.6 | 115.5 | 143.1 | 178.8 | 224.0 | 265.0 | 310.0 |
| | % | 31.5 | 20.8 | 23.9 | 24.9 | 25.3 | 18.3 | 17.0 |
| OB | $Ms | 226.1 | 298.7 | 380.0 | 475.0 | 590.0 | 730.0 | 890.0 |
| | % | 41.0 | 32.1 | 27.2 | 25.0 | 24.2 | 23.7 | 21.9 |
| PI | $Ms | 108.6 | 119.3 | 138.8 | 155.2 | 172.0 | 189.1 | 207.0 |
| | % | 11.3 | 9.9 | 16.3 | 11.8 | 10.8 | 9.9 | 9.5 |
| SSC | $Ms | 168.4 | 213.7 | 265.0 | 318.0 | 369.0 | 424.0 | 482.0 |
| | % | 42.7 | 26.9 | 24.0 | 20.0 | 16.0 | 14.9 | 13.7 |
| FX | $Ms | 61.1 | 113.0 | 219.6 | 496.4 | 888.6 | 1,200.0 | 1,500.0 |
| | % | 57.1 | 84.9 | 94.3 | 126.0 | 79.0 | 35.0 | 25.0 |
| ACD | $Ms | 750.0 | 812.0 | 900.5 | 1,006.2 | 1,125.0 | 1,215.2 | 1,369.0 |
| | % | 10.3 | 8.3 | 10.9 | 11.7 | 11.8 | 8.0 | 12.7 |
| CTI | $Ms | 222.2 | 253.5 | 384.0 | 528.9 | 712.5 | 947.9 | 1,234.1 |
| | % | 13.1 | 12.3 | 34.0 | 27.4 | 25.8 | 24.8 | 23.2 |
| Total | $Ms | 2,821.9 | 3,445.1 | 4,499.0 | 5,762.3 | 7,356.5 | 8,931.2 | 10,654.5 |
| Growth | % | 23.8 | 22.1 | 30.6 | 28.1 | 27.7 | 21.4 | 19.3 |

PBX and keyswitch system integration will be common. As more powerful micro-computers and larger low-cost disks become available, port and speech storage capacity differences will tend to disappear. Multifunction systems will become common; providing auto attendant, voice mail, and telephone call accounting in a single product will be one of the most popular configurations. We anticipate that the RBOCs will start to provide voice-mail services in a significant way, which should have a strong, positive effect on voice mail because it will further legitimize this capability and broaden the market significantly by extending its availability

**Table 13.11**

Industry Segment by Voice Processing Market Segment--1991

| Industry Segment | VM/AA | IVR | IP | OB | PI | SSC | ACD | CTI | Total | % |
|---|---|---|---|---|---|---|---|---|---|---|
| Finance | 99.8 | 97.9 | 2.3 | 104.4 | 2.3 | 11.3 | 129.9 | 53.7 | 501.6 | 14.0 |
| Transportation | 82.0 | 52.3 | 6.6 | 4.0 | 7.4 | 11.2 | 89.3 | 24.8 | 277.6 | 7.2 |
| Utilities | 39.5 | 29.6 | 4.4 | 24.6 | 4.4 | 11.0 | 73.1 | 21.5 | 208.1 | 5.0 |
| Telco | 158.7 | 52.9 | 5.1 | 10.9 | 42.2 | 30.7 | 81.2 | 24.1 | 405.8 | 13.3 |
| Education | 70.1 | 13.6 | 5.4 | 18.0 | 9.5 | 19.3 | 32.5 | 10.9 | 179.3 | 6.0 |
| Publishing | 80.0 | 6.8 | 52.4 | 47.0 | 22.5 | 17.0 | 73.1 | 24.6 | 323.4 | 10.0 |
| Retail | 42.1 | 7.0 | 5.4 | 46.5 | 8.1 | 10.8 | 56.8 | 16.5 | 193.2 | 5.3 |
| Wholesale | 44.9 | 10.4 | 5.4 | 5.4 | 6.9 | 10.7 | 8.1 | 3.3 | 95.1 | 3.7 |
| Medical | 73.6 | 12.9 | 6.8 | 2.4 | 2.3 | 19.2 | 48.7 | 15.2 | 181.1 | 5.2 |
| Insurance | 140.0 | 12.7 | 4.6 | 7.0 | 0 | 4.3 | 40.6 | 12.2 | 221.4 | 7.4 |
| Manufacturing | 182.4 | 23.3 | 3.5 | 13.1 | 1.1 | 38.3 | 121.8 | 31.4 | 414.9 | 11.5 |
| Government | 156.1 | 30.8 | 13.6 | 15.4 | 12.6 | 29.9 | 56.8 | 15.2 | 330.4 | 11.4 |
| Total | 1,169.2 | 349.9 | 115.5 | 298.7 | 119.3 | 213.7 | 811.9 | 253.4 | 3,331.9 | |

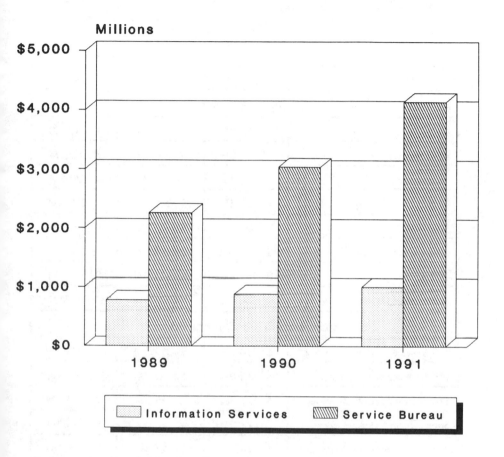

**Figure 13.8** Service provider revenue profile.

into the residential area. To serve the needs of the RBOCs, microcomputer-based VM suppliers will develop networking capability that will permit multiple smaller systems to function as though they were one large system. Digital telephone interfaces (i.e., T-1) will also be available. Consolidations among companies will increase. Large computer suppliers will act toward further consolidation to acquire a microcomputer-based market segment. Suppliers in other market segments will pursue this as a mechanism for expanding their business. The market for low-end VM products is extremely large and is presently at a low penetration level. Ninety-nine percent of all U.S. businesses have less than 100 telephone lines, and 75% have less than 10 telephone lines. This is the real market for VM systems, and where much of the growth will be realized.

**Table 13.12**
Voice Processing Service Operations

|  | *1989* | *1990* | *1991* |
|---|---|---|---|
| **Service bureaus** | | | |
| Voice mail | $ 159.7M | $ 265.0M | $ 357.8M |
| RCC voice mail | $ 32.7M | $ 44.8M | $ 62.7M |
| Telco voice mail | $ 2.0M | $ 15.0M | $ 29.0M |
| TAS | $ 296.5M | $ 298.0M | $ 313.0M |
| Telemarketing | $1,102.9M | $1,608.5M | $2,370.0M |
| Information provider | $ 163.0M | $ 182.6 | $216.3M |
| Transaction processing | $ 507.9M | $ 625.0M | $ 787.5M |
| Service bureau total | $2,264.7M | $3,038.9M | $ 4,136.3M |
| **Information service providers** | | | |
| 976 Services (IP portion) | $ 314.5M | $ 318.9M | $ 322.4M |
| 900 Services (IP portion) | $ 383.2M | $ 463.7M | $ 562.6M |
| Financial subscription services | $ 13.9M | $ 15.8M | $ 17.8M |
| Sponsor supported services | $ 21.0M | $ 26.4M | $ 33.7M |
| Advertiser supported services | $ 17.3M | $ 21.8M | $ 27.8M |
| RCC information services | $ 26.1M | $ 31.9M | $ 38.9M |
| **Information service providers total** | $ 776.0M | $878.5M | $1,003.2M |
| Service operations total | $3,040.7M | $3,917.4M | $5,139.5M |

## 13.11 IVR MARKET TRENDS AND FUTURE DIRECTIONS

VARs will become a dominant distribution channel for transaction-processing products, addressing a variety of niche vertical market areas. Mergers among companies in IVR and other market areas will increase during the next few years. The differences between IVR and information provider areas will blur, and suppliers will be heavily into each area. Suppliers will start to address the international market beyond the two to three vendors currently pursuing it.

The penetration level in IVR is less than 5%, and significant growth is likely. The primary constraint on market growth has been the lack of standardized, repetitive, noncustom products that can address market needs.

## 13.12 INFORMATION PROVIDER TRENDS AND FUTURE DIRECTIONS

The availability of interactive 900 services makes it possible to offer a nationwide audiotex service and be a catalyst for the entry of large, nationwide companies such as information providers. 976 will become an information service used strictly to reach a regional market.

Entry of large companies already in the publishing and broadcasting business will help to accelerate growth in this market area. These organizations are well positioned to address the promotional requirements of audiotex services. The TYPs will grow slowly during the next few years, while clients become convinced that this area is a worthwhile investment of their advertising dollars. The RBOCs and the independent publishers of yellow pages directories will be the prime drivers of this area.

## 13.13 OUTBOUND VOICE-PROCESSING TRENDS AND FUTURE DIRECTIONS

Growth in this market segment is driven by the telemarketing industry. Distribution channels will be expanded to include a significant VAR and dealer effort. This will provide the total solutions needed to permit this market area to register significant growth. Providing outbound services on a service bureau basis will become a major portion of this market during the next few years.

## 13.14 OVERALL VOICE-PROCESSING MARKET TRENDS

VARs will become a major force in the marketing and distribution of voice-processing products because they will be able to provide the support services users will demand. Mergers to obtain synergy will occur quite regularly during the next few years. Large companies that do not have a presence in the voice-processing area will acquire small voice-processing companies and thereby obtain an instant presence.

We anticipate that a voice-processing capability will be offered by all telephone switch suppliers such as AT&T, Northern Telecom, and TIE, and computer companies such as IBM, DEC, HP, Wang, and UNISYS. They will often offer this capability by forming strategic alliances with existing suppliers of voice-processing products. Some examples of this that have already occurred:

AT&T/Brooktrout
Hewlett-Packard/Octel

TIE/Brooktrout
Wang/Digital Sound
Xerox/VMX
NEC/Centigram
Northern Telecom/Centigram
IBM/Syntellect
Toshiba/VMX
Rockwell/InterVoice
NCR/InterVoice
IBM/Dialogic
IBM/Intellivoice
AT&T/Brooktrout
Fujitsu/Centigram
Teknekron/InterVoice
Tandem/Voicetek

These companies are finding that this approach provides rapid market entry with a minimal investment. In addition, these suppliers will also offer an "open world" architecture, which permits integration with a variety of external voice-processing products. Generally, the switch and computer companies are looking to participate in the voice-processing area to the extent that it helps them sell switches or computers. This is a defensive posture, and it is unlikely that they will be an aggressive factor in the voice-processing area. The few companies such as Rolm and Northern Telecom who have developed their own voice-processing products have offered products that were not as competitive as products from independent suppliers.

## REFERENCES

1. Creitz, W. W., "Understanding Voice Processing Markets: Opportunities in the 80s," *Online Voice-Processing Conference*, London, May 1985, pp. 107–117.
2. Teschner, W. C., *Voice Processing Markets, Products and Suppliers—1992*, Tern Systems, Concord, Massachusetts, March 1992.

# Chapter 14

## Voice Processing and Persons With Disabilities

Speech technology has been used to aid people with disabilities. The most fundamental capability has been to provide access to information that would not be available to a person because of his or her disability. Disabled individuals have frequently found employment when they have access to equipment that permits them to overcome their disabilities. The quality of life for a person with a disability can often be significantly improved with speech technology devices. Significant productivity and human resources benefits occur for government, industry, and persons with disabilities when information technology is enhanced to support this access.

Only in recent decades has equal opportunity for the disabled become a recognized objective of our society. Since the turn of the century, education and rehabilitation programs have promoted personal independence and economic self-sufficiency. In spite of these programs, individuals with disabilities fall far short of equality with their non-disabled peers. The American Foundation for the Blind estimates that two out of three working-age blind persons are unemployed. It is an ironic injustice that the revolution in technology, the ultimate advancement that could complete the assimilation of the disabled person into mainstream society, may instead create confining barriers. Without access to computers, persons with disabilities are in danger of falling further behind in reaching equality.

The development of devices designed to permit computer use by individuals with disabilities promises to make this individual truly the peer of the individual with no disabilities. Access technology transforms the computer into a prosthetic device that enables a disabled individual to master an expanding universe of information, activities, and opportunities [1]. As part of the Federal Rehabilitation Act, Congress has mandated that Government agencies purchase electronic equipment that meets specific guidelines for accessibility by persons with disabilities.

## 14.1 USE OF SPEECH TECHNOLOGY BY INDIVIDUALS WITH DISABILITIES

For users with very limited or no usable vision, converting information into voice form is an effective way to provide access to the information. Any of the telephone-oriented voice-processing services can be used by a blind person. The person can readily use voice mail or obtain rate information or an account balance. Text-to-speech converters are the most automatic way to convert computer information into audible form. One of the simplest ways to do this is to connect the text-to-speech device in series with a normal terminal attached to a computer. Many of the commercially available products come equipped with a line-splice configuration, as shown in Figure 14.1. Information from the computer can either be sent to the terminal display, to the text-to-speech device, or to both. Information generated at the terminal can be sent to the text-to-speech device to be heard. This is similar to the screen copy printer capability that is available on most PCs and terminals.

There are software packages that support text-to-speech and provide computing capabilities such as word processing, spreadsheets, and relational database processors. In most cases, the most effective packages are ones that interface with a popular language processor such as Lotus 1-2-3 or WordStar and provide the special functions needed to accommodate a blind person. Features such as spelling a word, cursor location, echo input, read columns, and speaking rate are provided by these packages.

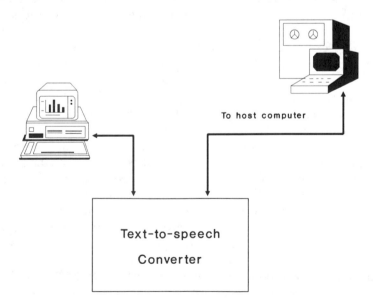

To host computer

Text-to-speech
Converter

**Figure 14.1** Text-to-speech line-splice configuration.

Reading machines for the blind read a document with an optical character reader and then send it to a text-to-speech device that converts it to audio. The most-well-known device of this sort has been provided for a number of years by Kurzweil Computer Products, a division of Xerox Corporation (see Fig. 14.2(a)). These machines originally cost $20,000 to $30,000, which put them out of the reach of many individuals. In September 1988, a product called the *Personal Reader* was introduced by Kurzweil Computer Products for $8,000. It has a hand-held scanner and weighs 19 pounds (see Fig. 14.2(b)). In this configuration, it is a highly portable device. A similar product is available with a flatbed scanner for $10,000. For

**Figure 14.2(a)** The Kurzweil reading machine. (Photograph courtesy of Xerox Imaging Systems, Inc.)

$12,000, a unit that includes both the hand-held and the flatbed scanner is available. The hand-held scanner includes a magnetic tracking page, which makes it relatively easy to line the scanner up with the text characters. To make this product more readily available to individuals, Xerox and the American Foundation for the Blind have established a foundation that will provide the units at a discount and will guarantee loans that are made for the purchase of the Personal Reader. The purchaser must meet a need criteria. In early 1992, Xerox introduced a PC-based version of the Personal Reader priced at $4,695 without the PC. A separate software product was also introduced for use by individuals with reading disabilities. The text being read is displayed and the user is able to scan through the text in a variety of ways.

Text-to-speech technology has been used to assist individuals who are nonverbal or vocally impaired. A nonverbal person can type what he or she desires to say, and the text-to-speech device will say it for them. Devices are available that have pushbuttons labeled with graphical symbols. These symbols identify the most common communication of a user. The user would press a particular pushbutton and the device verbalizes what is programmed for that pushbutton. For

**Figure 14.2(b)** Xerox/Kurzweil personal reader. (Photograph courtesy of Xerox Imaging Systems, Inc.).

individuals who are severely handicapped and are not able to physically press a pushbutton, a scanning capability is available. The choices are scanned, and the user makes a selection when the desired item is scanned. A variety of mechanisms for controlling the scanner are available, such as joysticks and optical pointers.

Individuals that suffer from dyslexia can use text-to-speech as a learning device. A person with dyslexia has a great difficulty with reading because letters become transposed. With text-to-speech, the dyslexic is able to understand audibly what he or she is not able to understand visually. Individuals with speaking disabilities can learn the proper pronunciation of words by viewing a visual display of a speech spectagram. The person sees what the spectagram looks like when the word is pronounced properly and then modifies his or her speech-generation effort to replicate the template of the properly pronounced word.

Individuals with mobility difficulties can successfully use speech-recognition technology to communicate to a computer, for example, for someone without the use of his or her limbs. Using speech recognition, robotic devices can be controlled to perform a function that the disabled individual is unable to perform.

Until the early 1990s, the price of high-quality text-to-speech products were expensive, typically costing $3,000 to $4,000. This has changed during the last few years. An example is the PC/DECtalk product that Digital Equipment Corporation announced in early 1992. Priced at only $1,195, it can be used with a conventional PC.

Recording for the Blind, Inc. is a private organization that puts books on audiocassette tapes for blind people and dyslexics. The books are primarily textbooks for student use. The Library of Congress also provides audio books, but these books are mostly for entertainment and have historically been created by individuals audibly reading a book into a recorder. However, this tends to be a very long process. Most of the reading is actually done by volunteers, who would typically read an hour or two a week, so audio books often take months to create. At a speaking rate of 180 words per minute, a 200-page book requires approximately 60 hours to complete. A year or more to record a book is not uncommon. With text-to-speech, however, a book can be placed on a cassette tape in a few days.

To communicate on the telephone, deaf people must use a *telecommunications device for the deaf* (TDD). The caller sends information by typing at a keyboard, sending the information as tones. To accept the message, the receiving end must be equipped with a TDD. Many of the voice-processing systems are providing TDD interfaces that may be set up to allow a deaf person to access a voice-processing service over a TDD. Information that is available to hearing individuals can then be accessed by a deaf person by using a TDD. TDD relay services are also available in which a deaf person is able to communicate with a hearing person over the telephone using a third-party operator. The operator will relay messages between the conversing parties—using the TDD in the direction of the deaf person and orally in the direction of the hearing person until the conversation ends.

## 14.2 FEDERAL GOVERNMENT SUPPORT OF THE DISABLED

In 1986, Congress reauthorized the Rehabilitation Act of 1973, as amended (public law 99-506), adding Section 508 on electronic accessibility ". . . to ensure that handicapped individuals may use electronic office equipment with or without peripherals." Congress mandated that guidelines for electronic equipment accessibility be established and adopted and that agencies shall comply with these guidelines with respect to electronic equipment, whether purchased or leased. The Department of Education and the *General Services Administration* (GSA) were directed to develop agency procurement guidelines to ensure access to electronic equipment by disabled individuals.

These guidelines have been developed. Copies are available from the *Clearinghouse on Computer Accommodations* (COCA), which is an organization within GSA that functions as a governmentwide clearinghouse for the disabled. This technical resource center assists agencies as they establish support services and responds to individual accommodation requests governmentwide. COCA provides demonstrations of accommodation products and strategies. In addition, COCA gives presentations at agency conferences and seminars and provides formal training in computer accommodation through the GSA Training Center. COCA also maintains a database of accommodation solutions received from government agencies and also has available a manager's handbook, *Managing End User Computing for Users with Disabilities*. The COCA staff can be reached at 202-523-1906 or by mail at GSA, Clearinghouse on Computer Accommodation, Room 2022, KGDO, 18th & F Streets N.W., Washington, DC, 20405 [2, 3].

The Americans with Disabilities Act was passed on July 26, 1990. In addition to barring employment discrimination against individuals with disabilities, it mandates that public facilities provide accessibility accommodations for individuals with disabilities. The access to public facilities portions went into effect on January 26, 1992, and mandates that a public accommodation shall take those steps that may be necessary to ensure that no individual with a disability is excluded, denied services, segregated or otherwise treated differently than other individuals.

## REFERENCES

1. Hutchins, S. A., "Computer-Animated Speech Processing for Speech Therapy," *American Voice Input Output Society proceedings,* San Francisco, California, October 1988.
2. COCA staff, *Managing End User Computing for Users With Disabilities*, GSA, Washington, D.C., December 1991.
3. COCA staff, *Access to Information Technology by Users With Disabilities*, GSA, Washington, D.C., October 1987.

# Appendix 1
## Voice Mail and Automated Attendant Product Suppliers

The suppliers of voice mail and automated attendant products are categorized by type of product and the market that is served in Table A1.1.

ACS Communications, Inc.
250 Technology Circle
Scotts Valley, CA 95066-3575
408-438-3883/800-538-0742

Active Voice, Inc.
101 Stewart Street
Seattle, WA 98101
206-441-4700

Advanced Interactive Systems, Inc.
1377 Main Street
Waltham, MA 02154
617-899-4700

Advanced Voice Technologies, Inc.
1865 Airline Drive, Suite 14,
Nashville, TN 37210
615-885-4170

Alston
A MARK IV Company
1600 S. Mountain Avenue
Duarte, CA 91010-2744
818-357-2121

American Communications & Engineering,
Inc.
2267 N. Agate Court
Semi Valley, CA 93065
805-581-3318/800-283-3318

American Telesystems
Seven Piedmont Center, Suite 200
Atlanta, GA 30305
404-266-2500

Amtelco
4800 Curtin Drive
McFarland, WI 53558
608-838-4194/800-356-9148

Applied Voice Technology, Inc.
P.O. Box 97025
Kirkland, WA 98083
206-820-6000/800-443-0806

Applied Intelysis
4340 Campus Drive, Suite 204
Newport Beach, CA 92660
714-852-1175

**Table A1.1**

Voice Mail/Automated Attendant Supplier Categorization

| Supplier | Personal | Depart-mental | PBX | Corporate/ SB | CO | TAS/ RCC | Dict-ation |
|---|---|---|---|---|---|---|---|
| Active Voice | | * | | | | | |
| ACS Communications | * | | | | | | |
| AIS, Inc. | | * | | | | | |
| Alston | | | | | | * | |
| AC&E | | * | | | | | |
| Amtelco | | | | | | * | |
| Applied Voice Technologies | | * | | | | | |
| AT&S | | * | | | | | |
| AT&T | | * | * | * | | | |

AT&S
2381 Dutch Fork Road
Chapin, SC 29036
803-732-7520

AT&T/IS
55 Corporate Drive
Bridgewater, NJ
201-361-1212/800-247-1212

AVA Technology, Inc.
267 Boston Post Road
Billerica, MA 01862
508-663-0900

AudioFAX, Inc.
2000 Powers Ferry Road, Suite 220
Marietta, GA 30067
404-933-7600/800-AUDIOFAX

Automation Electronics Corporation
11501 Dublin Boulevard
Dublin, CA 94568
415-828-2880/800-232-4653

Autotel Information Systems, Inc.
9401 Science Center Drive
Minneapolis, MN 55428
612-533-7888/800-328-8966

BCB Technologies
305 Healey Road/PO 315
Bolton, Ontario, L7E 5T3 Canada
416-857-0790/800-668-7875

BMC Group, Inc.
2177 Flintstone Drive, Suite O
Tucker, GA 30084
404-934-7613

**Table A1.1 (continued)**

| Supplier | Personal | Depart-mental | PBX | Corporate/ SB | CO | TAS/ RCC | Dict-ation |
|---|---|---|---|---|---|---|---|
| AVA Technology | | * | | | | | |
| AEC | | * | | | | | |
| BMC Group, | | * | | | | | |
| Boston Technoloogy | | * | | | * | | |
| Brooktrout Technology | | * | | | | | |
| Centigram Communications | | * | | * | * | * | |
| Cobotyx Corporation | | * | | | | | |
| Code-A-Phone | * | | | | | | |
| Compass Computer Systems | | * | | | | | |
| Complete PC, The | * | | | | | | |
| Computer Talk Technology | | * | | | | | |
| Comverse Technology | | * | | * | * | * | |
| Dacon | | * | | | | | |

Boston Technology, Inc.
100 Quannapowitt Parkway
Wakefield, MA 01880
617-246-9000

Brite Voice Systems, Inc.
7309 E. 21st Street North
Wichita, KS 67206
316-652-6500/800-SEE-BRITE

Brooktrout Technology, Inc.
144 Gould Street
Needham, MA 02192
617-449-4100

Centigram Corporation
91 East Tasman Drive
San Jose, CA 95134
408-942-0250

**Table A1.1 (continued)**

| Supplier | Personal | Depart-mental | PBX | Corporate/ SB | CO | TAS/ RCC | Dict-ation |
|---|---|---|---|---|---|---|---|
| Dial Tech | | * | | | | | |
| Dictaphone Corporation | | | | | | | * |
| Digital Sound Corporation | | * | | * | | | |
| Digital Speech Systems | | * | | | | | |
| Digitcom | | * | | | | | |
| Dytel Corporation | | * | | | | | |
| Eletech Electronics | | * | | | | | |
| Enhanced Systems | | * | | | | | |
| Fujitsu Business Communications | | | * | * | | | |
| Glenayre Electronics Corporation | | | * | * | | * | |
| IBM Corporation | | * | | | | | |
| In.Gate Technology | | | | * | | | |
| Innovative Technology | | * | | | | | |

Cobotyx Corporation, Inc.
38C Grove Street
Ridgefield, CT 06877
203-431-3000/800-288-6342

Code-A-Phone Corporation
16261 S.E. 130th Avenue
Clackamas, OR 97015
503-655-8940

Compass Technology, Inc.
Live Oak Office Center
2201 Cantu Office Center

Sarasota, FL 34232
813-371-8000

Computer Talk Technology, Inc.
225 East Beaver Creek, Suite 310
Richmond Hill, Ontario L4B 3K3
Canada
416-882-5000

Comverse Technology, Inc.
400 Crossways Park Drive
Woodbury, NY 11797
516-921-0659

**Table A1.1 (continued)**

| Supplier | Personal | Depart-mental | PBX | Corporate/SB | CO | TAS/RCC | Dict-ation |
|---|---|---|---|---|---|---|---|
| Insystecom | | * | | | | | |
| Intellisystems Corporation | | * | | | | | |
| Intellivoice Communications | | * | | | | | |
| Interactive Communication Systems | | * | | | | | |
| Kerygma Technologies | | * | | | | | |
| Lanier Voice Products | | | | | | | * |
| LEADtrack Services | * | | | | | | |
| Macrotel International Corporation | | * | | | | | |
| Magnum Software | * | | | | | | |
| Miami Voice | | * | | | | | |
| Microlog Corporation | | * | | | | | |
| Microvoice Corporation | | * | | | | | |

Dacon
123 Pleasant Avenue
Upper Saddle River, NJ 07458
201-825-4640/800-322-8686

Dial Tech
211 West 2nd Street
East Greenville, PA 18041
215-679-0443/800-622-0443

Dictaphone Corporation
3191 Broadbridge Avenue
Stratford, CT 06497
203-348-2751/800-255-0942

Digital Sound Corporation
6307 Carpinteria Avenue
Carpinteria, CA 93013
805-566-2000

Digital Speech Systems, Inc.
1840 North Greenville, Suite 156
Richardson, TX 75081
214-235-2999

Dytel Corporation
50 East Commerce Drive
Schaumburg, IL 60173
312-519-9850/800-223-2727

**Table A1.1 (continued)**

| Supplier | Personal | Depart-mental | PBX | Corporate/SB | CO | TAS/RCC | Dict-ation |
|---|---|---|---|---|---|---|---|
| Mitel Corporation | | | * | | | | |
| Moscom | | * | | | | | |
| MPSI | | * | | | | | |
| MultiVerse Communications | | * | | | | | |
| Natural Microsystems Corporation | * | | | | | | |
| Northern Telecom | | | * | | | | |
| Octel Communications Corporation | | * | | * | * | * | |
| Omnivoice | | | | | | * | |
| Parwan Electronics Corporation | | * | | | | | |
| Pika Technologies | | * | | | | | |
| Premier | | * | | | | | |
| Rolm Company | | | * | * | | | |
| Soft-Com | | * | | | | | |

Eletech Electronics
1262 E. Katella Avenue
Anaheim, CA 92805
714-385-1707

Enhanced Systems
6961 Peachtree Industrial Boulevard
Norcross, GA 30092
404-662-1503

Fujitsu Business Communications
3190 Miraloma Avenue

Anaheim, CA 82806-1998
714-630-7721

Glenayre Atlanta
4800 River Green Parkway
Duluth, GA 30136
404-623-4900/800-866-4002

In.Gate Technology
1333 Lawrence Expressway, Suite 440
Santa Clara, CA 95051
408-243-9150

## Table A1.1 (continued)

| Supplier | Personal | Depart-mental | PBX | Corporate/ SB | CO | TAS/ RCC | Dict-ation |
|---|---|---|---|---|---|---|---|
| Spectrum Ericsson Communications | | | * | | | | |
| Speech Solutions | | * | | | | | |
| Stok Softare | | * | | | | | |
| Strategic Dimensions, Inc. | | * | | | | | |
| Sudbury Systems, Inc. | | | | | | | * |
| Telecorp Systems | | * | | | | | |
| Telelaison | | * | | | | | |
| Telephonic Equipment Corporation | | * | | | | | |
| Toshiba | | | * | | | | |
| Treva Communications | | * | | | | | |
| Unisys | | * | | * | * | | |
| VMX | | * | | * | | * | |
| Voicemail International | | | | * | | | |

Innovative Technology, Inc.
P.O. Box 767370
1000 Holcomb Woods Parkway, Suite 422
Roswell, GA 30076
404-998-9970

Insyscom Corporation
1912-L Batavia Street
Orange, CA 92665
714-637-8007/800-266-6789

IntelliSystems, Inc.
9430 Topanga Canyon Boulevard, #205

Chatsworth, CA 91311
818-341-7000

Intellivoice, Inc.
1201 West Peachtree Street
Suite 4670
Atlanta, GA 30309

Interactive Communication Systems Corp.
23-25 Elm Street
Watertown, MA 02172
617-923-2299

**Table A1.1 (continued)**

| Supplier | Personal | Depart-mental | PBX | Corporate/ SB | CO | TAS/ RCC | Dict-ation |
|----------|----------|---------------|-----|---------------|-----|----------|------------|
| VoiceSoft | | | | * | | | |
| Voice Systems & Services | | * | | | | * | |
| Voicetek Corporation | | * | | | | | |
| Wang Laboratories, Inc. | | * | | * | | | |
| Wygant Scientific | | * | | | | | |
| Xiox Corporation | | * | | | | | |

Kerygma Technologies, Inc.
80 Modular Avenue
Commack, NY 11725
516-864-2357

Lanier Voice Products Division
1700 Chantilly Drive, N.E.
Atlanta, GA 30324
404-321-1244/800-241-1706

LEADtrack Services
P.O. Box 862215
Marietta, GA 30062-0001
800-663-4641

Liberty Communications
941 Thoms Run Road
P.O. Box 348
Pittsburgh, PA 15142
412-221-8810

Lynx Communications Corporation
53 Winchester Street
Newton, MA 02161
617-965-2000

Macrotel International Corp.
3540 N.W. 56th Street
Fort Lauderdale, FL 33309
305-484-4000/800-826-1627

Miami Voice
5215 N.W. 74th Street,
Miami, FL 33166
305-593-6077

Microlog Corporation
20270 Goldenrod Lane
Germantown, MD 20874
301-428-3227/800-562-2822

Microvoice Corporation
6 Morgan, Suite 116
Irvine, CA 92718
714-588-2739

Messaging Processing Systems, Inc.
834 Tyvola Road, Suite 112
Charlotte, NC 28217
704-527-8888

Moscom Corporation
3750 Monroe Avenue
Pittsford, NY 14534
716-381-6000

MultiVerse Communications
148 West 77th Street, Suite 3A
New York, NY 10024
212-580-0541

Natural Microsystems Corporation
8 Erie Drive,
Natick, MA 01760
617-655-0700/800-533-6120

Northern Telecom
2305 Mission College Road
Santa Clara, CA 95054
408-988-5550/800-328-8800

Octel Communications Corporation
890 Tasman Drive
Milpitas, CA 95035-7439
408-942-6500

Onmivoice
280 North Park Avenue, Suite 108
Warren, OH 44482
216-393-3246

Parwan Electronics Corporation
47 Gordons Corner Road
Marlboro, NJ 07746
908-536-7500

Pika Technologies
155 Terrence Matthews Crescent
Kanata, Ontario, Canada
613-591-1555

Premier
600 Industrial Parkway
Industrial Airport, KS 66031
913-791-7000

Rolm
4900 Old Ironsides Way
Santa Clara, CA 95054
408-986-1000

Soft-Com, Inc.
140 West 22nd Street
New York, NY 10011
212-242-9595/800-627-4550

Spectrum Ericsson
45 Crossways Park Drive
Woodbury, NY 11797
516-822-9810/800-828-8255

Speech Solutions
139 Townsend Street, Suite 301
San Francisco, CA 94107
415-243-8300

Startel
17661 Cowan Avenue
Irvine, CA 92714
714-863-8700

Stok Software, Inc.
92-30 56th Street
Elmhurst, NY 11373
718-699-9393

Strategic Dimensions, Inc.
375 Franklin Road, Suite 460
Marietta, GA 30067
404-423-9485

Sudbury Systems, Inc.
31 Union Avenue
Sudbury, MA 01776
508-443-1100/800-876-8888

Talking Technology
1125 Atlantic Avenue
Alameda, CA 94501
510-522-3800

Telecorp Systems, Inc.
1000 Holcomb Woods Parkway, Ste 410A
Roswell, GA 30076
404-587-0700/800-347-9907

Teleliason
3501 Rue Ashby
St. Laurent, Quebec H4R 2K3
514-333-5333

Telephonic Equipment Corporation
17401 Armstrong Avenue
Irvine, CA 92714
714-250-9400/800-854-8269

The Complete PC, Inc.
1983 Concourse Drive
San Jose, CA 95131
408-434-0145/800-634-5558

Toshiba
9740 Irvine Boulevard
Irvine, CA 92718
714-583-3700/800-222-5805

UNISYS
Township Line & Jolly Rd. MS B330
Blue Bell, PA 19424-0001
215-986-2359

VMX, Inc.
2115 O'Nell Drive
San Jose, CA 95131
408-441-1144/800-284-4VMX

Voice Communications Software Corp.
3825 Atherton Road
Rocklin, CA 95677
916-632-3232

Voicemail International, Inc.
2953 Bunker Hill Lane
Santa Clara, CA 95054
408-980-4000

VoiceSmart Corporation
170 East Linden Avenue
Englewood, NJ 07631
201-568-3338/800-878-7627

Voicetek Corporation
19 Alpha Road
Chelmsford, MA 01824
508-250-9393

Voice Systems and Services, Inc.
One Technology Center
Mannford, OK 74044
918-865-1000

Wang Laboratories, Inc.
One Industrial Way
Lowell, MA 01851
508-459-5000

Wygant Scientific, Inc.
921 S.W. Morrison
547 Galleria Building
Portland, OR 97205
503-227-6901/800-NUVOICE

# Appendix 2

## Interactive Voice Response Product Suppliers

Access International, Inc.
1853 Bernice Road
Lansing, IL 60438
708-895-3495

American Communications & Engineering
30961 West Agoura Road
Westlake Village, CA 91361
818-706-0161/800-283-3318

Apex Voice Communications
251 Kearny Street, Suite 710
San Francisco, CA 94108
415-291-0737/800-727-3970

Applied Voice Technology, Inc.
P.O. Box 97025
Kirkland, WA 98083
206-820-6000/800-443-0806

Argos Computer Systems, Inc.
363 7th Avenue
New York, NY 10001
212-736-0720

Arkansas Systems, Inc.
8901 Kanis Road
Little Rock, AR 72205
501-227-8471

AT&T Business Communication Systems
55 Corporate Drive
Bridgewater, NJ 08807
908-658-8747

Burr-Brown Corporation
P.O. Box 11400
Tucson, AZ 85734
602-741-2239

CDP Systems, Inc.
2005 Pan Am Circle, Suite 800
Tampa, FL 33607
813-874-1358/800-ASK-CDP1

CE Corporation
8 Chrysler
Irvine, CA 92718
714-583-0792/800-854-6861

Centigram Communications Corporation
91 East Tasman Drive
San Jose, CA 95134
408-944-0250

Cognitronics Corporation
25 Crescent Street
Stamford, CT 06906
203-327-5307/800-243-2594

Computer Associates
400 Blue Hill Drive
Westwood, MA 02090-2198
617-329-7700

Computer Communications Specialists, Inc.
6683 Jimmy Carter Boulevard
Norcross, GA 30071
404-441-3114

Computer Consoles, Inc.
97 Humboldt Street
Rochester, NY 14609-7493
716-482-5000/800-833-7477

Computer Talk Technology, Inc.
225 East Beaver Creek, Suite 310
Richmond Hill, Ontario L4B 3P4
416-882-5000

CTI Information Services
8012 Goodhurst Drive
Gaithersburg, MD 20882
301-990-2564

Datap
2575 Cumberland Parkway
Atlanta, GA 30339
404-433-9450

DataWay Systems
24133 Northwestern Highway, Suite 100
Southfield, MI 48075-2568
313-356-0011

Diatek Corporation
5720 Oberlin Drive
San Diego, CA 92121
619-453-9560/800-854-2904

Di/Com Ltd.
3041 Lexington Road
Nicholasville, KY 40356
606-885-2273

Denniston & Denniston, Inc.
3250 N. Arlington Heights Road
Suite 111
Arlington Heights, IL 60004
708-398-8500

Digital Sound Corporation
6307 Carpinteria Avenue
Carpinteria, CA 93013
805-566-2000

Electronic Tele-Communications, Inc.
3620 Clearview Parkway
Atlanta, GA 30340
404-455-4890

EPOS Corporation
507 Stage Road, P.O. Box 2219
Auburn, AL 36830
205-826-7056

Expert Systems, Inc.
1010 Huntcliff, Suite 2235
Atlanta, GA 30350
404-642-7575

Granada Systems Design, Inc.
245 Fifth Avenue
New York, NY 10016
212-686-6945/800-472-6444

HTI Voice Solutions
333 Turnpike Road
Southboro, MA 01772
508-485-8400

Hypercom, Inc.
1741 East Morten
Suite A
Phoenix, AZ 85020
602-870-4993

IBM Corporation
44 South Broadway
White Plains, NY 10601
914-288-3508

Information Associates
3000 Ridge Road East
Rochester, NY 14622
716-467-7740

Interact, Inc.
770 North Cotner Street, Suite 401
Lincoln, NE 68505
402-464-8786

International Electronics, Inc.
32 Wexford Street
Needham Heights, MA 02194
617-449-6646

International Telesystems, Inc.
Suite 101, 9128 152nd Street
Surrey, B.C. Canada, V3R 4E7
604-589-1086

InterVoice, Inc.
17811 Waterview Parkway
Dallas, TX 75252
214-669-3988

IOCS
400 Totten Pond Road
Waltham, MA 02254-9033
617-890-2299/800-451-1033

Linker Systems
13612 Onkayha Circle
Irvine, CA 92720
714-552-1904

Microdimension, Inc.
7345 Production Drive
Mentor, OH 44060-4858
216-974-8070

Microlog Corporation
20270 Goldenrod Lane
Germantown, MD 20874
301-428-3227/800-562-2822

Missing Link Computer Technology, Inc.
52 Forest Avenue
Paramus, NJ 07652-5214
201-845-0303/800-999-6890

Pelton Systems, Inc.
1078 Carol Lane, Suite 202
Lafayette, CA 94549
415-283-0232

Perception Technology Corporation
Shawmut Park
Canton, MA 02021-1409
617-821-0320/800-PTC-3002

Periphonics Corporation
4000 Veterans Memorial Highway
Bohemia, NY 11716
516-467-0500

Pertek
849 Fairmount Avenue
Baltimore, MD 21204
301-494-6607

Simpact Voice Products Group
1782 La Costa Meadows Drive
San Marcos, CA 92068
619-471-0342

Speech Solutions
139 Townsend Street, Suite 301
San Francisco, CA 94107
415-243-8300

SwitchLink Systems Corporation
10220 SW Greenburg Road, Suite 360
Portland, OR 97223
503-245-2400

Syntellect, Inc.
15810 North 28th Avenue
Phoenix, AZ 85023
602-789-2800

TALX Corporation
6850 Borman Court
St. Louis, MO 63146
314-434-0046

Telecorp Systems, Inc.
1000 Holcomb Woods Parkway, Suite 410A
Roswell, GA 30076
404-587-0700/800-347-9907

Telxon Canada Corporation, Inc.
2651 John Street, Unit #6
Markham, Ontario L3R2W5
416-475-8866

Telephone Response Technology, Inc.
1624 Santa Clara Drive, Suite 200
Roseville, CA 95661
916-784-7777

UNISYS
Township Line & Jolly Road, MS B330
Blue Bell, PA 19424-0001
215-986-2359

UniVoice
3204 Gulf Gate Drive
Sarasota, FL 34231
813-925-8800

URIX Corporation
187 Gibraltor Road
Horsham, PA 19044
215-443-0600

U.S. Telecom, Inc.
112 East 32nd Street, Suite D
Joplin, MO 64803
417-781-7000/

Vicorp Interactive Systems
540 Tremont Street

Boston, MA 02116
617-542-9233

Voicetek Corporation
19 Alpha Road
Chelmsford, MA 01824
508-250-9393

Volt Delta Resources
1133 Avenue of the Americas
New York, NY 10036
212-827-2617

Votrax
1794 Rankin
Troy, MI 48083
313-588-2050

V-PEC, Inc.
2300 Hampten Boulevard
Reading, PA 19604
215-921-8881

# Appendix 3
# Information Provider Product Suppliers

Access Radio
1805 N.E. Jensen Beach Boulevard
Jenson Beach, FL 34957
407-334-5000/800-334-5123

American Communications & Engineering
2267 North Agate Court
Simi Valley, CA 93065
805-581-3318

Apex Voice Communications
14900 Ventura Boulevard, Suite 200
Sherman Oaks, CA 94108
818-379-8400/800-727-3970

AT&T Business Communication Systems
55 Corporate Drive
Bridgewater, NJ 08807
908-658-8747

AT&T Information Systems
Basking Ridge, NJ
800-222-0400

AUDIOtechs, Inc.
39 Bemis Street
Newton, MA 02160
617-966-3336

AVA Technology, Inc.
267 Boston Road, Suite 5
Billerica, MA 508-663-0900

BCB Technologies, Inc.
305 Healey Road, Box 315
Bolton, Ontario L7E 5T3
416-857-0790/800-668-7875

Brite Voice Systems, Inc.
7309 East 21st North
Wichita, KS 67206-1080
316-652-6500/800-SEE-BRITE

Communications & Information Service Corp.
4310 Spring Valley Road
Dallas, TX 75244
214-960-9281

Compression Labs
2860 Junction Avenue
San Jose, CA 95134
800-538-7542

ConferTech International
2801 Youngfield Street, Suite 240
Golden, CO 82218
303-233-9051

Darome
8750 West Bryn Mawr Avenue, Suite 850
Chicago, IL 60631
312-399-1610

Dial Tech International
211 West 2nd Street
East Greenville, PA 18041
215-679-0443/800-622-0443

DiRAD Technologies, Inc.
21 Aviation Road
Albany, NY 12205
518-438-6000

Digitron Telecommunications
44 Green Street
Huntington, NY 11743
516-271-9405

DSP Technology Corporation
1325 Capital Parkway
Carrollton, TX 75006
214-242-TALK

## Table A3.1
### Information Provider Product Supplier Classification

| Supplier | Sponsored information services | 976 & 900 | Talking yellow pages | Conference bridges |
|---|---|---|---|---|
| Access Radio | * | | | |
| AC & E | * | * | | |
| American Data Voice Systems | * | | | |
| Apex Voice Communications | * | * | | |
| Applied Voice Technologies | * | | | |
| AT&T | * | * | | * |
| Audio/Digital Systems | * | | | |
| AVA Technology | * | | | |
| BCB Electronic Sales | * | | | |
| Brite Voice Systems | * | * | * | |
| CISCorp | * | | * | |
| ConferTech International | | | | * |
| Connex Internatioal | | | | * |
| Darome | | | | * |
| DataDial | * | | | |
| Dialtech | * | | | |
| Digitran Telecommunications | * | | | |
| DiRAD Technologies | * | | | |
| DSP Technology Corporation | * | | | |
| Enhanced Systems | * | | | |
| ETC | * | | | |
| Gralin Associates | * | * | | |
| Granite Telcom | * | * | | |
| Hacowie Corp. | * | | | |
| Integrated Data Concepts | * | * | | |
| Intellivoice | * | | | |
| Interalia Communications | * | | | |

Table A3.1 (continued)

| Supplier | Sponsored information services | 976 & 900 | Talking yellow pages | Conference bridges |
|---|---|---|---|---|
| Livewire Speech Systems | * | * | | |
| M/A-Com MAC | | | | * |
| Microlog Corporation | * | | | |
| MultiLink | | * | | * |
| Perception Technology | * | * | * | |
| Periphonics Corporation | * | | | |
| Phone Trader | * | * | | |
| Precision Components | | | | * |
| RAAC Technologies, Inc. | * | * | | |
| Renegade C Software | | * | | |
| Shure Teleconferencing Syst. | * | | | |
| Simpact Voice Products | * | * | | |
| SpanLink | * | * | * | |
| SpeechSoft | * | * | | |
| Stok Software | * | * | | |
| T1 Systems | * | * | | |
| Teladate | * | * | | |
| Telcom Design | * | * | | |
| Teleconferencing Syst. Int'l | | | | * |
| Telecorp Systems | * | | | |
| Tellabs | | | | * |
| Treva Communications | * | * | | |
| TRT | * | | | |
| Telephonic Equipment Corp. | | | | * |
| Television Telecomm. Systems | * | * | | |
| Unex | | | | * |
| URIX Corporation | * | * | | |
| U.S. Audiotex | * | * | * | |
| U.S. Sprint | * | * | | |
| U.S. Telecom, Inc. | * | * | | |
| VICORP | * | | | |
| Voicetek Corporation | * | * | | |
| Votrax | * | | | |
| Westell | | | | * |

Electronic Tele-Communications, Inc.
3620 Clearview Parkway
Atlanta, GA 30340
404-455-4890

Gralin Associates, Inc.
3613 Old Easton Road
Doylestown, PA 18901
215-340-2411

Granite Telcom
669 East Industrial Park Drive
Manchester, NH 03103
603-424-3900

Howcowie Corporation
376 Route 17M
Monroe, New York 10950
914-782-6767

Integrated Data Concepts
P.O. Box 93425
Los Angeles, CA 90027
213-469-2312

Intellivoice, Inc.
One Atlantic Center
1201 West Peachtree Street, Suite 4670
Atlanta, GA 30309
404-875-3535

Livewire Speech Systems, Inc.
5397 Eglinton Avenue West, Suite 103
Etobicoke, Ontario, M9C 5K6
416-622-6723/800-668-4723

M/A-Com MAC
5 Omni Way
Chelmsford, MA 01824
617-272-3100

Microlog Corporation
20270 Goldenrod Lane
Germantown, MD 20874
800-562-2822

MultiLink, Incorporated
One Market Street
Lynn, MA 01901
617-595-7577

Perception Technology Corporation
Shawmut Park
Canton, MA 02021-1409
617-821-0320

Periphonics Corporation
4000 Veterans Memorial Highway
Bohemia, NY 11716
516-467-0500

Phone Trader
516 SE Morrison, Suite 221
Portland, OR 97214
800-638-8838

Renegade C Software, Inc.
2464 El Camino Real, Suite 525
Santa Clara, CA 95051
408-727-7764

Shure Teleconferencing Systems
222 Hortney Avenue
Evanston, IL 60202
800-447-4873

Simpact Voice Products Group
1782 La Costa Meadows Drive
San Marcos, CA 92068
619-471-0342

SpeechSoft, Inc.
2575 Palisades Avenue
Riverside, NY 10463
212-549-0783

Stok Software, Inc.
92-30 56th Street
Elmhurst, NY 11373
718-699-9393

T1 Systems, Inc.
1658 Cole Boulevard
Golden, CO 80401
303-237-0440

Teladate
190 East 9th Avenue, Suite 600
Denver, CO 80203
303-744-1111

Telcom Design, Inc.
417 2nd Avenue West
Seattle, WA 98119-4012
206-282-0110

Teleconferencing Systems International
South Grove Village, IL
312-228-5444

Telecorp Systems, Inc.
1000 Holcomb Woods Parkway, Suite 410A
Roswell, GA 30076
404-587-0700/800-347-9907

Tellabs
Lisle, IL
312-969-8800

Telephone Response Technology, Inc.,
1624 Santa Clara Drive, Suite 200
Roseville, CA 95661
916-784-7777

Telephonic Equipment Corporation
17401 Armstrong Avenue
Irvine, CA 92714
714-250-9400/800-854-8269

Televation Telecommunication Systems, Inc.
2723 Curtiss Street
Downers Grove, IL 60515
312-852-9695

URIX Corporation
187 Gibraltor Road
Horsham, PA 19044
215-443-0600

U.S. Audiotex
415 Herondo, Suite 339
Hermosa Beach, CA 90259
213-318-8859

U.S. Telecom, Inc.
112 East 32nd Street, Suite D
Joplin, MO 64803
417-781-7000/800-835-7788

VICORP
54 Tremont Street
Boston, MA 02116
617-542-9233

Voicetek Corporation
19 Alpha Road
Chelmsford, MA 01824
508-250-9393

Votrax
2407 Research Drive
Farmington Hills, MI 48335
313-442-0900

# Appendix 4
## Passive Intercept Product Suppliers

Adtech
6725 Mesa Ridge Road, Suite 104
San Diego, CA 92121
619-455-5353/800-334-0836

ETC
3620 Clearview Parkway
Atlanta, GA 30340-2178
404-455-7972

Automation Electronics Corporation
11501 Dublin Boulevard
Dublin, CA 94568
415-828-2880/800-232-4653

ATIS, Ltd.
1225 Northmeadow Parkway, #114
Roswell, GA 30076
404-446-7234/800-688-4744

Code-A-Phone Corporation
16261 S.E. 130th
Clackamas, OR 97015
503-655-8940

Cognitronics Corporation
25 Crescent Street
Stamford, CT 06906
203-327-5307/800-243-2594

Com-Dev, Inc.
2006 Whitfield Industrial Way
Sarasota, FL 34243-9708
813-753-6411

Colonial Data Services Corp.
80 Pickett District Road
New Milford, CT 06776
203-355-3178

Northern Telecom
Cook Electric Division
6201 Oakton Street
Morton Grove, IL 60053
312-967-6600

Dacon
123 Pleasant Avenue
Upper Saddle River, NJ 07458
201-825-4640/800-322-8686

Digital Recorders, Inc.
P.O. Box 14068
Research Triangle Park, NC 27709-4068
919-361-2155

Eltrex
2 Columbia Street
Amherst, NH
603-886-3500/800-432-7631

Granite Telcom
669 East Industrial Park Drive
Manchester, NH 03103
603-424-3900/800-GRANTEL

Heliotrope General, Inc.
3733 Kenora Drive
Spring Valley, CA 92077
619-460-3930/800-552-8838

Interalia Communications, Inc.
6277 Bury Drive
Eden Prairie, MN 55346
612-934-7766

MacKenzie Laboratories, Inc.
5507 Peck Road
Arcadia, CA 91006
818-579-0440

Metro Tel
485-13 South Broadway
Hicksville, NY 11801
516-937-3420

Nel-Tech Labs, Inc.
P.O. Box 1030
Londonderry, NH 03053
603-434-8234

Prohold
55 Ridgeway Avenue, Suite A
Santa Rosa, CA 95401-4777
707-579-5150

Racom, Inc.
5504 State Road
Cleveland, OH 44134
216-351-1755/800-722-6664

Science Dynamics
1919 Springdale Rd.
Cherry Hill, NJ 08003
609-424-0068

Skutch Electronics, Inc.
209 Kenroy Lane #7
Roseville, CA 95678
916-786-6186/800-535-5315

Takacom Corporation of America
10722 Los Vaqueros Circle
Los Alamitos, CA 90720
714-761-3844/800-421-1858

Television Telecommunications Systems
2723 Curtiss Street
Downers Grove, IL 60515
312-852-9695

Viking Electronics, Inc.
1531 Industrial Street
Hudson, WI 54016
715-386-8861

# Appendix 5

# Outbound Call-Processing System Suppliers

Amcat
9601 Broadway Extension
Oklahoma City, OK 73114

Analysts International Corporation
600 Emerson Road, Suite 200
St. Louis, MO 63141
314-997-1746

ATM Systems, Inc.
1111 International Parkway, Suite 230
Richardson, TX 75081
214-669-2333

British Telecom, PLC
2-12 Gresham Street
London, U.K. EC 2V 7 AG
44 0 71 356 8219

Brock Control Systems, Inc.
2859 Paces Ferry Road, Suite 1000
Atlanta, GA 30339
404-431-1200/800-221-0775

Business Systems Resource, Inc.
1000 Winter Street
Waltham, MA 02154
617-890-2105

Call Management Products, Inc.
2150 West 6th Avenue, Unit N
Broomfield, CO 80020
303-465-0651

Communicator Asystance Systems
80 Everett Avenue
Chelsea, MA 02150
617-884-3510

Community Alert Network
301 Nott Street
Schenectady, NY 12305-1039
518-382-8007

Comtel Broadcasting Corporation
CBC Plaza
508 East Sixth Street
Sheridan, IN 46069
317-758-4415/800-248-5323

CRC Information Systems, Inc.
435 Hudson Street
New York, NY 10014
212-620-5678

Davox
4 Federal Street
Billerica, MA 01821
508-667-4455

Dial Tech International
211 West 2nd Street
East Greenville, PA 18041
215-679-0443/800-622-0443

DBD Telebroadcasting Inc.
163 Limestone Crescent
North York, Ontario M3J 2R1
416-665-7997

Dialogic Communications Corporation
1106 Harpeth Industrial Court
P.O. Box 8
Franklin, TN 37064
615-790-2882

Digital Products Corporation
4021 NE 5th Terrace

Fort Lauderdale, FL 33334
305-564-0521

Digital Systems International
7659 178th Place Northeast
P.O. Box 908
Redmond, WA 98052
206-881-7544

DRW
10025 Valley View Road, Suite 130
Eden Prairie, MN 55344
612-9433-1331

Early, Cloud & Company
2374 Post Road
Warwick, RI 02886
401-849-0500/800-322-3042

## Table A5.1
### Outbound Call Processing Suppliers

| Suppliers | ADRMP | TSR-based | Telephone ports | TSR stations |
|---|---|---|---|---|
| Amcat | | * | 36 | 12 |
| AT&T | | * | 192 | 64 |
| ATM Systems | | * | 64 | 16 |
| Audiocom, Inc. | * | | 1 | |
| British Telecom, PLC | | * | 200 | 100 |
| Brock Control Systems, Inc. | | * | 600 | 200 |
| Business Systems Resources, Inc. | | * | 100 | 50 |
| Call Management Products | | * | 120 | 120 |
| Communicator Asystance Systems | | * | 64 | 16 |
| Community Alert Network | * | | 32 | NA |
| Comtel Broadcasting | * | | 1 | NA |

## Table A5.1 (continued)

| Suppliers | ADRMP | TSR-based | Telephone ports | TSR stations |
|---|---|---|---|---|
| CRC Information Systems | | * | 120 | 80 |
| Database Systems Corporation | | * | 128 | 64 |
| Davox | | * | 128 | 64 |
| DFD Telebroadcasting, Inc. | * | * | 128 | 64 |
| Dialogic Communications Corp | * | * | 1 | NA |
| Dial Tech International | * | | 24 | NA |
| Digital Products Corporation | * | | 1 | NA |
| Digital Systems Corporation | | * | 64 | 24 |
| Digitran Telecommunications | * | | 32 | NA |
| DRW | | * | 128 | 40 |
| Early, Cloud & Company | | * | 1,500 | 700 |
| Electronic Information Systems | | * | 120 | 80 |
| Enator, Ltd. | | * | 200 | 100 |
| Granite Telecom | * | | 24 | NA |
| GWA Information Systems, Inc. | | * | 400 | 200 |
| Information Access Technology | | * | 32 | 64 |
| Information Management Associates | | * | 120 | 80 |
| International Telesystems | | * | 64 | 96 |
| InterVoice, Inc. | | * | 24 | 72 |

**Table A5.1 (continued)**

| Suppliers | ADRMP | TSR-based | Telephone Ports | TSR Stations |
|---|---|---|---|---|
| IT Research, Inc. | | * | 22 | 22 |
| Melita International | * | * | 48 | 96 |
| Micro Delta | * | | 1 | NA |
| Microlog Corporation | * | | 24 | NA |
| MPSI | * | | 24 | NA |
| Natural Microsystems | * | | 8 | NA |
| Noble Systems Corporation | | * | 32 | 8 |
| NPRI | | * | 1,000 | 800 |
| Rockwell International | | * | 256 | 96 |
| Stok Software, Inc. | * | | 32 | NA |
| Teknekron Infoswitch | | * | 72 | 126 |
| Telecorp Systems | * | | 1 | NA |
| TeleDirect International, Inc. | | * | 24 | 8 |
| Telesystems-Source | | * | 48 | 24 |
| TKM | | * | 48 | 16 |
| Trans World Telephone Corp. | | * | 48 | 16 |
| U.S. Telecom | * | | 1 | NA |
| Voad | * | | 1 | NA |
| Voice Plus, Inc. | * | | 24 | NA |
| VSSI | * | | 24 | NA |
| Wygant Scientific | * | | 24 | NA |

Electronic Information Systems, Inc.
1351 Washington Boulevard
Stamford, CT 06902
203-351-4800/800-765-4347

Enator, Ltd.
Boston House, The Little Green
Richmond Surrey, TW9 1Q2
44 81 948 6000

GWA Information Systems, Inc.
1432 Main Street
Waltham, MA 02154
617-890-1838

Information Access Technology, Inc.
1100 East 6600 South, Suite 300
Salt Lake City, UT 84121
801-265-8800

Information Management Associates
6527 Main Street
Trumbull, CT 06611
203-261-4777

International Telesystems Corporation
600 Herndon Parkway
Herndon, VA 22070
703-478-9808/800-999-1482

InterVoice, Inc.
17811 Waterview Parkway
Dallas, TX 75252
214-669-3988

IT Research
3717 West 50th Street
Minneapolis, MN 55410
800-657-0110

MAMS (Manufacturing Administration &
    Management Systems, Inc.)
P.O. Box 978
Glenwood Landing, NY 11547
518-671-8336

Melita International
6611 Bay Circle 220
Norcross, GA 30071
404-446-7800/800-342-5635

Mer Communication Systems, Inc.
350 Fifth Avenue, Suite 1910
New York, NY
212-594-7871/800-933-TABS

Micro Delta Corporation
318 South West 32nd Avenue
Deerfield Beach, FL 33442
305-429-8785

Microlog Corporation
20270 Goldenrod Lane
Germantown, MD 20874
800-562-2822

Missing Link Computer Systems
52 Forest Avenue
Paramus, NJ 07652-5214
201-845-0303

Messaging Processing Systems, Inc.
834 Tyvola Road, Suite 112
Charlotte, NC 28217
704-527-8888

Natural Microsystems Corporation
8 Erie Drive
Natick, MA 01760
617-655-0700

Noble Systems Corporation
3297 Northcrest Road, Suite 200
Atlanta, GA 30340
404-851-1331

NPRI
602 Cameron Street
Alexandria, VA 22314
703-683-9090/800-526-1984

Rockwell International
1431 Opus Place
Downers Grove, IL 60515
800-722-5959

Sigma Software
10801 Bismarck Avenue
Northridge, CA 91326
818-368-6132

Stok Software, Inc.
92-30 56th Street
Elmhurst, NY 11373
718-699-9393

Teknekron Infoswitch Corporation
4401 Cambridge Road
Fort Worth, TX 76155
817-354-0661

Telecorp Systems, Inc.
1000 Holcomb Woods Parkway, Suite 410A
Roswell, GA 30076
404-587-0700/800-347-9907

TeleDirect International, Inc.
736 Federal Street
Davenport, IA 52803
319-324-7720/800-747-5562

Telesystems Marketing, Inc.
11320 Random Hills Road, Suite 200
Fairfax, VA 22030
703-385-1212

TKM
90 Tiverton Court
Markham, Ontario L3R 9V2
416-491-3575

TWT International
2550 Medina Road
Medina, OH 44256
216-722-5500/800-331-8484

U.S. Telecom, Inc.
112 East 32nd Street, Suite D,
Joplin, MO 64803
417-781-7000

Voad Systems
19004 74th Avenue West
Marysville, WA 98036
206-672-0393

Voice Plus, Inc.
39899 Balentine Drive, Suite 375
Newark, CA 94560
415-490-6000

Voice Systems and Services, Inc.
One Technology Center
Mannford, OK 74044
918-865-1000

Wygant Scientific, Inc.
921 SW Morrison, 547 Galleria Bldg.
Portland, OR 97205
503-227-6901/800-NUVOICE

# Appendix 6
## Operator Service Providers

## OSP Suppliers

Advantage Operator Services, Inc.
609 West 9th Street
Austin, TX 78701
800-777-6577

American Central
1114 Lost Creek Boulevard, Suite 210
Austin, TX 78746
512-328-8500

American Network Exchange, Inc.
5295 Town Center Road
Boca Raton, FL 33432
407-394-9780

American Public Communictions, Inc.
3200 Broadway, Suite 360
Texas Commerce Bank Building
Garland, TX 75043
214-278-9464

American Telecommunications Corp.
1001 South Sherman Street
Richardson, TX 75081
214-690-9200

Automated Communications, Inc.
9100 East Mississippi Avenue

Suite 1300
Denver, CO 80222
303-756-4333

Call Technology
100 Stevens Drive
Lester, PA 19113
215-595-1100

Central Corporation
2810 E. Oakland Park Blvd. Suite 204
Fort Lauderdale, FL 33306
305-563-4116

Com Systems, Inc.
15716 Stag Street
Van Nuys, CA 91409
818-988-3010

Intellicall Operator Services
12790 Merit Drive, Suite 624, Box 124
Dallas, TX 75251
214-701-0000

International Telecharge
108 South Akard
Dallas, TX 75202
214-748-2723

National Data Corporation
National Data Plaza
Atlanta, GA 30329-2010
404-728-2000

National Telephone Services
6100 Executive Boulevard, 4th Floor
Rockville, MD 20852
301-468-0307

NY Com, Inc.
60 Hudson Street, Suite M-16
New York, NY 10013
212-619-1717

Operator Assisted Systems, Inc.
14800 Quorum, Suite 180
Dallas, TX 75240
214-239-6274

Operator Service Company
1220 Broadway, Suite 1700
Lubbock, TX 79401

Operator Services America
34700 Pacific Coast Highway

Capistrano Beach, CA 92624
714-248-0401

Payline Systems, Inc.
921 S.W. Washington, Suite 250
Portland, OR 97205
503-243-2930

PhoneTel Technologies, Inc.
3843 Saint Clair
Cleveland, OH 44114
216-241-2555

Tel Com International, Inc.
162 North Franklin Street
Chicago, IL 60606
312-807-4400

TelEquip Labs
1501 LBJ Freeway, Suite 150
Dallas, TX 75234
214-620-3139

Tel Fiber Net
810 Greenbriar Circle, Suite 500
Chesapeake, VA 23320
804-353-7573

## Table A6.1
### Operator Service Providers

| OSP Company Name | Regional OSP | Nationwide OSP |
|---|:---:|:---:|
| ACC Long Distance Corporation | * | |
| Advantage Operator Services | * | |
| Americall Business Systems | * | |
| American Central | | * |
| American Network Exchange | * | |
| American Public Communications | | * |
| American Telecommunications | | * |
| American Telenet Systems | | * |
| AT&T | | * |
| ATC | * | |

## Table A6.1 (continued)

| OSP Company Name | Regional OSP | Nationwide OSP |
|---|:---:|:---:|
| Automated Communications, Inc. | * | |
| Call Technology Corporation | * | |
| Capital Network System, Inc. | * | |
| Central Corporation | | * |
| Charter Network | * | |
| ClayDesta Communication | * | |
| ClearTel | * | |
| Coastal Automated Communications | | * |
| Com Systems, Inc. | * | |
| Conquest Telecommunication Services | * | |
| Elcotel | * | |
| First Phone of New England | * | |
| Global Access Communications | * | |
| Hobic Plus | * | |
| Intellicall Operator Services | * | |
| International Pacific, Inc. | * | |
| International Telecharge | * | |
| LiTel Telecommunications | * | |
| Long Distance Savers, Inc. | * | |
| Long Distance Service, Inc. | * | |
| Long Distance USA | | * |
| LTS, Inc. | * | |
| MCI Communications | | * |
| Metromedia/ITT Long Distance | * | |
| Mid-Atlantic Telecom, Inc. | * | |
| National Communication Network | | * |
| National Data Corp. | | * |
| National Telephone Services | | * |
| NYCOM Info. Systems | | * |
| Operator Assisted Systems | * | |
| Operator Service Company | * | |
| Operator Services America | * | |
| Opticom | * | |

**Table A6.1 (continued)**

| OSP Company Name | Regional OSP | Nationwide OSP |
|---|:---:|:---:|
| Payline Systems, Inc. | * | |
| PhoneTel Technologies, Inc. | * | |
| Resurgens Communications Group | | * |
| TelCom International | | * |
| Teledial America | * | |
| TelEquip Labs | | * |
| Tele-Fibernet | * | |
| Telephone Solutions | * | |
| Tel-Share U.S., Inc. | * | |
| Tel-Star Operator Service | * | |
| Total Access Communications | * | |
| Transtel Communications, Inc. | * | |
| United Communications, Inc. | | * |
| United Telephone | * | |
| US Fiberline Communications | | * |
| US Link Long Distance | * | |
| US Long Distance | | * |
| US Operators | | * |
| US Sprint Communications | | * |
| VYVX Telecom, Inc. | | * |

Telesphere International, Inc.
2 Mid-America Plaza, Suite 500
Oakbrook, IL 60181
312-954-7700

Tel-Star Operator Services
901 Avenue C
West Point, GA 31833
404-643-9923/800-367-5104

Total Access Communication
1170 Burnett #S
Concord, CA 94520
415-788-1660

United Communications, Inc.
50 West Broad Street

Suite 3700
Columbus, OH 43215
614-221-0033

U.S. Fiberline Communications, Inc.
6745 Convoy Court
San Diego, CA 92111
619-268-0700/800-748-6888

US Long Distance
1022 Wirt Road, Suite 312
Houston, TX 77055
713-688-5600

Zero Plus, Inc.
4742 Madison Ave.
Sacramento, CA 95841
916-334-9600

**Table A6.2**
OSP support companies

| Organization | OSP support companies | | | | |
| --- | --- | --- | --- | --- | --- |
| | Billing clearing house | Validation service | Equipment vendor | Call rating | IXC |
| ABC | | | * | | * |
| Allnet | | | | | * |
| AT&T | | | | | * |
| ATC Long Distance | | | | | * |
| Cable & Wireless Communications | | | | | |
| Card*Tel | | * | | * | |
| CCMI/McGraw-Hill | | | * | | |
| CTI Corporation | | | * | | |
| Digital Switch Corporation | | | * | | |
| Digital Services | | | * | | |
| Harris Corporation | | | | | |
| J.C. Penney | | * | | | |
| MCI Communications | | | | | * |

## Table A6.2 (continued)

| Company | | | | | |
|---|:--:|:--:|:--:|:--:|:--:|
| Metromedia | * | | | | |
| Micro Dimensions | | | | | |
| Mitel Datacom | | | * | | |
| NACT | | | * | | |
| Northern Telecom | | | * | | |
| National Data Corporation | | | * | | |
| Near Space Communications | | | | * | * |
| OLBS, Inc. | | | * | | |
| Operator Assistance Network | | | | | * |
| Pentagon Computer Data | | | | | * |
| Rockwell | | | | | |
| SoutherNet | | | | | |
| SwitchLink Systems Corporation | * | | | | |
| Summa Four | | | * | | |
| Stromberg-Carlson | | | * | | |
| Tele-tech Services | | | * | | |
| Teltronics | | * | | | |
| Telus Communications | | | * | | |
| U.S. Fiberline Communications | * | | | | |
| U.S.Sprint Communications | * | | | | |
| U.S. West Service Link | * | | | | |
| Williams Telecommunications | | | | * | * |
| Zero Plus Dialing, Inc. | * | | | | |

**Table A6.3**
OSP Equipment Suppliers

| Supplier | Switch | OSP automation | Switch and OSP automation |
|---|---|---|---|
| ABC | * | | * |
| CTI Corporation | | * | |
| Digital Services | * | | * |
| DSC Corporation | * | | * |
| Harris | * | | * |
| Micro Dimensions | | * | |
| Mitel Datacom | * | | |
| National Applied Computer Technologies | * | | |
| Near Space Communications | * | | * |
| Northern Telecom | * | | * |
| SwitchLink Systems Corporation | | * | |
| Summa Four | * | | |
| Stromberg-Carlson | * | | * |
| Teltronics | | * | |

## OSP Switch Providers

Advanced Business Communications, Inc.
4401 Beltway Parkway South
Dallas, TX 75244
214-386-3500

Digital Services
3261 South Highland Drive, Suite 605
Las Vegas, NV 89109
703-735-9211/800-635-2276

DSC Communications Corporation
1000 Coit Road
Plano, TX 75075
214-519-3000

Harris Corporation
One Digital Drive
P.O. Box 1188
Novato, CA 94948
415-472-2500

National Applied Computer Technologies
744 South 400 East
P.O. Box 1870
Orem, UT 84057
801-225-6248

Near Space Communications
730 Avenue F
Plano, TX 75074
214-423-3904

Rockwell International
P.O. Box 568842
Dallas, TX 75356-8842
214-996-6547

Stromberg-Carlson
400 Rinehart Road
Lake Mary, FL 32746
407-333-5000

## OSP Subsystem Providers

CCMI/McGraw-Hill
McGraw-Hill Information Services Company
Computer & Communications Information
    Group
500 North Franklin Turnpike
Ramsey, NJ 07446

CTI Corporation
601 North Glenville, Suite 165
Richardson, TX 75081
214-480-8110

EASI, Inc.
5965 Peachtree Corners East, Bldg. C
Norcross, GA 30071
404-447-6340

Mitel Datacom
13873 Park Center Road, Suite 553

Herndon, VA 22071
703-471-1000

MicroDimensions, Inc.
7345 Production Drive
Mentor, OH 44060-4858
216-974-8070

SwitchLink Systems Corp.
10300 Southwest Greenburg Road
Suite 480
Portland, OR 97223
503-245-2400

Teltronics
5105 New Tampa Highway
Lakeland, FL 33801
813-688-6831

## IXCs

Allnet
30300 Telegraph Road
Birmingham, MI 48010
800-631-4000

ATC Long Distance
Atlanta, GA
404-688-2475/800-456-2648

Cable & Wireless Communications, Inc.
1919 Gallows Road
Vienna, VA 22182
703-790-5300

MCI
11330 19th Street N.W., Suite 800
Washington, D.C. 20036
800-888-0800

Metromedia
1 Harmon Place
Secaucus, NJ
201-348-3244/212-606-4300

SoutherNet
Suite 200, 61 Perimeter Park, NE

Atlanta, GA 30341-1342
404-458-4927

Telus Communications
Miami, FL
305-624-2400

Telecom*USA
Atlanta, GA
800-868-2600

U.S. Sprint
840 Wirt Road, Suite 312
Kansas City, MO 64114
816-276-6000/800-877-6546

U.S. Fiberline Communications, Inc.
6745 Convoy Court
San Diego, CA 92111
619-268-0700/800-748-6888

Williams Telecommunications Group
P.O. Box 21348
Tulsa, OK 74121
800-642-2299

## Validation Services Suppliers

Card*Tel
1500 N.W. 49th Street
Suite 600
Fort Lauderdale, FL 33309
305-491-7800/800-759-CARD

National Data Corporation
National Data Plaza
Atlanta, GA 30329-2010
404-728-2000

## Billing Services

Card*Tel
1500 N.W. 49th Street
Suite 600
Fort Lauderdale, FL 33309
305-491-7800/800-759-CARD

National Data Corporation
National Data Plaza
Atlanta, GA 30329-2010
404-728-2000

On-Line Business Systems, Inc.
115 Sansome St.
San Francisco, CA 94211
415-391-9555

Operator Assistance Network
6611 Valjean Avenue
Van Nuys, CA 91406
213-414-0009

Operator Services Providers Association
6611 Valjean Avenue
Suite 201
Van Nuys, CA 91406
818 786-6772

Pentagon Computer Data, Ltd.
6033 West Martin
Oak Park, IL 60302
312-780-7109

Zero Plus Dialing, Inc.
9311 San Pedro, Suite 300
San Antonio, TX 78216
800-456-8371

# Appendix 7

## Suppliers of Subsystems and Tools

ACS Communications, Inc.
250 Technology Circle
Scotts Valley, CA 95066-3575
800-538-0742

Advanced Compression Technology, Inc.
31368 Via Colinas, Suite 104
Westlake Village, CA 91362
818-889-3618

Advanced Products & Technologies
15444 N.E. 95th Street
Redmond, WA 98052
206-883-8297

Aerotel, Ltd.
5 Hazoref Street
Holon, Israel
972-3-559-3222

Antex Electronics
16100 South Figueroa Street
Gardena, CA 90248
213-532-3092

Audiosears Corporation
2 South Street
Stamford, NY 12167
607-652-7305

Bicom
2387 Black Rock Turnpike
Fairfield, CT 06430
203-374-0211

Cascade Technologies, Inc.
1001 Sixth Avenue
New York, NY 10018
212-768-7380

Chelsea Software, Inc.
P.O. Box 369
Chelsea, OK 74016
918-789-3185/800-842-6485

Covox, Inc.
675-D Conger Street
Eugene, OR 97402
503-342-1271

CDP Systems
2005 Pan Am Circle, Suite 800
Tampa, FL 33607
800-275-2371

DataVoice Corporation
1853 McCraren Road
Highland Park, IL 60035
312-831-4488

Dialogic Corporation
129 Littleton Road
Parsippany, NJ 07054
201-334-8450

DigiDesign
1360 Willow Road, Suite 101
Menlo Park, CA 94025
415-327-8811

Digital Equipment Corporation
146 Main Street

Maynard, MA 01754
508-467-6560

DigiVox Corporation
991 Commercial Street
Palo Alto, CA 94303
415-494-6200/800-DIGIVOX

Emerson & Stern Associates, Inc.
10150 Sorrento Valley Road, Suite 210
San Diego, CA 92121
619-457-2526

## Table A7.1
Suppliers of system components and development tools

| Supplier | Voice processing boards | AGTKs | High quality speech boards | Speech Transmission | Headset microphones | Wireless (radio) systems |
|---|---|---|---|---|---|---|
| ACS | | | | | * | |
| ACT, Inc. | | | * | | | |
| Aerotel, Ltd | * | | | | | |
| Antex Electronics | | | * | | | |
| Apex Voice Communications | | * | | | | |
| Audiosears | | | | | * | |
| Bicom | * | | | | | |
| Cascade Technologies, Inc. | | * | | | | |
| C-AT | | | | | | * |
| CDP Systems | | * | | | | |
| Chelsea Software | | * | | | | |
| Covox | | | * | | | |
| DataVoice | | | * | | | |
| Dialogic Corporation | * | | | | | |
| DigiDesign | | | * | | | |
| DEC | | * | | | | |
| DigiVox Corporation | | * | | | | |
| Expert Systems | | * | | | | |
| Excel, Inc. | * | | | | | |
| Farallon Computing | | | * | | | |

## Table A7.1 (continued)

| Supplier | Voice processing boards | AGTKs | High quality speech boards | Speech Trans- mission | Headset micro- phones | Wireless (radio) systems |
|---|---|---|---|---|---|---|
| GN NetCom | | | | | * | |
| IBM | | * | | | | |
| Innovative Technology, Inc. | * | | | | | |
| ISD | * | | | | | |
| Linkon Corporation | | * | | | | |
| Natural Microsystems | * | | | | | |
| NewVoice | * | | | | | |
| Nicollet Technology | * | | | | | |
| Northeast Innovations | * | | | | | |
| Magnum Software | | * | | | | |
| Parity Software Development | | * | | | | |
| Pika Technologies, Inc. | * | * | | | | |
| Plantronics | | | | | | |
| Promptus Communications | * | | | | | |
| Republic Telcom | | | | * | | |
| Rhetorex | * | | | | | |
| Shure Brothers | | | | | * | |
| SpeechSoft | | * | | | | |
| Stok Software | | * | | | | |
| Street Electronics | * | | | | | * |
| Swintek | | | | | | |
| Talking Technology | * | | | | | |
| Texas Instruments | * | * | | | | |
| Time & Space Processing | | | | * | | |
| TRT | | * | | | | |
| UNIDATA | | | | * | | |
| UniVoice Products, Inc. | * | | | | | |
| U.S. Telecom | | * | | | | |
| Voice Learning Systems | | * | | | | |
| Voicetek Corporation | | * | | | | |
| Voice Information Systems | | * | | | | |
| Voice Systems Technology, | | * | | | | |
| Voysys Corporation | * | | | | | |
| Wespercorp | * | | | | | |

Expert Systems, Inc.
1010 Huntcliff, Suite 2235
Atlanta, GA 30350
404-642-7575

Excel, Inc.
P.O. Box 327
355 Old Plymouth Road
Sagamore Beach, MA 02562
508-833-1144

Farallon Computing, Inc.
2150 Kittredge
Berkeley, CA 94704
415-849-2331

GN Netcom
6400 Flying Cloud Drive
Minneapolis, MN 55344
800-826-4656

IBM Entry Systems Division
11400 Burnett Road
Austin, TX 78758
512-823-2252

Innovative Technology, Inc.
P.O. Box 767370, Suite 422
1000 Holcomb Woods Parkway
Roswell, GA 30076
404-998-9970

Linkon Corporation
12226 East 54th Street
New York, NY 10022
212-753-2544

Magnum Software
21115 Devonshire Street, Suite 337
Chatsworth, CA 91311
818-700-0510

Natural Microsystems Corporation
8 Erie Drive
Natick, MA 01760
617-655-0700/800-533-6120

NewVoice
8500 Leesburg Pike, #409
Vienna, VA 22182-2409
703-448-0570

Nicollet Technologies, Inc.
11437 Valley View Road
Eden Prairie, MN 55344
612-942-9200/800-942-8722

Northeast Innovations
P.O. Box 120
Concord, NH 03302
603-736-8260

Open + Voice, Inc.
13771 N. Central Expressway, Suite 832
Dallas, TX 75243-1017
214-497-9024

Parity Software Development Corporation
1721 Chestnut Street, Suite 303
San Francisco, CA 94123
415-931-8221

Pelton Systems, Inc.
1171 Monticello Road
Lafayette, CA 94549
415-283-0232

Pika Technologies, Inc.
155 Terrence Matthews
Kanata, Ontario K2M 2A8
613-591-1555

Plantronics
345 Encinal Street
Santa Cruz, CA 95060
800-544-4660

Promptus Communications, Inc.
207 High Point Avenue
Portsmouth Business Park
Portsmouth, RI 02871
401-683-6100/800-777-5267

Republic Telcom Systems Corporation
6150 Lookout Road
Boulder, CO 80301
303-530-8600

Rhetorex, Inc.
1671 Dell Avenue # 208
Campbell, CA 95008
408-370-0881

Speech Soft
32 Manners Road
Ringoes, NJ 08551
609-466-1100

Stok Software, Inc.
93-30 56th Avenue
Elmhurst, NY 11373
718-699-9393

Street Electronics
1140 Mark Avenue
Carpinteria, CA 93013
805-684-4593

Talking Technology, Inc.
1125 Atlantic Ave.,
Alameda, CA 94501
510-522-3800/800-568-4884

Targa Systems Corporation
Cityplace
Hartford, CT 06103
203-275-6585

Telephone Response Technology, Inc.
1624 Santa Clara Drive, Suite 200
Roseville, CA 95661
916-442-1878

Texas Instruments
P.O. Box 2909 MSs 2081
Austin, TX 78769
512-250-6005

Time and Space Processing, Inc.
3410 Central Expressway
Santa Clara, CA 95051
408-730-0200

Unidata Corporation
610 Winters Avenue
Paramus, NJ 07652
201-262-8833

UniVoice Products, Inc.
1377 Main Street
Waltham, MA 02154-9521
617-736-0030

Urex
27 Industrial Avenue
Chelmsford, MA 01824
508-692-9505

U.S. Telecom, Inc.
211 Main Street, Suite 401
Joplin, MO 64802
417-781-7000

Voice Information Systems, Inc.
24 North Merion Avenue #353
Bryn Mawr, PA 19010
215-747-5035/800-234-VISI

VoiceSmart
The Grant Center
2160 North Central, 2nd Floor
Fort Lee, NJ 07026

Voice Systems Technology, Inc.
1320 Hamilton Street, Suite 202
Somerset, NJ 08873
800-866-0355

Voysys Corporation
680 West Maude Avenue
Sunnyvale, CA 94086
408-737-2300

Wespercorp
1821 East Dyer Road
Santa Anna, CA 92505
714-261-0606

Zaisan, Inc.
31069 Genstar Road
Hayward, CA 94545
800-221-7060

## Industrial-PC Product Suppliers

American Advantech Corporation
1460 Tully Road, Suite 602
San Jose, CA 95122
408-293-6797

Burr-Brown
1141 W. Grant Road, MS 131
Tucson, AZ 85705
602-746-1111

DAC Systems
375 Coram Avenue
Shelton, CT 06484
203-924-7000

Daisy Data, Inc.
333 South Enola Drive
Enola, PA 17025
717-732-8800

Diversified Technology
112 East State Street
Ridgefield, MS 39158
601-856-4121/800-443-2667

I-Bus, Inc.
9596 Chesapeake Dr.
San Diego, CA 92123
619-569-0646/800-382-4229

IBM Corporation
Manufacturing Systems Products
Box 1328-4327
Boca Raton, FL 33432
800-526-6602

Industrial Computer Source
4837 Mercury Street
San Diego, CA 92111
619-279-0084

Intecolor Corporation
2150 Boggs Road
Duluth, GA 30136
404-623-9145

Integration Technology Systems
350 Hochberg Road
Monroeville, PA 15146
412-327-7137

Lynx Real-time Systems, Inc.
550 Division Street
Campbell, CA 95008
408-370-2233

PCQT North America, Inc.
12930 Saratoga Avenue, Suite B7
Saratoga, CA 95070
408-255-1131

Pro-Log Corporation
2560 Garden Road
Monterey, CA 93940
408-372-4573/800-538-9570

Qualogy Corporation
1751 McCarthy Boulevard
Milpitas, CA 95035
408-434-5302

RAAC Technologies, Inc.
219 North Milwaukee Street
Milwaukee, WI 53202
414-277-1889

Radix Microsystems, Inc.
19545 N.W. Von Neuman Drive
Beaverton, OR 97006
503-690-1229

Systems Manufacturing Technology, Inc.
1080 Linda Vista Drive
San Marcos, CA 92069
619-744-3590

Texas Microsystems, Inc.
10618 Rockley Road
Houston, TX 77099
713-933-8050/800-627-8700

Xycom, Inc.
750 North Maple Road
Saline, MI 48176
313-429-4971/800-367-7300

Ziatech Corporation
3433 Roberto Court
San Luis Obispo, CA 93401
805-541-0488/800-541-5088

## Product Development Tools

These suppliers provide basic components and tools for the development of voice processing components. Table A7.3 lists and categorizes them.

## Table A7.2
### Suppliers of Voice Processing Product Development Tools

| Supplier | Speech compression algorithms | DSP development systems | Speech signal analysis |
|---|:---:|:---:|:---:|
| Ariel Corporation | | * | * |
| Atlanta Signal Processors, Inc. | * | | |
| AT&T | | * | |
| Ceredata Research | | | * |
| Communications, Automation & Control | | * | * |
| Dalanco Spry | | | * |
| DigiDesign | | | * |
| DSP Design Tools | | * | * |
| Electronic Speech Systems, Inc. | | * | |
| Entropic Processing | | | * |
| Extrema Systems International Corporation | * | | |
| GW Instruments | | | * |
| Hecht-Neilsen Neurocomputers | * | | |
| Hyperception, Inc. | | * | * |
| Kay Elemetrics | | | * |
| Micro Technology Unlimited | | | * |
| NEC Corporation | | * | |
| Sonitech | | * | * |
| Spectral Innovations | | * | |
| Spectrum Signal Processing, Inc. | | * | * |
| Texas Instruments | | * | |
| The DSP Group | | | * |
| Voicecraft, Inc. | * | | |

Ariel Corporation
433 River Road
Highland Park, NJ 08904
201-249-2900

Atlanta Signal Processors, Inc.
770 Spring Street
Atlanta, GA 30308
404-892-7265

CereData Research
2058 Felix #1

Memphis, TN 38104
901-274-8354

Communications, Automation, and Control
1642 Union Boulevard, Suite O
Allentown, PA 18103
215-776-6669

Dalanco Spry
2900 Connecticut Street, Suite 241
Washington, D.C.
202-232-7999

DSP Design Tools
4101 Green Pond Road
Bethlehem, PA 18017
215-691-0693

Electronic Speech Systems, Inc.
3216 Scott Boulevard
Santa Clara, CA 95054
415-644-8120

Entropic Processing, Inc
10011 North Foothill Boulevard
Cupertino, CA 95014

Extrema Systems International Corporation
10805 Parkridge Boulevard
Reston, VA 22091
703-648-3181

GW Instruments, Inc.
P.O. Box 2145
Cambridge, MA 02141
617-625-4096

Hecht-Neilsen Neurocomputers
5501 Oberlin Drive
San Diego, CA 92121-1718
619-546-8877

Hyperception, Inc.
9550 Skillman
LB125
Dallas, TX 75243

Kay Elemetrics Corp.
12 Maple Avenue
Pine Brook, NJ 07058

Micro Technology Unlimited
156 Wind Chime Court
Raleigh, NC 27615
919-870-0344

NEC Corporation
532 Broad Hollow Road
Melville, NY 11747
516-752-9700

Sonitech International, Inc.
83 Fullerbrook Road
Wellesley, MA 02181
617-235-6824

Spectral Innovations
4633 Old Ironsides Drive
Santa Clara, CA 95054
408-727-1314

Spectrum Signal Processing, Inc.
Suite 301, Discovery Park
3700 Gilmore Way,
Burnaby, B.C. V5G4M1
604-438-7266

The DSP Group
1900 Powell Street
Emeryville, CA 94608
415-655-7311

Voicecraft, Inc.
815 Volante Place
Goleta, CA 93117
805-683-2800

# Appendix 8

## Facsimile Response and Distribution Product Suppliers

3X USA Corporation
One Executive Drive
Fort Lee, NJ 07024
201-592-6874/800-327-9712

Abaton Technology
4831 Milmont Drive
Fremont, CA 94538
415-683-2226

ABS Systems, Inc.
2500 Shames Drive
Westbury, NY 11590
516-333-7900/800-825-5944-DEMO

Accelerated Voice, Inc.
28 Stillman, Suite 200
San Francisco, CA 94107
415-774-0789/800-779-0027

Accu-Weather, Inc.
619 West College Avenue
State College, PA 16801
814-234-9601

ACI Telecom
330 South 108th Avenue
Omaha, NE 68154
402-390-7600

Add*On America
433 N. Mathilda Avenue
Sunnyvale, CA 94086-4222
408-746-1590/800-292-7771

Adtech Micro Systems, Inc.
43120 Christy Street
Fremont, CA 94538
415-659-0756

Advanced Microcomputer Systems
1321 Northwest 65th Place
Fort Lauderdale, FL 33309
305-975-9515

Advantage Systems Corporation
5 Choke Cherry Road
Rockville, MD 20850
301-840-2900

Alacrity Systems, Inc.
43 Newburg Road
Hackettstown, NJ 07840
908-813-2400

Alcom, Inc.
2464 Embarcadero Way
Palo Alto, CA 94303
415-493-3800

All The FAX
917 Northern Boulevard
Great Neck, NY 11021
516-829-0556

American Communications & Engineering,
Inc.
30961 West Agoura Road
Westlake Village, CA 91361
818-706-0161

American Data Technology, Inc.
44 West Bellevue Drive, # 6

Pasadena, CA 91105
818-578-1339

Alternative Technology Corporation
P.O. Box 357
Hasting-on-Hudson, NY 10706-0357
914-478-5904

Applied Voice Technologies, Inc.
11410 N.E. 112nd Way
P.O. Box 97025
Kirkland, WA 98083
206-641-1760/800-443-0806

**Table A8.1**

Facsimile Processing Product Supplier Categorization

| Supplier | Fax modem | Fax server | Fax message system | Fax response system | Facsimile service bureau | |
|---|---|---|---|---|---|---|
| | | | | | Messaging | Response |
| 3X USA Corporation | * | | | | | |
| ABS Systems | | | | * | | |
| Abaton | * | | | | | |
| Accelerated Voice | | | | * | | * |
| ACI Telecom | | | * | | | |
| Accu-Weather | | | | | | * |
| Advanced Micro Systems | * | | | | | |
| Advantage Systems | | | | | | * |
| Alacrity Systems, Inc. | | * | | | | |
| Alcom | | * | | | | |
| All The Fax | | * | | | | |
| American Data Technology | | | | | | |

**Table A8.1 (continued)**

| Supplier | Fax modem | Fax server | Fax message system | Fax response system | Facsimile service bureau | |
|----------|-----------|------------|--------------------|---------------------|--------------------------|--------|
| | | | | | Messaging | Response |
| Apple Computer | * | | | | | |
| Applied Voice Technology | | | * | * | | |
| AST Research, Inc. | * | | | | | |
| AT&S | | | | * | | |
| AT&T | * | | * | | * | |
| ATC | | | | * | | |
| Audiofax | | | * | * | | |
| Bell South IS | | * | | | | |
| Biscom | * | * | * | | | |
| Black Box Corporation | * | | | | | |
| Brite Voice Systems | | | | * | | |
| Brooktrout Technology | * | | | * | | |
| Brother International Corp. | * | | | | | |
| Cable & Wireless | | | | | * | |

AT&S, Inc.
2381 Dutch Fork Road
Chapin, SC 29036
803-732-7520

AT&T Enhanced FAX
5000 Hadley Road, Room 10B13
South Plainfield, NJ 07080
800-624-5672

AudioFax
2000 Powers Ferry Road, Suite 220
Marietta, GA 30067
404-933-7600/800-444-7961

Bell South Information Systems, Inc.
1967 Lakeside Parkway, Suite 412
Tucker, GA 30084
404-621-3117/800-621-4736

**Table A8.1 (continued)**

| Supplier | Fax modem | Fax server | Fax message system | Fax response system | Facsimile service bureau | |
|---|---|---|---|---|---|---|
| | | | | | Messaging | Response |
| Calculus, Inc. | * | * | | | | |
| Castelle | | * | | | | |
| Cardiff Software, Inc. | | * | | | | |
| Cardinal Technologies | * | | | | | |
| CC:Mail, Inc. | | * | | | | |
| Centigram Communications | | | * | * | | |
| Chinon America | * | | | | | |
| Choice Technology Group | * | | | | | |
| Circuit Research Corp | * | * | | | | |
| Cobotyx Corporation | | | | * | | |
| Compass Technology | | | | * | | |
| Complete PC, The | * | | | | | |
| CompLink, Ltd. | | * | | | | |

Best Data Products, Inc.
9304 Deering Avenue
Chatsworth, CA 91311
818-773-9600/800-632-2378

Biscom
85 Rangeway Road
Billerica, MA 01821
508-670-5521

Black Box Corporation
P.O. Box 12800

Pittsburgh, PA 15241-0800
412-746-5565

Brite Voice Systems, Inc.
7309 East 21st North
Wichita, KS 67206-1080
316-652-6500

Brooktrout Technology, Inc.
144 Gould Street
Needham, MA 02192
617-449-4100

## Table A8.1 (continued)

| Supplier | Fax modem | Fax server | Fax message system | Fax response system | Facsimile service bureau | |
|----------|-----------|------------|--------------------|--------------------|-------|--------|
| | | | | | Messaging | Response |
| Computer Friends, Inc. | * | | | | | |
| Computer Automation, Inc. | * | * | | | | |
| Computer Peripherals, Inc. | * | | | | | |
| Computer System Integration | | | | * | | |
| Computers Unlimited | | * | | | | |
| ComSEL | | | | | | * |
| Comverse Technology, Inc. | | | * | | | |
| Connex Systems | | * | | | | |
| Consumers Software | | * | | | | |
| Copia International | | | | * | | |
| COS, Inc. | | * | | | | |
| Cracchiolo & Feder, Inc. | | * | | | | |

Cable & Wireless
1919 Gallows Road
Vienna, VA 22182
800-969-9998

Calculus, Inc.
522 Mercury Drive
Sunnyvale, CA 94086-4018
408-395-5899

Cardinal Technologies, Inc.
1827 Freedom Road

Lancaster, PA 17601
717-293-3000/800-722-0094

Castelle
3255-3 Scott Boulevard
Santa Barbara, CA 95054
408-496-0474/800-359-7654

Centigram Communications Corporation
91 East Tasman Drive at North First Street
San Jose, CA 95134
408-942-3500

**Table A8.1 (continued)**

| Supplier | Fax modem | Fax server | Fax message system | Fax response system | Facsimile service bureau | |
|---|---|---|---|---|---|---|
| | | | | | Messaging | Response |
| Cypress Research Corporation | | * | | | | |
| Danyl | | * | | | | |
| Data Processing Design | | * | | | | |
| Data Race | * | | | | | |
| DCE Corporation | * | | | | | |
| DCS | | * | | | | |
| DemoSource | | * | | | | |
| DEC | | * | | | | |
| Dialogic Corporation | * | | | | | |
| DigiBoard | * | | | | | |
| Digital Data Systems | * | | | | | |
| DMG, Inc. | | * | | | | |
| Dove Computer Corporation | * | | | | | |

cc:Mail
2141 Landings Drive
Mountain View, CA 94043
800-448-2500

Chinon America, Inc.
660 Maple Avenue
Torance, CA 90503
213-533-0274

Choice Technology Group, Ltd.
11545 West Bernado Court #200

San Diego, CA 92127
619-487-5640/800-767-7656

Circuit Research Corporation
4 Townsend West, Suite 3
Nashua, NH 03063
603-880-4000

Cobotyx Corporation, Inc.
55 Kenosia Drive
Danbury, CT 06810
203-438-9298/800-288-6342

Table A8.1 (continued)

| Supplier | Fax modem | Fax server | Fax message system | Fax response system | Facsimile service bureau | |
|---|---|---|---|---|---|---|
| | | | | | Messaging | Response |
| Dunn Communications | | | | | * | |
| ECAP Systems | | * | | | | |
| EEC Systems, Inc. | | * | | | | |
| EPG America, Inc. | | * | | | | |
| E-Fax Communications | | | | | * | * |
| Electronic Modules, Inc. | | | * | | | |
| Enable Software/Higgins | | * | | | | |
| Enhanced Systems, Inc. | | | * | * | | |
| ESCO Systems, Inc. | * | | | | | |
| Everex Corporation | * | | | | | |
| Exar Corporation | * | | | | | |
| Facsimile Marketing, Inc. | | | | | * | * |
| FAX900, Inc. | | | | | | * |

CommSEL
415 Bayside Drive
Newport Beach, CA 92660
714-723-4800/800-727-2537

Compass Technology, Inc.
Live Oak Office Center
2201 Cantu Court #116
Sarasota, FL 34232
813-371-8000

The Complete PC, Inc.
1983 Concourse Drive

San Jose, CA 95131
408-434-0145

CompLink, Ltd.
1419 Avenue J
Brooklyn, NY 11230
718-338-9646

Computer Automation, Inc.
1819 Firman Drive, Suite 137
Richardson, TX 75081
214-680-9913

## Table A8.1 (continued)

| Supplier | Fax modem | Fax server | Fax message system | Fax response system | Facsimile service bureau | |
|---|---|---|---|---|---|---|
| | | | | | Messaging | Response |
| Faxback, Inc. | | | * | * | | |
| Faxbank Systems, Inc. | | | * | * | | |
| Faximum Software | | * | | | | |
| FaxPump Systems, Inc. | | | | * | | |
| FaxtNOW | | | | | | * |
| Fax Interactive, Inc. | | | | | * | * |
| FaxLogic, Inc. | | | | * | | |
| FAX Response Internation | | | | | | * |
| Frecom Communications | * | | | | | |
| Fujitsu Imaging | * | | | | | |
| Gammalink | * | * | | | | |
| GemFax | | | | | * | |
| Global Information Services | | | | | * | |

Computer Friends, Inc.
14250 N.W. Science Park Drive
Portland, OR 97229
503-626-2291/800-547-3303

Computer Peripherals, Inc.
667 Rancho Conejo Boulevard
Newbury Park, CA 91320
805-499-5751/800-854-7600

Computers Unlimited
2407 Montana Avenue

Billings, MT 59101
406-248-1632

Computer Systems Integration
222 South Main Street
Providence, RI 02903
401-331-1117

Comverse Technology, Inc.
400 Crossways Park Drive
Woodbury, NY 11797
516-921-0659

## Table A8.1 (continued)

| Supplier | Fax modem | Fax server | Fax message system | Fax response system | Facsimile service bureau | |
|---|---|---|---|---|---|---|
| | | | | | Messaging | Response |
| Global Vision Communication | * | | | | | |
| Guardian Communication Industries | | * | | | | |
| GUIS America | * | | | | | |
| Hays Microsystems | * | | | | | |
| Hewlett-Packard | | * | | | | |
| Hitachi | | | * | | | |
| Holmes Microsystems | * | | | | | |
| Horizon Service Bureau | | | | | | * |
| Hybrid Fax | * | | | | | |
| Ibex | | | | * | | |
| IBM Corporation | | * | | | | |
| IdealDial | | | | | | * |
| IDR Unicom, Inc. | | * | | | | |

Connex Systems
9341 Coutland Drive
Rockford, MI 49351
800-748-0212

Consumers Software, Inc.
700-73 Water Street
Vancouver, B.C. V6B1A1 Canada
800-663-8935

Copia International
1964 Richton Drive

Wheaton, IL 60187
708-682-8898

COS, Inc.
9 Huron Way
Lawrenceville, NJ 08648
609-771-6705

Cracchiolo & Feder, Inc.
440 E. Broadway, Suite 600
Tucson, AZ 85711
602-327-1357

## Table A8.1 (continued)

| Supplier | Fax modem | Fax server | Fax message system | Fax response system | Facsimile service bureau | |
|---|---|---|---|---|---|---|
| | | | | | Messaging | Response |
| Imavox Corporation | * | * | | | | |
| Infotel | | | | | | * |
| Innosoft International | | * | | | | |
| Instant Information | | | | | | * |
| Intel Corporation | * | * | | | | |
| Interfax | | | | | | * |
| IOCS | | | | * | | |
| IVM Systems | | | * | | | |
| Intervoice | | | | * | | |
| InTouch Software | | * | | | | |
| Kerygma Technologies | | | * | | | |
| Kurzweil AI | | * | | | | |
| Kuster Ross Data Systems | | | * | * | | |
| LEADtrack | | | * | | | |

Cypress Research Corporation
766 San Aleso Avenue
Sunnyvale, CA 94086
408-745-7200

Danville May Group, Inc.
54 Guelph Road
Elora, Ontario N0B 1S0
519-846-0474

Danyl
1509 Glen Avenue

Moorestown, NJ
609-234-8000/800-732-6868

Data Processing Design, Inc.
1400 North Brasher
Anaheim, CA 92807
714-970-1515/800-843-1317

Data Race Corporation
12758 Cimarron Path, Suite 108
San Antonio, TX 78249
512-692-3909

**Table A8.1 (continued)**

| Supplier | Fax modem | Fax server | Fax message system | Fax response system | Facsimile service bureau | |
|---|---|---|---|---|---|---|
| | | | | | Messaging | Response |
| Logicraft | | * | | | | |
| Macronics, Inc. | * | | | | | |
| MCI | | | | | * | |
| MEC | | * | | | | |
| Metafile Information Systems | | * | | | | |
| Micro Electonic Technology | * | | | | | |
| Microlink International | * | | | | | |
| Microlog | | | | * | | |
| Missing Link | | | | * | | |
| Multi-Tech Systems | * | | | | | |
| Multiverse Communications | | | | * | | |
| Murata | * | | | | | |
| National Semiconductor | * | * | | | | |

DCE Corporation
50 Glenbrook Road, Suite 1E
Stamford, CT 06902
203-359-5737

DCS, Inc.
12700 Park Central, Suite 308
Dallas, TX 75251
214-458-9711/800-999-2495

DemoSource
8646 Corbin Avenue
Northridge, CA 91324

Digiboard, Inc.
6751 Oxford Street
St Louis Park, MN 55426
612-922-8055/800-344-4273

Digital Equipment Corporation
146 Main Street
Maynard, MA 01754
508-897-5111

Digital Data Systems, Inc.
30100 Telegraph Road, Suite 251
Birmingham, MI 48010-2952
313-258-1122

**Table A8.1 (continued)**

| Supplier | Fax modem | Fax server | Fax message system | Fax response system | Facsimile service bureau | |
|---|---|---|---|---|---|---|
| | | | | | Messaging | Response |
| NBS Systems | | * | | | | |
| NCD | | * | | | | |
| Networking Dynamics Corp. | | * | | | | |
| Newport Simulfax Network | | | | | * | * |
| Nuntius | | | | * | | |
| OAZ Communications | * | * | | | | |
| Octel Communications | | | | * | | |
| Omnium Corp. | * | | | | | |
| Omtool Ltd. | | * | | | | |
| Open Systems Engineering | | * | | | | |
| Open + Voice | | | * | | | |
| Optus Software | | * | | | | |
| Orchid Technology | * | | | | | |

Dialogic Corporation
300 Littleton Road
Parsippany, NJ 07054
201-334-8450

Dove Computer Corporation
1200 North 23rd Street
Wilmington, NC 28405
800-622-7627

Dunn Communications
3330 Peachtree Road N.E., Suite 500

Atlanta, GA 30326
404-266-0400

DynamicFAX
2470 Eastrock Drive
Rockford, IL 61108
815-398-9009

ECAP Systems, Inc
83 Ste-Euphemie
Casselman, Ontario K0A1M0
613-764-3889

Table A8.1 (continued)

| Supplier | Fax modem | Fax server | Fax message system | Fax response system | Facsimile service bureau | |
| --- | --- | --- | --- | --- | --- | --- |
| | | | | | Messaging | Response |
| Orion Network Communications | | * | | | | |
| Panasonic Corp. | * | | | | | |
| Paradox Development Corp. | | * | | | | |
| Periphonics Corporation | | | | * | | |
| Prairie Systems | | | | * | * | * |
| Product R&D Corporation | * | | | | | |
| Prometheus Products, Inc. | * | | | | | |
| Ricoh Corporation | * | | | | | |
| Share Communications | | * | | | | |
| Sitel Interactive | | | | | | * |
| SNET | | | | | * | |
| SoftNet Inc. | | * | | | | |
| Soft*Switch | | * | | | | |

EEC Systems, Inc.
Millbrook Park
327 Boston Post Road
Sudbury, MA 01776
508-443-5106

E-FAX Communications, Inc.
1611 Telegraph Avenue, Suite 901
Oakland, CA 94612
415-987-7222

Electronic Modules, Inc.
10410 Vista Park Road

Dallas, TX 75238
214-340-6789/800-677-0767

Enable Software/Higgins Group
1150 Marina Village Parkway, Suite 101
Alameda, CA 94501
415-430-8875/800-888-0684

Enhanced Systems, Inc.
6961 Peachtree Industrial Boulevard
Norcross, GA 707355
404-662-1503

Table A8.1 (continued)

| Supplier | Fax modem | Fax server | Fax message system | Fax response system | Facsimile service bureau | |
|---|---|---|---|---|---|---|
| | | | | | Messaging | Response |
| SpectraFAX Corp. | * | | * | * | | |
| Sprint Gateways | | | | | * | * |
| Starfax, Inc. | | | | | * | * |
| STF Technologies, Inc. | * | | | | | |
| Sunset Systems | | | * | | | |
| Support Net, Inc. | | * | | | | |
| Swift Global Communications | | | | | * | |
| T1 Systems, Inc. | | | | * | | |
| T-4 Systems | | * | | | | |
| TEC-Advice S.A. | * | * | | | | |
| Technology Partners AB | | * | | | | |
| Teleglobe Canada, Ltd. | | | | | * | |
| Telemarketing Technology | | | | | | * |

EPG America, Inc.
130 William Street
New York, NY 10038
212-406-1720

Ergonomic Solutions
P.O. Box 7052
Plainville, CT 06062
203-793-0445

Everex Systems, Inc.
48431 Milmont Drive
Fremont CA 94538
415-498-1111/800-821-0806

Facsimile Marketing, Inc.
3 Landmark Square, Suite 403
Stamford, CT 06901
203-323-4368

FAX900, Inc.
One Indian Head Plaza
Nashua, NH 03060
603-889-8411/800-688-7171

Table A8.1 (continued)

| Supplier | Fax modem | Fax server | Fax message system | Fax response system | Facsimile service bureau | |
|---|---|---|---|---|---|---|
| | | | | | Messaging | Response |
| TEO Technologies, Inc. | * | | | | | |
| Teubner & Associates | | * | | | | |
| The Fax Group | * | * | | | | |
| The Pan Network | | | | | | * |
| The Turbo Group | | | * | | | |
| Touchbase Systems, Inc. | * | | | | | |
| Treva Communications | | | * | | | |
| TRT | | | | * | | |
| Universal Data Systems, Inc. | * | | | | | |
| UNISYS | | | * | | | |
| Vocal Telecommunications | | | | * | | |
| Voice Interactive Processing | | | | | | * |
| VoiceLink | | | | | | * |

FaxBack, Inc.
Cornell Oaks Corporate Center
1520 N.W. Greenbriar Parkway
Beaverton, OR 97006
503-690-6390/800-873-8753

Faxbank Systems, Inc.
2380 Wycliff Street
St. Paul, MN 55114
612-646-1336/800-SEL-FAXX

Faximum Software
1497 Marine Drive, Suite 300

West Vancouver, B.C. V7T 1B8
604-925-3600

The Fax Group
12625 High Bluff Drive #111
San Diego, CA 92130
619-792-6400

FAX Interactive Inc.
1650 Oakbrook Drive, Suite 425
Norcross, GA 30093
404-447-0004

**Table A8.1 (continued)**

| Supplier | Fax modem | Fax server | Fax message system | Fax response system | Facsimile service bureau | |
|---|---|---|---|---|---|---|
| | | | | | Messaging | Response |
| Voxem | | * | | | | |
| VoxLink Corporation | | * | | | | |
| V-Systems | | * | | | | |
| Wang Information Systems | | * | | | | |
| Wilco International | | * | | | | |
| Worldfax Services, Inc. | | | | | * | * |
| Xecom, Inc. | * | | | | | |
| Xerox | * | | | | | |
| Zoltrix, Inc. | * | | | | | |
| Zoom Telephonics | * | | | | | |

FaxPump Systems
Campbell, CA
800-922-7100

FAX Response International, Inc.
2829 Townsgate Road, Suite 190
Westlake Village, CA 91361
800-933-9900/800-933-2948

FaxtNOW
1633 Westwood Boulevard, Suite 204
Los Angeles, CA 90024
213-477-2707

Frecom Communications Company
46309 Warm Springs Road
Fremont, CA 94539
415-438-5041

Gammalink
133 Caspian Court
Sunnyvale, CA 94089
408-744-1430

GemFax
10440 West Nine Mile
Oak Park, MI 48237
313-399-8800/800-445-1561

Global Information Services
2 Executive Drive, 7th Floor
Fort Lee, NJ 07024
201-592-0714

Guardian Communication Industries, Inc.
6400 Roberts Street, Suite 492
Burnaby, B.C. Canada V5G 4C9
604-294-4300

GUIS America, Inc.
3675 Placentia Court
Chino, CA 91710
714-590-0801

Hays Microcomputer Products
P.O. Box 105203
Atlanta, GA 30348
404-449-8791

Hewlett-Packard Company
19310 Pruneridge Avenue
Cupertino, CA 95014
800-752-0900

Holmes Microsystems, Inc.
2620 South 900 West
Salt Lake City, UT 84119
801-975-9929

Hybrid Fax
978 Hamilton Court
Menlo Park, CA 94025
415-324-0600

Ibex
P.O. Box 148
Placeville, CA 95667
916-621-4342

IBM Corporation
37th Street, Dept. 14T
Rochester, MN 55901
507-253-4011

IdealDial
1536 Cole Boulevard, Suite 315
Golden, CO 80401
303-233-0300

Imavox Corporation
3350 Scott Boulevard, Bldg. 38-02
Santa Clara, CA 95054
800-969-4628

InfoTel
217 Lucas Street, Suite E
Mt. Pleasant, SC 29464
800-388-3528

Innosoft International, Inc.
250 West First Street, Suite 240
Claremont, CA 91711
714-624-7907

Inset Systems
71 Commerce Drive
Brookfield, CT 06804
203-775-5866/800-828-8088

Instant Information
66 Long Wharf
Boston, MA 02110
617-523-7636

Intel Corporation
MS CO03-07
5200 N.E. Elam Young Parkway
Hillsboro, OR 97124-6497
800-538-3373

InterFax, Inc.
320 Soquel Way
Sunnyvale, CA 94086-4101
408-245-2600

International Voice Messaging Systems, Inc.
563 West 500 South, Suite 300
Bountiful, UT 84010
801-292-8190

InterVoice, Inc.
17811 Waterview Parkway
Dallas, TX 75252
214-669-3988

InTouch Software
32 Ross Common, P.O. Box 806
Ross, CA 94957
415-461-3600

IOCS
400 Totten Pond Road
Waltham, MA 02254-9033
617-890-2299/800-451-1033

Kerygma Technologies, Inc.
80 Modular Avenue
Commack, NY 11725
516-864-2357

KISS Software Corporation
P.O. Box 743
Tenafly, NJ 07670-0743
201-816-0033

LEADtrack Services
P.O. Box 862215
Marietta, GA 30062-0001
404-594-7860/800-663-4641

Logicraft, Inc.
22 Cotton Road
Nashua, NH 03063
603-880-0300

Macronics, Inc.
1348 Ridder Park Dr.
San Jose, CA 95131
408-453-8088

Micro Electronic Technologies
35 South Street
Hopkinton, MA 01748
508-435-9057/800-766-7466

Microlog Corporation
20270 Goldenrod Lane
Germantown, MD 20874
301-428-3227

Microsystems Engineering Corporation
2400 West Hassell Road
Hoffman Estates, IL 60195
708-882-0111

MCI Telecommunications, FAX Services
2000 M Street, 8th Floor
Washington, D.C. 20036
800-888-32FAX

Missing Link Computer Technology, Inc.
52 Forest Avenue

Paramus, NJ 07652-5214
201-845-9622/800-999-6890

Multi-Tech Systems, Inc.
2205 Woodale Drive
Mounds View, MN 55112
612-785-3500/800-328-9717

Multiverse Communications
148 West 77th Street
New York, NY 10024
212-580-0541

Murata
5560 Tennyson Parkway
Plano, TX 75024
214-403-3300

National Semiconductor
2900 Semiconductor Drive
Santa Clara, CA 95052-8090
800-538-8510

Nationwide Computer Dynamics
1730 S. El Camino Real, Suite 208
Encinitas, CA 92024
619-943-1800/800-346-4200

NBS Systems, Inc.
15 Mullen Road
Enfield, CT 06082
203-741-2244

Networking Dynamics Corporation
1234 N. Edgemont Street, Suite 214
Hollywood, CA 90099-2696
213-668-0077

Newport Associates, Ltd.
7400 E. Orchard Road, Suite 320
Englewood, CO 80111
800-733-5515

Nuntius
1904 Merrill Drive
St. Charles, MO 63301
314-768-0109

OAZ Communications
48420 Kato Road
Fremont, CA 94538
800-NET-FAX5

Octel Communications Corporation
890 Tasman Drive
Milpitas, CA 95035-7439
408-942-6500

Omtool Ltd.
13 Industrial Way
Salem, NH 03079
603-898-8900

Open Systems Engineering
Box 396
Granby, CT 06035
203-653-0032/800-736-5032

Open + Voice, Inc.
13771 North Central Expressway, Ste. 832
Dallas, TX 75243-1017
214-497-9022

Optus Software, Inc.
100 Davidson Avenue
Somerset, NJ 08873-9931
201-271-9568/800-962-7422

Orchid Technology
45365 Northport Loop West
Fremont, CA 94538
415-683-0300

Orion Network Communications, Inc.
6600 Peachtree-Dunwoody Road
Atlanta, GA 30328

The Pan Network
P.O. Box 162
Skippack, PA 19474
215-584-0300

Panasonic Corporation
2 Panasonic Way
Secaucus, NJ 07094
201-348-7000

Paradox Development Corporation
6215 Ferris Square
San Diego, CA 92121
519-535-0765

Perception Technology Corporation
Shawmut Park

Canton, MA 02021-1409
617-821-0320

Periphonics Corporation
4000 Veterans Memorial Highway
Bohemia, NY 11716
516-467-0500

Prairie Systems
600 North 93rd Street, Suite 100
Omaha, NE 68114
402-391-1020

Product R&D Corporation
1194 Pacific Street, Suite 201
San Luis Obispo, CA 93401
805-546-9713/800-321-9713

Prometheus Products, Inc.
7225 S.W. Bonita Road
Tigard, OR 97223
503-624-0571/800-477-3473

Ricoh Corporation
5 Dedrick Place
West Caldwell, NJ 07006
201-882-7000

Share Communications
15377 N.E. 90th Street
Redmond, WA 98052
206-867-1222

Sitel Interactive
110 Gibraltor Road, Suite 231
Horsham, PA 19044
800-777-2033

Skyworld Technology
1100 Burnhamthorpe Road West
Mississauga, Ontario L5C 4G4
416-897-2153

SoftSwitch
640 Lee Road
Wayne, PA 19087-5698
215-651-5353

Southern New England Telephone (SNET)
54 Wall Street
New Haven, CT 06511
800-345-4329

SofNet, Inc.
775 Franklin Road, Suite 101
Marietta, GA 30067
404-499-0007

SpectraFAX Corporation
209 South Airport Road
Naples, FL 33942
813-643-5060

Sprint Telemedia
P.O. Box 7910
Shawnee Mission, KS 66207
913-661-8000/800-SELL-900

Starfax, Inc.
1430 West Blancke Street
Linden, NJ 07036
201-862-3000

Sunset Systems
16631 South Pacific Avenue
Box 237
Sunset Beach, CA 90742
213-592-4944

Support Net
8440 Woodfield Crossing Boulevard
Suite 340
Indianapolis, IN 46240-4300
317-469-4189/800-255-3390

Swift Global Communications, Inc.
997 Glen Cove Avenue
Glen Head, NY 11545-1599
516-676-8000

Syntellect, Inc.
21200 Black Canyon Highway
Phoenix, AZ 85027
602-264-5900

T1 Systems, Inc.
1658 Cole Boulevard
Golden, CO 80401
303-237-0440

T4 Systems
3 Inwood Circle
Little Rock, AK 72211
501-227-6637

TEC-Advice S.A.
P.O Box 850
CH-1800 Vevey Switzerland
41-21-922-6323

Telemarketing Technologies, Inc.
234 South 77th Street
Omaha, NE 68114
800-535-6979

TEO Technologies, Inc.
50 Mural Street
Richmond Hill, Ontario L4B 3H6
416-882-6082

Teubner & Associates, Inc.
P.O. Box 1994
Stillwater, OK 74076
405-624-2254/800-343-7070

Telephone Response Technology, Inc.
1624 Santa Clara Drive, Suite 200
Roseville, CA 95661
916-784-7777

Touchbase Systems, Inc.
160 Laurel Avenue
Northport, NY 11768
516-261-0423/800-541-0345

Treva Communications, Inc.
1781 Fox Drive
San Jose, CA 95131
408-452-1112/800-899-4EOS

The Turbo Group
7000 Boulevard East
Guttenberg, NJ 07093
201-662-8827

UNISYS Corporation
Township Line & Jolly Road, MS B330
Blue Bell, PA 19424-0001
215-986-2359

VoCal Telecommunications
77 West Las Tunas Drive, Suite 202
Arcadia, CA 91007
818-447-9425

Voice Interactive Processing, Inc.
1680 38th Street, Suite 400
Boulder, CO 80301
303-442-7800/800-688-2188

VoiceLink
906 University Place
Evanston, IL 60201
708-467-1100

Voxem
200 River Road
Red Bank, NJ 07701
201-576-1566

VoxLink Corporation
P.O. Box 23306
Nashville, TN 37202
615-331-0275

V-Systems, Inc.
39 Brookhollow Drive
Santa Barbara, CA 92705
714-545-6442

Wang Information Systems, Inc. (WISC)
One Industrial Way
Lowell, MA 01851
508-459-5000

Wilco International, Inc.
61 Broadway
New York, NY 10006
212-269-3970

WorldFax Services, Inc.
4747 West Water Avenue, Suite 1804
Tampa, FL 33614

Xecom, Inc.
374 Turquoise Street
Milpitas, CA 95035
408-945-6640

Xpedite Systems, Inc.
446 Highway 35 South
Eatontown, NJ 07724
800-227-9379

Zoom Telephonics, Inc.
207 South Street
Boston, MA 02111
617-423-1072

# Appendix 9
# Speech- and Voice-Recognition Product Suppliers

**Base Product Capability**

### Table A9.1
Speech and Voice Recognition Supplier Categorization

| Supplier | Speech recognition | Voice recognition | Support products |
|---|---|---|---|
| ACS Telecom | * | | |
| Adaptive Solutions | * | | |
| Advanced Products & Technology | * | | * |
| Alpha Microsystems | * | * | * |
| Applied AI Systems | * | | |
| Articulate Systems | * | | |
| Astronics | * | | |
| AT&T Conversant Systems | * | | * |
| Automated Business & Services, Inc. | * | | |
| Avanti | * | | |

Table A9.1 (continued)

| Supplier | Speech recognition | Voice recognition | Support products |
|---|---|---|---|
| Bellcore | * | | |
| BI, Inc. | | * | |
| Burr-Brown | * | | |
| California Medical Software | * | | |
| Cherry Electrical Products | * | | |
| Clinical Information Advantages | * | | |
| Command Corporation | * | | |
| Communications-Applied Technology | | | * |
| Compuspeak Labs | * | | * |
| Computer Consoles, Inc. | * | | * |
| Computer Voice Systems, Inc. | * | | |
| Covox | * | | |
| Cyberlog | * | | * |
| Daxus | * | | |
| Dialogic Corporation | * | | |
| Digital Equipment Corporation | * | | |
| Digital Sound Corporation | * | | * |
| Denniston & Denniston | * | | |
| Diatek | * | | |
| Dictaphone Corporation | * | | |

## Table A9.1 (continued)

| Supplier | Speech recognition | Voice recognition | Support products |
|---|:---:|:---:|:---:|
| Dragon Systems | * | | |
| Electronic Warfare Associates | | * | |
| Emerson & Stern Associates | * | | |
| Fujitsu America | * | | |
| Gradient Technology | * | | |
| Guardian Systems | | * | |
| Hearsay, Inc. | * | | |
| Hewlett-Packard | * | | |
| HY-TEK Manufacturing | * | | |
| IBM | * | | |
| International Electronics | | * | |
| I.T.S. Communications | * | | |
| ITT | * | * | |
| Kurzweil AI | * | | |
| Lanier | * | | |
| Logica | * | * | |
| MacSema | * | | |
| Mainstream | * | | |
| Mastervoice | * | | |

## Table A9.1 (continued)

| Supplier | Speech recognition | Voice recognition | Support products |
|---|:---:|:---:|:---:|
| McDonnell Douglas Health Systems | * | | |
| Mimic | * | | |
| MTI, Inc. | * | | |
| NanoPac | * | | |
| Origin Technology | * | | |
| Prab Command | * | | * |
| Rhetorex | * | | |
| Ricoh | * | | |
| Scott Instruments | * | | |
| Shure Brothers | | | * |
| Speech Recognition | * | | |
| Speech Systems, Inc. | * | | |
| Summa Four | * | | |
| Supersoft | * | | * |
| Swintek | | | * |
| Synchronetics | * | | |
| Systems & Services | * | | * |
| Technologica | * | | |
| Telxon | * | | |

## Table A9.1 (continued)

| Supplier | Speech recognition | Voice recognition | Support products |
|---|---|---|---|
| Texas Instruments | * | * | |
| The Complete PC | * | | |
| Transceptor Technologies, Inc. | * | | |
| Verbex | * | | |
| Verbotics | * | | |
| Vocollect | * | | |
| Voice Command & Control | * | | |
| Voice Connexion | * | | |
| Voice Control Products | * | | |
| Voice Control Systems | * | * | |
| Voice Learning Systems | * | | |
| Voice Processing Corporation | * | | |
| Voice Systems, Inc. | | * | |
| Vorec | | * | |
| Votan | * | * | |
| Wang | * | | |

## System Suppliers

### Table A9.2
Speech and Voice Recognition Supplier Categorization

| Supplier | Base technology | Board supplier | VAR | Systems integrator |
|---|---|---|---|---|
| ACS Telecom | | | * | |
| Adaptive Solutions | * | | | |
| Advanced Products & Technology | * | | | * |
| Alpha Microsystems | | * | | * |
| Applied AI Systems | | | * | |
| Articulate Systems | | * | * | |
| Astronics | | | * | |
| AT&T Business Communications Systems | * | * | | * |
| Automated Business & Services | | | * | |
| Avanti | | | * | |

Adaptive Solutions, Inc.
1499 N.W. Compton Drive
Beaverton, OR 97006
503-690-1236

Advanced Products & Technologies
15444 N.E. 95th Street
Redmond, WA 98052
206-883-8297

Aicomm, Inc.
4020 Westchase Boulevard, Bldg #115
Raleigh, NC 27607
919-839-0002

Alpha Microsystems
3501 W. Sunflower Avenue
Santa Anna, CA 92704
714-957-8500/800-253-3434

Applications Express
179 Avenue-at-the-Common
Shrewsbury, NJ 07702
908-389-366

Applied AI Systems, Inc.
Gateway Business Park
340 March Road, Suite 500
Kanata, Ontario K2K 2E4
613-592-3030

## Table A9.2 (continued)

| Supplier | Base technology | Board supplier | VAR | Systems integrator |
|---|---|---|---|---|
| Bellcore | * | | | |
| BI, Inc. | | | * | |
| Burr-Brown | | | * | |
| California Medical Software | | | * | |
| Cherry Electrical Products | | * | | |
| Clinical Information Advantages | | | * | |
| Command Corporation | * | * | | * |
| Compuspeak Labs | * | | | * |
| Computer Consoles, Inc. | | | * | * |
| Computer Voice Systems, Inc. | | | * | |
| Covox | * | * | | |
| Cyberlog | | | | * |
| Daxus | | | * | |
| Dialogic Corporation | | * | | |
| Digital Equipment Corporation | | * | | |
| Digital Sound Corporation | * | * | | * |
| Denniston & Denniston | | | * | |

## Table A9.2 (continued)

| *Supplier* | *Base technology* | *Board supplier* | *VAR* | *Systems integrator* |
|---|:---:|:---:|:---:|:---:|
| Diatek | | | * | |
| Dictaphone Corporation | | * | * | * |
| Dragon Systems | * | * | | * |
| Electronic Warfare Associates | | | * | |
| Emerson & Stern Associates | * | * | | |
| Fujitsu America | * | * | | |
| Gradient Technology | * | * | | |
| Guardian Systems | | | * | |
| Hearsay, Inc. | * | * | | |
| Hewlett-Packard | | | | * |
| HY-TEK Manufacturing | | | * | |
| IBM | | * | | |
| International Electronics | * | * | | * |
| I.T.S. Communications | | | * | |
| ITT | * | * | | |
| Kurzweil AI | * | * | | * |
| Lanier | | | | * |
| Logica | | | * | |

**Table A9.2 (continued)**

| Supplier | Base technology | Board supplier | VAR | Systems integrator |
|---|---|---|---|---|
| MacSema | * | | * | |
| Mainstream | | | * | |
| McDonnell Douglas Health Systems | | | * | |
| Mimic | * | | | |
| MTI, Inc. | | | * | |
| NanaPac | | | * | |
| Origin Technology | * | | | * |
| Prab Command | | | * | |
| Rhetorex | | * | | |
| Ricoh | * | * | | |
| Scott Instruments | * | * | | |
| Speech Recognition | * | | | |
| Speech Systems, Inc. | * | * | | * |
| Summa Four | | * | | |
| Supersoft | | | * | |
| Synchronetics | | | | * |
| Systems & Services | | | * | |
| Technologica | * | * | | |

## Table A9.2 (continued)

| Supplier | Base technology | Board supplier | VAR | Systems integrator |
|---|---|---|---|---|
| Telxon | | | | * |
| Texas Instruments | * | * | | |
| Transceptor Technologies, Inc. | | | * | |
| Verbex | * | * | | * |
| Verbotics | | * | | * |
| Vocollect | | * | | * |
| Voice Command & Control | * | * | * | |
| Voice Connexion | * | * | | * |
| Voice Control Products | * | * | | |
| Voice Control Systems | * | * | | * |
| Voice Learning Systems | * | * | | * |
| Voice Processing Corporation | * | * | | |
| Voice Systems, Inc. | * | | | |
| Vorec | * | * | | * |
| Votan | * | * | | * |
| Wang | | | | * |

Articulate Systems, Inc.
600 West Cummings Park
Woburn, MA 01801
617-935-5656/800-443-7077

Astronics, Inc.
101 Wayne Avenue, Suite 540
Silver Spring, MD 20910
301-650-8866

AT&T Business Communications Systems
55 Corporate Drive
Bridgewater, NJ 08807
908-658-8747

Avanti Computer Associates, Inc.
157 Valley Run Drive
Cherry Hill, NJ 08002
609-354-1620

Bellcore
290 West Mt. Pleasant Avenue
Rm4D-114
Livingston, NJ 07039
800-527-1080

BI, Incorporated
6400 Lookout Road
Boulder, CO 80301
303-530-2911

Burr-Brown
1141 W. Grant Road, MS 131
Tucson, AZ 85705
602-746-1111

Clinical Information Advantages, Inc.
51 Sawyer Road, Suite 450
Waltham, MA 02154
617-893-1221

Command Corp. Inc.
6045 Atlantic Boulevard, Suite 400
Norcross, GA 30071
404-662-1598

Communications-Applied Technology
11250-14 Roger Bacon Drive
Reston, VA 22090
703-481-0068

Compuspeak Labs
15095 West 116
Olathe, KS 66062
913-491-3444

Computer Consoles, Inc.
97 Humboldt Street
Rochester, NY 14609-7493
716-482-5000

Covox, Inc.
675-D Conger Street
Eugene, OR 97402
503-342-1271

Daxus Corporation
One Oliver Plaza
Pittsburgh, PA 15222-2603
412-566-5100

Denniston & Denniston, Inc.
3250 North Arlington Heights Road

Suite 111
Arlington Heights, IL 60004

Dialogic Corporation
129 Littleton Road
Parsippany, NJ 07054
201-334-8450

Diatek Corporation
5720 Oberlin Drive
San Diego, CA 92121
619-453-9560/800-854-2904

Dictaphone Corporation
3191 Broadbridge Avenue
Stratford, CT 06497-2559
203-381-7000

Digital Equipment Corporation
146 Main Street
Maynard, MA 01754
508-493-6788

Digital Sound Corporation
2030 Alameda Padre Serra
Santa Barbara, CA 93103
805-569-0700

Dragon Systems, Inc.
320 Nevada Street
Newton, MA 02158
617-965-5200

Electronic Telecommunications Corporation
3620 Clearview Parkway
Atlanta, GA 30340-2178
404-455-7972

Electronic Warfare Associates, Inc.
2071 Chain Bridge Road
Vienna, VA 22182-2622
703-893-4820

Emerson & Stern Associates, Inc.
10150 Sorrento Valley Road, Suite 210
San Diego, CA 92121-1604
619-457-2526

Fujitsu America, Inc.
3055 Orchard Drive
San Jose, CA 95134-2022
408-432-1300

Gradient Technology, Inc.
95B Connecticut Drive
Burlington, NJ 08016
609-387-8688

Granada Systems Design, Inc.
245 Fifth Avenue
New York, NY 10016
212-686-6945

Hearsay, Inc.
1825 74 Street
Brooklyn, NY 11204
718-256-1607

HTI Voice Solutions
333 Turnpike Road
Southborough, MA 01772
508-485-8400

HY-TEK Manufacturing Company
Adaptive Systems Divsion
1980 Route 30
Sugar Grove, IL 60554
312-466-7664

IBM Corporation
IBM Telemarketing Operations
3035 Center Green, Plaza 2
Boulder, CO 80301
800-426-3388

International Electronics, Inc.
32 Wexford Street
Needham Heights, MA 02194
617-449-6646

Intervoice, Inc.
17811 Waterview Parkway
Dallas, TX 75252
214-669-3988

I.T.S. Communications
643 Crosstown Parkway
Kalamazoo, MI 49007
616-344-6300/800-9999-ITS

ITT Defense Communications Div.
492 River Road
Nutley, NJ 07110
201-284-3000

Kurzweil AI
411 Waverly Oaks Road
Waltham, MA 02154
617-893-5151/800-23-VOICE

Lanier Voice Products
1700 Chantilly Drive, N.E.
Atlanta, GA 30324
404-321-1244/800-241-1706

Learnout & Hauspie Speech Products n.v
800 W. Cummings Park, Suite 3900
Woburn, MA 01801
617-932-4118

MacSema
29383 Lamb Drive
Albany, OR 97321
800-344-7228

Mainstream Solution
5541 E. Tulare Avenue #30
Fresno, CA 93727
209-251-4400

Mastervoice
10523 Humbolt Street
Los Alamitos, CA 90720
213-594-6581

Mimic, Inc.
P.O. Box 705
Islington, MA 02090
617-329-9593

NEC Corporation
401 Ellis Street, MV 4580
Mountain View, CA 94039
415-965-6000

Moscom
300 Main Street
East Rochester, NY 14445
415-490-7600/800-877-4756

Origin Technology, Inc.
520 Weddell Drive, Suite 4-5
Sunnyvale, CA 94089
408-734-0885

Periphonics Corporation
4000 Veterans Memorial Highway
Bohemia, NY 11716
516-467-0500

Reflectone, Inc.
5125 Tampa West Boulevard
Tampa, FL 33634
813-885-7481

Rhetorex, Inc.
1671 Dell Avenue # 208
Campbell, CA 95008
408-370-0881

Ricoh Corporation
2071 Concourse Drive
San Jose, CA 95131
408-434-6700/201-882-2085

Robot World
Rochester, NY
716-334-7168

S.C.I Systems, Inc.
8600 South Memorial Parkway
P.O. Box 4000
Huntsville, AL 35502
205-882-4800

Scott Instruments Corporation
1111 Willow Springs Drive
Denton, TX 76205
817-566-3174

Shure Brothers, Inc.
222 Hartrey Avenue
Evanston, IL 60202-3696
312-866-2509

Simpact Voice Products Group
1782 La Costa Meadows Drive
San Marcos, CA 92068
619-471-0342

Spectrum Management Group, Inc.
7330 San Pedro Avenue, #104
San Antonio, TX 78216
512-340-4792

Speech Recognition Systems, Inc.
1895 Mount Hope Avenue
Rochester, NY 14620
716-271-0600

Speech Systems Incorporated
18356 Oxnard Street
Tarzana, CA 91356
818-881-0885

Summa Four, Inc.
2456 Brown Avenue
Manchester, NH 03103
603-625-4050

Swintek
587 Division Street
Campbell, CA 95008-6905
408-378-8091

Syntellect, Inc.
15810 North 28th Avenue
Phoenix, AZ 85023
602-789-2800

Technologica Systems, Ltd.
155 N. Michigan Avenue, Suite 764
Chicago, IL 60601
312-938-1919

Telxon Canada Corporation, Inc.
2651 John Street, Unit #6
Markham, Ontario L3R2W5
416-475-8866

Texas Instruments
MS 2081, P.O. Box 2909
Austin, TX 78769
512-250-6005

Verbex Voice Systems, Inc.
1090 King Georges Post Rd./ Bldg 107
Edison, NJ 08837
201-225-5225

Verbotics, Inc.
P.O. Box 110149
Carrollton, TX75011-0149
214-991-8887

Vocollect, Inc.
664 Linden Avenue
East Pittsburgh, PA 15112
412-829-8145

Voice Learning Systems
2265 Westwood Boulevard, Suite 9
Los Angeles, CA 90064
213-475-1036/800-531-5314

Voice Connexion
17835 Skypark Circle, Suite C
Irvine, CA 92714
714-261-2366

Voice Control Products, Inc.
1140 Broadway
New York, NY 10001
212-683-4684

Voice Control Systems, Inc.
14140 Midway Road, Suite 100
Dallas, TX 75244
214-386-0300

Voice Systems, Inc.
4555 Corporate Drive
Troy, MI 48007-7085
313-641-0088

Voice Systems Plus, Inc.
526 Forest Way
Bolingbrook, IL 60440
708-972-1000

Voice Technologies
120 Village Square #143
Orinda, CA 94563
415-283-7586

Volt Delta Resources
1133 Avenue of the Americas
New York, NY 10036
212-827-2617

Vorec Corporation
155 White Plains Road
Tarrytown, NY 10591
914-631-8213

# Appendix 10
## Text-to-Speech Product Suppliers

AcuVoice, Inc.
111 N. Market Street, Suite 708
San Jose, CA 95113
408-289-1661

Advanced Products & Technologies
15444 N.E. 95th Street
Redmond, WA 98052
206-883-8297

AICOM Company
2375 Zanker Road, Suite 205
San Jose, CA 95131
408-922-0855

Artic Technologies
55 Park Street
Troy, MI 48083
313-588-7370

Bellcore
290 West Mount Pleasant Avenue
Rm 4D-114
Livingston, NJ 07039
800-527-1080

Berkeley Speech Technologies, Inc.
2409 Telegraph Avenue
Berkeley, CA 94704
415-841-5083

Centigram Communications Corporation
91 East Tasman Drive
San Jose, CA 95134
408-944-0250

Cybercorp
1 Linden Plaza
Great Neck, NY 11021
516-482-5389

Digital Equipment Corporation
146 Main Street
Maynard, MA 01754
508-493-6788

Electronic Speech Systems, Inc.
3216 Scott Boulevard
Santa Clara, CA 95054
415-644-8120

Emerson & Stern Associates, Inc.
10150 Sorrento Valley Road, Suite 210
San Diego, CA 92121-1604
619-457-2526

First Byte
3100 South Harbor Boulevard
Santa Ana, CA 92704
714-432-1740/800-523-8070

Fon-EX
P.O. Box 565
New Hope, PA 18938
215-862-FONX

Hearsay, Inc.
1825 74 Street
Brooklyn, NY 11204
718-256-1607

IBM Entry Systems Division
11400 Burnett Road
Austin, TX 78758
512-823-2252

Infovox AB
P.O. Box 2503
S 171 02 Solna, Sweden
46-8-735-8090

Learnout & Hauspie Speech Products n.v
800 W. Cummings Park, Suite 3900
Woburn, MA 01801
617-932-4118

Periphonics Corporation
4000 Veterans Memorial Highway

Bohemia, NY 11716
516-467-0500

Street Electronics
6420 Via Real
Carpinteria, CA 93013
805-684-4593

Swisscomp, Inc.
5312 56th Commerce Park Boulevard
Tampa, FL 33610
813-628-0906

Texas Instruments
MS 2081, P.O. Box 2909
Austin, TX 78769
512-250-6005

Verbex Voice Systems, Inc.
1090 King Georges Post Road, Bldg. 107
Edison, NJ 08837
908-225-5225

Voice Connexion
17835 Skypark Circle, Suite C
Irvine, CA 92714
714-261-2366

# Appendix 11
# ACD Suppliers

AAC Corporation
5915 Airport Road, Suite 615
Mississauga, Ontario L4V 1T1
416-678-0333

Affinitec
2252 Welsch Industrial Court
St. Louis, MO 63146
314-569-3450

**Table A11.1**
ACD Suppliers

| Supplier | PBX option | Stand-alone systems | ACD software |
|----------|:----------:|:-------------------:|:------------:|
| AAC Corporation | | | * |
| Affinitec | | | * |
| Alcatel/Cortelco | * | | |
| Aspect Telecommunications | | * | |
| AT&T | * | | |
| CADcom Telesystems | | * | |
| Cintech | | | * |
| Cobotyx Corporation | | * | |

## Table A11.1 (continued)

| Supplier | PBX option | Stand-alone systems | ACD software |
|---|---|---|---|
| Comdial | * | | |
| Cybernetics Systems | | | * |
| Data Plus, Inc. | | * | |
| Digital Transmission, Inc. | * | | |
| Ericsson Business Communications | * | | |
| Executone Information Systems | * | * | |
| Fujitsu Business Communications | * | | |
| Harbinger Group | | | * |
| Harris Corporation | * | * | |
| Hitachi | * | | |
| HTL Management, Ltd | | | * |
| Innings Telecom | | | * |
| Intecom, Inc. | * | | |
| Inter-Tel Equipment Corporation | * | * | |
| Mitel, Inc. | * | | |
| Monitec Systems, Inc. | | | * |

Alcatel/Cortelco
P.O. Box 831, Fulton Drive
Corinth, MS 38834
601-287-5281/800-288-3132

Aspect Telecommunications Corporation
1733 Fox Drive
San Jose, CA 95131
408-441-2200/800-541-7799

AT&T
295 North Maple Avenue
Basking Ridge, NJ 07920
201-221-2000

ATM Systems
1111 International Parkway, Suite 230
Richardson, TX 75081
214-669-2333

**Table A11.1 (continued)**

| Suppliers | PBX option | Stand-alone systems | ACD software |
|---|---|---|---|
| MTC Systems | | | * |
| NEC | * | | |
| Northern Telecom | * | | |
| Nova Systems | | | * |
| PaceCom technologies | | | * |
| Perimeter Technology | | | * |
| Professional Resource Management | | | |
| Redcom Laboratories | | | |
| Rockwell International | | * | |
| Rolm Company | * | | |
| Scientific Development Technologies | | | * |
| Scoop Systems | | | * |
| Shared Resources Exchange | | * | |
| Siemens Information Systems | * | | |
| Solid State Systems (Cortelco) | * | | |
| Source Data Systems | | * | |

CadCom TeleSystems
1296 Atlanta Road
Marietta, GA 30060
404-422-3600/800-537-1827

Cybernetic Systems International
999 Ponce de Leon Boulevard
Coral Gables, FL 33134
305-443-1651

Data Plus, Inc.
7420 Fullerton Road, Suite 110
Springfield, VA 22153
800-368-3747

Digital Transmission, Inc.
4343 Commerce Court, Suite 215
Lisle, IL 60532
708-505-1221

## Table A11.1 (continued)

| Suppliers | PBX option | Stand-alone systems | ACD software |
|---|---|---|---|
| Takacom | | | * |
| Tandiron Electronic Industries | * | | |
| TC Telemanagement | | | * |
| TCS Management Group, Inc. | | | * |
| Tekenekron Infoswitch | | * | |
| Telcom Technologies, Inc. | | * | |
| Telecalc | | | * |
| Telecorp Products | | | * |
| Telegenix | | | * |
| Telenova/Lexar Business Systems | * | | |
| Telephonic Equipment Corporation | | * | |
| Telrad Telcommunications | | * | |
| Telephone Support Systems, Inc. | | * | |
| TIE Communications | * | * | |
| Unifi Communications | | * | |
| Xtend | | | * |

Ericsson Business Communications
1900 W. Crescent Avenue
Anaheim, CA 92801
714-533-5013

Executone Information Systems, Inc.
6 Thorndale Circle
Darien, CT 06820
203-655-6500

Fujitsu Business Communications
3190 Mira Loma Avenue
Anaheim, CA 92806
714-630-7721

Harbinger Group
17 North Avenue
Norwalk, CT 06851
203-849-9000

Harris Corporation
Digital Telephone Systems Division
300 Bel Marin Keys Boulevard
Novato, CA 94949

Hitachi America
Norcross, GA
404-446-8820

HTL Telemanagement, Ltd.
3901 National Drive, Suite 160
Burtonsville, MD 20866
301-236-0780

Innings Telecom, Inc.
1241 Denison Street, Unit 31
Markham, Ontario L3R 4B4
416-470-7070

InteCom, Inc.
601 InteCom Drive
Allen, TX 75002
800-INTE-800

Inter-Tel Equipment Corporation
6505 West Chandler Boulevard
Chandler, AZ 85226
602-961-9000

Mitel, Inc.
5400 Broken Sound Boulevard N.W.
Boca Raton, FL 33431
407-994-8500/800-MITEL-SX

Monitec Systems, Inc.
230-1333 Johnston Street
Vancouver, B.C. V6H 3R9
604-689-1481

MTC Systems
95 Don Mills Road, Suite 708
Don Mills, Ontario M3C 1W3

NEC America, Inc.
8 Old Sod Farm Road
Melville, NY 11747
516-753-7000

Northern Telecom Inc.
200 Athens Way
Nashville, TN 37228
615-734-4000/800-667-8437

Nova Systems
1030 Massachusetts Avenue
Cambridge, MA 02138
617-882-2900

Pace Com Technologies
14040 N.E. 8th Street
Bellevue, WA 98007
206-641-8217

Perimeter Technology
102 Perimeter Road
Nashua, NH 03063
603-882-2900/800-962-4662

Professional Resource Management
949 Topanga Drive
Palatine, IL 60067
312-359-3990

Redcom Laboratories
One Redcom Center
Victor, NY 14564-0995
716-924-7550

Rockwell International Corporation
1431 Opus Place
Downers Grove, IL 60515
312-708-8000/800-722-5959

Rolm Company
4900 Old Ironsides Drive
Santa Clara, CA 95050
408-986-1000

Scientific Develpoment
800 W. Fifth Avenue 108A
Naperville, IL 60563
312-355-7332

Scoop Systems
7 Mounthaven Drive Box 1638
Livingston, NJ 07039
201-740-0609/800-243-SCOOP

Shared Resources Exchange, Inc.(SRX)
3480 Lotus
Plano, TX 75075
214-985-2773

Siemens Information Systems, Inc.
5500 Broken Sound Boulevard
Boca Raton, FL 33431
800-327-0636

Solid State Systems
1300 Shiloh Road N.W.
Kennesaw, GA 30144
404-423-2229

Source Data Systems
Cedar Rapids, IA
319-393-3343

Startel Corporation
17661 Cowan Avenue
Irvine, CA 92714
800-STARTEL

Takacom Corporation of America
10722 Los Vaqueros Circle
Los Alamitos, CA 90720
714-761-3844/800-421-1858

Tandiron Electronic Industries, Inc.
5733 Myerlake Circle
Clearwater, FL 34620
813-536-3222

TC Telemanagement
3820 Northdale Boulevard, 301A
Tampa, FL 33624
813-063-6320

TCS Telemanagement
Parkview Towers, Suite 800
210 25th Avenue North
Nashville, TN 37203
615-327-0811

Teknekron Infoswitch
4401 Cambridge Road
Fort Worth, TX 76155
800-346-4436

Telcom Technologies, Inc.
761 Corporate Center Drive
Pomona, CA 91768

Telecalc
4122 S.E. 128th
Bellevue, WA 98006
206-643-0300

Telecorp Products
20830 Rutland Drive, #106
Southland, MI 48075
313-569-7100/800-634-1012

Telenova/Lexar Business Systems
Camarillo, CA
800-73-LEXAR

Telephonic Equipment Corporation
17401 Armstrong Avenue
Irvine, CA 92714
714-250-9400

Telephone Support Systems, Inc.
2001 Marcus Avenue
Lake Success, NY 11040
516-867-2500

Telrad Telecommunications
Woodbury, NY
516-921-8300

TIE/Communications
4 Progress Avenue
Seymour, CT 06483
800-843-3231

Unifi Communications
4 Federal Street
Billerica, MA 01821
508-663-7570

Xtend Communications
171 Madison Avenue, 7th Floor
New York, NY 10016
212-725-2010

# Appendix 12
# C-TI Product Suppliers

21st Century Solutions, Inc.
1511 N. Elm
Palatine, IL 60067
708-705-6474/708-304-6420

ACIUS
Cupertino, CA
408-252-4444

Acxiom/BSA Division
1500 Lawrence
Ocean, NJ 07712
908-493-8062

Advanced Interactive Systems
1377 Main Street
Waltham, MA 02154
617-899-4700

AGS Information Services (a NYNEX
    Company)
11820 Parklawn Drive
Rockville, MD 20852
301-770-4600

ALE Systems
3334 Kings Charter Drive
Ashland, VA 23005
804-550-1370

Amcat
9601 Broadway Extension
Oklahoma City, OK 73114
800-342-7329

Amcom Software, Inc.
5555 West 78th Street
Minneapolis, MN 55439
612-829-7445/800-852-8935

Ameritech Information Systems
500 West Madison, Suite 1700
Chicago, IL 60606
312-906-4106

Amerex Technology, Inc.
909 Third Avenue, 19th Floor
New York City, NY 10022
212-759-0610

Amtelco
4800 Curtin Drive
McFarland, WI 53558
608-838-4194

Analysts International Corporation
600 Emerson Road, Suite 200
St. Louis, MO 63141
314-997-1746

**Table A12.1**
C-TI Product Suppliers

| Suppliers | Switch | System integrators | Host application | Computer API suppliers |
|---|---|---|---|---|
| 21st Century Solutions | | | * | |
| ACIUS | | | * | |
| Action Plus Software | | | * | |
| Acxiom/BSA Division | | * | * | |
| Advanced Interactive Systems | | * | * | |
| Advanced Software, Inc. | | | * | |
| Advanced Solutions | | * | | |
| Advanced Systems Technology, Inc. (Japan) | | | * | |
| After Hours Software | | | * | |
| AG Communication Systems | * | | | |
| AGS Information Services | | * | | |
| ALE Systems | | * | * | |
| Allied Group Information Systems | | | * | |
| Alta Telecom | | * | | |
| Amcat | | * | | |
| Amcom Software, Inc. | | * | * | |
| Amerex Technology, Inc. | | * | | |
| Ameritech Information Systems | | * | | |
| Amtelco | * | * | * | |
| Analysts International Corporation | | * | * | |
| Appinitec | | * | * | |
| Apple Computer | | | | * |
| Applied Micros | | * | * | |
| Applied System Technologies | | * | * | |
| Applied Telematics, Inc. | | * | * | |
| Aristacom International | | * | | |

Table A12.1 (continued)

| Suppliers | Switch | System Integrators | Host application | Computer API suppliers |
|---|---|---|---|---|
| AS/3X Group, The | | * | | |
| Aspect Telecommunications | * | | | |
| AT&T | * | * | * | |
| ATM Systems | | * | * | |
| Aurora Systems, Inc. | | * | | |
| Automation Technologies | | | * | |
| Baldwin, Hackett & Meeks, Inc. | | * | * | |
| Beacon Software, Inc. | | | * | |
| BellSouth Information Systems, Inc. | | * | | |
| Berg Konsult AG (Sweden) | | | * | |
| Biz*Base, Division of Creagh Computer | | | * | |
| BranchData AB (Sweden) | | | * | |
| British Telcom, PLC (UK) | | * | * | |
| Brock Control Systems, Inc. | | * | * | |
| Business Systems Resources, Inc. | | * | * | |
| BusinessWise | | * | | |
| Call Center Solutions, Inc. | | * | | |
| Call Management Products | | * | | |
| CCS Enterprises, Inc. | | | * | |
| Chronos Software, Inc. | | | * | |
| Cintech Telemanagement | | * | | |
| CML Technologies, Inc. (Canada) | | * | * | |
| Cobotyx Corporation | * | | | |
| CoCoN (Germany) | | | * | |
| Command (Germany) | | | * | |
| CommercialWare, Inc. | | * | * | |

## Table A12.1 (continued)

| Suppliers | Switch | System integrators | Host application | Computer API suppliers |
|---|---|---|---|---|
| Communications Group, The | | * | * | |
| Communicator Asystance Systems | | * | | |
| Compco, Inc. | | * | | |
| Computer Consoles, Inc. (NTI) | | * | * | |
| Computer Horizons Corporation | | * | | |
| Computer Sciences Corporation | | * | | |
| Computer Task Group, Inc. | | * | | |
| ComTel Computer Corporation | | * | * | |
| Contact Software International, Inc. | | | * | |
| Contact Plus Corporation | | | * | |
| Cortelco | * | | | |
| Cothern Computer Systems | | * | | |
| CRC Information Systems | | * | * | |
| Croyle & Associates, Inc. | | * | | |
| Cybernetics Systems International Corporation | | | * | |
| Cypress Research | * | | | |
| Database Systems Corporation | | * | * | |
| Data Code, Inc. | | | * | |
| DataCorp Business Systems, Inc. | | * | * | |
| Data Group, The | | * | * | |
| DataSave (Germany) | | | * | |
| Davis Software Engineering, Inc. | | * | | |
| Davox | | * | | |
| DayFlo TRACKER Corporation | | | * | |
| DCS Software & Consulting, Inc. | | * | * | |

## Table A12.1 (continued)

| Suppliers | Switch | System integrators | Host application | Computer API suppliers |
|---|---|---|---|---|
| Ericsson | * | | | |
| Evergreen Ventures Corporation | | | * | |
| Excel | * | | | |
| Executone | * | | | |
| Ficke & Associates | | * | * | |
| Fukushima Information Servoces Co., Ltd. (Japan) | | | * | |
| Futurus Corporation | | | * | |
| Global Telling Corporation | | * | * | |
| Granada Systems Design | | * | * | |
| GTE Government Information Services | | * | * | |
| GWA Information Systems, Inc. | | * | * | |
| Harris Corporation | * | | | |
| HBF Group | | * | * | |
| HDV (Germany) | | | * | |
| Hewlett-Packard | | | | * |
| Hill Arts & Entertainment Systems, Inc. | | * | * | |
| IBM Corporation | * | * | * | * |
| IBS Corporation | | * | | |
| Image Stream Communications | | * | * | |
| IMI Computing, Inc. | | * | * | |
| Info Group, The | | * | * | |
| Information Access Technology | | * | * | |
| Information & Communication Services | | * | * | |
| Information Builders, Inc. | | * | | |

**Table A12.1 (continued)**

| Suppliers | Switch | System integrators | Host application | Computer API suppliers |
|---|---|---|---|---|
| Information Management Associates | | * | * | |
| Information Technology Laboratory Co., Ltd. (Japan) | | | * | |
| Information Management Consultants, Inc. | | | * | |
| Innings Telecom | | * | | |
| Instor Corporation | | * | | |
| Intecom | * | | | |
| Integrated Northcoast Group | | * | * | |
| Intellivoice Communications | | * | | |
| Interactive Systems, Inc. | | * | * | |
| InterApps | | | * | |
| International Management Systems | | * | | |
| Intenational Solutions, Inc. | | | * | |
| International Telesystems Corporation | | * | * | |
| Intervoice, Inc. | | * | | |
| ISI InfoSystems, Inc. (Canada) | | | * | |
| IT Research, Inc. | | * | | |
| Jameson Industries | | * | | |
| JAM Information Systems | | * | * | |
| Japan Business Computer Co., Ltd. (Japan) | | | * | |
| Japan System Marketing Co., Ltd. (Japan) | | | * | |
| Kanebo Co., Ltd. (Japan) | | | * | |
| Keltech Information Systems | | * | * | |
| KMA Associates | | * | * | |
| KOMTEC | | * | | |

## Table A12.1 (continued)

| Suppliers | Switch | System integrators | Host application | Computer API suppliers |
|---|---|---|---|---|
| Lante | | | * | |
| Lawson Associates | | * | * | |
| LH Specifications (Germany) | | | * | |
| Lubbock Data Center, Inc. | | * | * | |
| Mapsys, Inc. | | * | | |
| Marketing Information Systems | | | * | |
| MarTel Group, The | | | * | |
| Melita International | * | * | * | |
| MicroAutomation | | * | | |
| MicroDimensions | | * | * | |
| Microframe, Inc. | | * | * | |
| Mini Computer Software Specialists | | * | * | |
| Mitel (Canada) | * | * | * | |
| Mitsubishi Corporation (Japan) | | | * | |
| Mr. Software | | | * | |
| Nabnasset Corporation | | * | | |
| Natural Microsystems Corporation | * | | | |
| NEC | * | * | | |
| Nippon Dentsu Kensetsu Co., Ltd. (Japan) | | | * | |
| Noble Systems Corporation | | * | * | |
| Northern Telecom, Inc. | * | | | |
| NPRI | | * | * | |
| Omniphone | | * | * | |
| PCBX Systems | * | | | |
| Performance Software, Inc. | | | * | |
| Polaris Software | | | * | |

## Table A12.1 (continued)

| Suppliers | Switch | System integrators | Host application | Computer API suppliers |
|---|---|---|---|---|
| Policy Management Systems Corporation | | * | * | |
| Profile Technologies, Inc. | | | * | |
| ProtoCall | | * | * | |
| Questcomp | | | * | |
| RadioPlan (Germany) | | | * | |
| Redcom | * | | | |
| Remote Control International | | | * | |
| Richmond Technologies & Software | | | * | |
| Ring Medical | | | * | |
| Robinson Group, The | | * | * | |
| Rochelle Communications | * | | | |
| Rockwell International | * | * | * | |
| Rolm Company | * | * | | |
| Sales & Marketing Systems, Inc. | | | * | |
| Sales Technologies, Inc., SNAP | | | * | |
| S & S Co., Ltd. (Japan) | | | * | |
| SCC, Inc. | | * | * | |
| Schaller & Rottorf (Germany) | | | * | |
| SD-Scicon UK, Ltd. (UK) | | * | * | |
| Siemens (Germany) | * | * | | |
| Smith, Cardner & Associates | | * | * | |
| SMS | | * | * | |
| Software Alternatives, Inc. | | * | * | |
| Software of the Future | | | * | |
| Software Ventures | | * | | |
| Solid State Systems (Cortelco) | * | | | |

## Table A12.1 (continued)

| Suppliers | Switch | System integrators | Host application | Computer API suppliers |
|---|---|---|---|---|
| SouthWare Innovations, Inc. | | * | * | |
| Speech Dynamics (Canada) | | | * | |
| SRX | * | | | |
| Stratus Computer | | | | * |
| Streetwise Systems | | * | | |
| Summa Four | * | | | |
| SW Bell | | * | | |
| Synon, Inc. | | * | | |
| Syspro Corporation | | | * | |
| Systec Co., Ltd. (Japan) | | | * | |
| System Development Corporation | | * | | |
| Systems Implementation, Inc. | | * | | |
| Tandem Computers | | | | * |
| TEC Solutions | | * | | |
| Teknekron Infoswitch | * | * | | |
| Telecom Finland | | | * | |
| Tel Control | * | | | |
| Telco Research | | * | * | |
| Telecommunications Int'l Consultants | | * | | |
| Telcom Technologies | * | | | |
| Tele Control, Inc. | * | | | |
| Telecorp Systems | | * | * | |
| TeleDirect International, Inc. | | * | * | |
| Telemagic Canada | | * | * | |
| Teleos Communications | * | | | |
| Telesystems Marketing, Inc. | | * | * | |
| TelIdent, Inc. | * | * | * | |

## Table A12.1 (continued)

| Suppliers | Switch | System integrators | Host application | Computer API suppliers |
|---|---|---|---|---|
| TelRelation | | * | * | |
| Time/Design | | | * | |
| TJ and K, Inc. | | * | | |
| TKM Communications (Canada) | | * | | |
| Touch Talk | | * | | |
| Touchtone Software International | | * | * | |
| Trans World Telephone Corp. | | * | * | |
| Travis DataTrak | | * | * | |
| Uchidata Co., Ltd. (Japan) | | | * | |
| Unitec Co., Ltd. (Japan) | | | * | |
| Universal Technics Co., Ltd. (Japan) | | | * | |
| Vector Systems Analysis (Canada) | | | * | |
| Vicorp Interactive Systems | | * | | |
| Voice Integrators, Inc. | | * | | |
| Volt Delta Resources | | * | * | |
| Voxcom | | * | * | |
| Wesson, Taylor, Wells & Associates | | * | | |
| Wohndata (Germany) | | | * | |
| Wygant Scientific | | * | | |
| Xtend Communications | | * | * | |
| Yezerski Roper, Ltd. (UK) | | * | | |
| Zybel Microsystems | | | * | |

Applied Micros, Inc.
12946 Dairy Ashford, Suite 100
Sugarland, TX
713-240-5555/800-827-9666

Applied Telematics, Inc.
487 Devon Park Drive, Suite 213
Wayne, PA 19087
215-687-3701/800-272-2441

Argos Computer Systems
110 West 32nd Street
New York, NY 10001
212-736-0720

Aristacom International
1320 Harbor Bay Parkway, Suite 180
Alameda, CA 94501
415-748-1533/800-223-7245

AS/3X Group
183 Lowell St.
Andover, MA 01810
508-475-2732

ATM Systems
1111 International Parkway, Suite 230
Richardson, TX 75081
214-669-2333

Aurora Systems, Inc.
40 Nagog Park, Suite 101
Acton, MA 01720
508-263-4141

BellSouth Information Systems, Inc.
300 Riverchase Galleria, Suite 1750
Birmingham, AL 35244
404-621-3188/800-621-4736

British Telcom, PLC
2-12 Gresham Street
London EC 2V 7 AG
44 0 71 356 8219

Brock Control Systems, Inc.
2859 Paces Ferry Road, Suite 1000
Atlanta, GA 30339
404-431-1200/800-221-0775

Business Systems Resources, Inc.
1000 Winter Street
Waltham, MA 02154
617-890-2105

BusinessWise
595 Millich Drive, Suite 210
Campbell, CA 95008
408-866-5960

Call Center Solutions, Inc.
P.O. Box 219
Madison, NJ 07940
201-593-0339

Call Management Products
2150 W. 6th Avenue, Unit N
Broomfield, CO 80020
303-465-0651

Cintech Telemanagement Systems
3006 Vernon Place
Cincinnati, OH 45219
513-861-2000/800-833-3900

Compco, Inc.
5120 Paddock Village Court
Brentwood, TN 37027
615-373-3636

CommercialWare, Inc.
470 Washington Street
Norwood, MA 02062-2337
617-551-0650

Communications Group, Inc.
443 South Gulph Road
King of Prussia, PA 19406
215-265-6615

Communicator Asystance Systems
80 Everett Avenue
Chelsea, MA 02150
617-884-3510

Computer Horizons Corporation
49 Old Bloomfield
Mountain Lakes, NJ 07046
201-402-7400

Computer Task Group, Inc.
7918 Jones Branch Road, Suite 500
McLean, VA 22102
703-790-1557/800-992-5350

Cothern Computer Systems
120 North Congress Street, Suite 700
Jackson, MS 39201
601-969-1155

CRC Information Systems
435 Hudson Street
New York, NY 10014
212-620-5678

Croyle & Associates, Inc.
1647 NW 85th Street
Clive, IA 50325
515-240-4689

Cybernetics Systems International Corporation
999 Ponce de Leon Boulevard
Coral Gables, FL 22134
305-443-1651

Database Systems Corporation
Database Plaza
1118 E. Missouri Avenue
Phoenix, AZ 85014
602-265-5968

DataCorp Business Systems, Inc.
28300 Euclid Avenue
Wickliffe, OH 44092
216-731-8000/800-327-3274

Data Group, The
77 South Bedford Street
Burlington, MA 01803
617-272-4100/800-247-1300

Davis Software Engineering, Inc.
1950 Stemmons Freeway, Suite 3044
Dallas, TX 75207
214-746-5210/800-373-2668

Davox
4 Federal Street
Billerica, MA 01821
617-667-4455

DCI
P.O. Box 38908
Denver, CO 80238
800-237-7378

DCS Software & Consulting, Inc.
12700 Park Central, Suite 308
Dallas, TX 75251
214-458-9711/800-999-2495

Dialogic Communications Corporation
1106 Harpeth Industrial Court
P.O. Box 8
Franklin, TN 37064
615-790-2882

Digisoft Computers, Inc.
92nd and 2nd Street
New York, NY
212-289-0991

Digital Systems International
7659 178th Place N.E.
P.O. Box 908
Redmond, WA 98052
206-881-7544/800-877-VOICE

Digital Techniques
402 West Bethany Drive
Allen, TX 75002
214-727-4234/800-634-4976

Distribution Resources
6061 South Willow Way
Englewood, CO 80111
303-889-4518

DRW
10025 Valley View Rd., Suite 130
Eden Prairie, MN 55344
612-9433-1331

Dynamic Communication
P.O. Box 38908
Denver, CO 80238-0908

Early, Cloud & Company
2374 Post Road
Warwick, RI 02886
401-849-0500/800-322-3042

Electronic Information Systems
1351 Washington Boulevard
Stamford, CT 06902
203-351-4800

Enator, Ltd.
Boston House, The Little Green
Richmond Surrey, TW9 1Q2
44 81 948 6000

Ficke & Associates
4733 Cornell Road
Cincinnati, OH 45241
513-489-9599

Gold Systems, Inc.
P.O. Box 1227
Boulder, CO 80306
303-447-2837

Granada Systems Design
245 Fifth Avenue
New York, NY 10016
212-686-6945/800-472-6444

GTE Government Information Services
P.O. Box 2924, MS 416
Tampa, FL 33601-2924
813-273-3000

GWA Information Systems, Inc.
1432 Main Street
Waltham, MA 02154
617-890-1838

Hill Arts & Entertainment Systems, Inc.
37 Soundview Road
Guilford, CT 06437
203-453-1718

IBS Corporation
12628 Highbluff Drive, Suite 700
San Diego, CA 92130
619-792-0273

IMI Computing, Inc.
One Pickwick Plaza
Greenwich, CT 06830
203-661-4404

Info Group
46 Park Street
Framingham, MA 01701
508-872-8383

Information Access Technology
1100 East 6600 South, Suite 300
Salt Lake City, UT 84121
801-265-8800

Information & Communication Services
221 Hickory Street
Mankato, MN 56001
507-387-1898

Information Builders, Inc.
1250 Broadway
New York, NY 10001
212-736-4433

Information Management Associates
6527 Main Street
Trumbull, CT 06611
203-261-4777

Intellivoice Communications
One Atlantic Center
1201 West Peachtree Street
Atlanta, GA 30309
404-875-3535

Interactive Systems, Inc.
P.O. Box 25024
Salt Lake City, UT 84125
801-972-1170

International Telesystems
600 Herndon Parkway

Herndon, VA 22070
703-478-9808/800-999-1482

InterVoice, Inc.
17811 Waterview Parkway
Dallas, TX 75252
214-669-3988

IT Research, Inc.
3717 West 50th Street
Minneapolis, MN 55410
800-657-0110

JAM Information Systems
16100 Chesterfield Parkway South
Chesterfield, MO 63017
314-536-1000

KOMTEC
Datenverarbeitung m.b.h.
Theaterstr. 24, 8700 Wurzburg
0931-538-21

Marketing Information Systems
1840 Oak Avenue
Evanston, IL 60620
708-491-3885/800-243-3885

Mar Tel Group, The
3601 Main Street
Kansas City, MO 64111
816-531-7776/800-234-3515

Melita International
6611 Bay Circle 220
Norcross, GA 30071
404-446-7800/800-342-5635

Microframe, Inc.
21 Meridian Road
Edison, NJ 08820
908-494-4570

Mini Computer Software Specialists
20975 Swenson Drive
Waulkesha, WI 53186-4064
414-798-8560

Missing Link Computer Systems
52 Forest Avenue
Paramus, NJ 07652-5214
201-845-0303

Nabnasset Corporation
410 Great Road, Suite B-4
Littleton, MA 01460
508-486-3244

Noble Systems Corporation
3297 Northcrest Road, Suite 200
Atlanta, GA 30340
404-851-1331

NPRI
602 Cameron Street
Alexandria, VA 22314
703-683-9090/800-526-1984

Policy Management Systems Corporation
One PMSC Center
Blythewood, SC 29016
803-735-4335

Remote Control International
5928 Pascal Court, Suite 150
Carlsbad, CA 92008
619-431-4000/800-992-9952

The Robinson Group
2411 West 14th Street
Tempe, AZ 85281
602-731-8900

Rockwell International
1431 Opus Place
Downers Grove, IL 60515
800-722-5959

Shared Medical Systems
2201 Broadway
Oakland, CA 94612
415-444-3434

Siemens AG
Austria
222-60171-5400

Sigma Software
10801 Bismarck Avenue
Northridge, CA 91326
818-368-6132

System Development Corporation
835 Hanover Street, Suite 305

Manchester, NH 03104
603-624-6907

Telco Research, Inc.
1207 17th Avenue South
Nashville, TN 37212
615-329-0031

Telecorp Systems, Inc.
1000 Holcomb Woods Parkway
Roswell, GA 30076
404-587-0700/800-334-9907

TeleDirect International, Inc.
736 Federal Street
Davenport, IO 52803
319-324-7720

TeleSystems Marketing, Inc.
11320 Random Hills Road, Suite 200
Fairfax, VA 22030
703-385-1212

TJ and K, Inc.
P.O. Box 26616
San Francisco, CA 94126
415-346-7675

TKM
90 Tiverton Court
Markham, Ontario L3R 9V2
416-491-3575

Touch Talk
46 Hidden Valley Airpark
Denton, TX 76205
817-497-7280

Trans World Telephone Corp.
2550 Medina Road
Medina, OH 44256
800-331-8484/216-722-5500

Travis DataTrak
42 Pleasant Street
Watertown, MA 02172
617-926-2929

Vicorp Interactive
540 Tremont Street
Boston, MA 02116
617-542-9233

Voice Integrators, Inc.
45 Whitney Road
Mahwah, NJ 07430
201-891-2226

Volt Delta Resources
1133 Avenue of the Americas
New York, NY 10036
212-827-2608

# Appendix 13

## Service Bureaus and Support Service Suppliers

1-900-Publishing, Inc.
27 W 24th Sreet, 6th Floor
New York, NY 10010
212-645-9666

The 9 Call Corporation
One Kendall Square, Bldg. 300
Cambridge, MA 02139
617-577-8855

900 Call Association
3608 NW 58th Street
Oklahoma City, OK 73112
405-947-5627

The 900 Connection, Inc.
575 Lexington Avenue, Suite 2601
New York, NY 10022

900 Selective Marketing
41 Vreeland Avenue
Totowa, NJ 07512
201-890-0898

900 Services, Inc.
5437 North 103rd Street
Omaha, NE 68134
402-573-1000/800-232-0900

900 Ventures, Inc.
5143 Cass-Elizabeth

Waterford, MI 48327
313-683-6060

900 America
720 S. Colorado Boulevard, Suite 275
Denver, CO 80222
303-692-8888/800-748-2900

A & J Recording Studios, Inc.
225 57th Street
New York, NY 10019
212-247-4860

Accelerated Voice
25 Stillman Street, #200
San Francisco, CA 94107
415-543-7998/800-779-0027

Access Equipment & Consulting
11560 N. Poema Place, Suite 102
Chatsworth, CA 91311
818-407-1208/800-233-1499

Accu-Weather, Inc.
619 W. College Ave.
State College, PA 16801
814-237-0309

AdTech, Inc.
San Diego, CA
800-334-0836

A-D Info Systems, Inc.
375 East Pine
Long Beach, NY 11561
516-431-2539

All My Features, Inc.
1873 North Clybourne, Suite 200
Chicago, Il 60614
312-935-8779

Alert Communications
5515 York Boulevard
Los Angeles, CA 90042
213-254-7171/800-233-7487

Allnet Communication Services
30300 Telegraph Road
Birmingham, MI 48010
313-647-6920/800-982-4422

## Table A13.1
Suppliers of Space, Equipment and Services for Information Providers

| *Supplier* | *Audiotex service bureau* | *Support service supplier* | *Syndicated audio information services* |
|---|:---:|:---:|:---:|
| 1-900-Publishing, Inc. | | * | |
| 900 Call Association | * | * | |
| 900 Selective Marketing | | * | |
| 900 Services, Inc. | | * | |
| 900 Ventures, Inc. | | * | |
| 900 America | | * | |
| 919 Computer Corporation | * | * | |
| AAA Audiotext, Inc. | * | * | |
| Accelerated Voice | * | * | |
| Access Equipment & Consulting | | * | |
| AccuWeather | * | * | * |
| ACP Corporation | * | * | |
| A-D Info Systems, Inc. | * | * | |
| All My Features, Inc. | | * | |
| AdTech | | * | |
| Alert Communications | * | * | |
| Almarc | * | * | |
| American International Communications | * | * | |
| American Message Tel | * | * | |
| Amirigon Audiotext Services | * | * | |
| A&J Recording Studios, Inc. | | * | |
| AC&E | * | | |
| Ameritech Audiotex Services | * | * | |
| Answer Quest, Inc. | * | * | |
| Applied Telematics, Inc. | * | | |
| Associated Press | | | * |

Almarc
8380 Santa Monica Boulevard #200
West Hollywood, CA 90069
213-656-7875

Alpha Group
808 North Spring Street, Suite 211
Los Angeles, CA 90012
213-617-913

American Airlines Direct Marketing
4201 Casmbridge Road, Mail drop 1306
Fort Worth, TX 76155
817-355-8200/800-325-2580

Amres Telemarketing
1280 W. Peachtree Street N.W.
Suite 325
Atlanta, GA 30367
404-873-6308/800-USA-8787

### Table A13.1 (continued)

| Supplier | Audiotex service bureau | Support service supplier | Syndicated audio information services |
|---|:---:|:---:|:---:|
| ATX Audiotex Productions | | * | |
| AT&T InfoWorx | * | * | |
| AudioCast | * | * | |
| Audio Communications, Inc.(ACI) | | * | |
| Audiocom | * | * | |
| Audio Marketing Systems | | | |
| Audio Response Services | * | * | |
| Audiotext Facilities Management | * | * | |
| Audio-Text Ventures | * | * | |
| Audio Voice, Inc. | * | * | |
| Aviation Data Link, Inc. | | | * |
| Barkley Communications, Inc. | * | | |
| Bellatrix Communications | * | | |
| B.F.D. Productions | | | |
| Blair Audiotex Productions | * | | |
| Buffalo Audiotex | | | |
| Call-hold Marketing! | * | | |
| Call Interactive | * | | |
| Celebration Computer Systems | * | | |
| CISCORP | * | | |
| CMI | | | |
| Confer-Call | * | | |
| Creative Ad-Vantage | | | |
| Dalcomp | * | | |
| DataDial, Inc. | * | | |
| Dialogue Technologies Corporation | * | | |
| Dial-it Services | * | | |
| Diamond Entertainment | * | | |
| Direct Response Communications | | | |
| Distinguished Phone Services | * | | |
| Dow Jones Information Services | | | * |

Table A13.1 (continued)

| Supplier | Audiotex service bureau | Audio support service supplier | Syndicated audio information services |
|---|---|---|---|
| Fleetweather, Inc. | | * | |
| Fourth Media, The | * | * | |
| Gateway Group, The | * | * | |
| Gigaphone | * | * | |
| GM Productions, Inc. | | * | |
| Hello, Inc. | * | * | |
| Hold Company, Inc. | * | * | |
| HSN 800/900 Corporation | * | * | |
| IdealDial Corporation | * | * | |
| Infoline Technology | * | * | |
| Information Systems & Services | * | * | |
| Instacom 900 Corporation | * | * | |
| Integrated Data Concepts | * | * | |
| Interactive Communications Unlimited | * | * | |
| Interactive Telemedia | * | * | |
| International Teleprograms | * | * | |
| International Telemedia Group | * | * | |
| International Voice Exchange | * | * | |
| Janes, Preston D. & Sons | * | * | |
| Jingle Phone Productions | | * | |
| Kupczyk, Kris & Associates | * | * | |
| Lip Service | | * | |
| LO-AD Communications | * | * | |
| Marketing Messages | | * | |
| Mass Communications | * | * | |
| MCI | * | | * |

Amrigon Audiotext Services
2750 South Woodward
Bloomfield Hills, MI 48013
313-332-2300

American Communications & Eng.
2267 North Agate Court
Simi Valley, CA 93065
805-581-3318/800-283-3318

American International
5595 E 7th Street, Suite 110
Long Beach, CA 90804
213-430-6663

Ameritech Audiotex Services, Inc.
600 South Federal Street, Suite 122
Chicago, IL 60605
312-939-3130/800-432-0080

Table A13.1 (continued)

| Supplier | Audiotex service bureau | Audio support service supplier | Syndicated audio information services |
|---|---|---|---|
| Motion Productions | | * | |
| National Audio-Text of U.S. | * | * | |
| National Audiotex Marketing Co. | * | * | |
| National Dial Centers | * | * | |
| National Phone Services | * | * | |
| National Telcom | * | * | |
| NEP Communications | * | * | |
| Network Telephone Services | * | * | |
| Nine Call Corporation | * | * | |
| On Hold Productions | | * | |
| ORO Communications Technology | * | * | |
| Pacific Bell | * | | |
| Pacific Information Services | * | * | |
| Perception Electronic Publishing | * | * | |
| Phone 800 & 900 Programs | * | * | |
| Phone Base Systems | * | * | |
| Phone Programs | * | * | |
| Phoneworks | * | * | |
| Pick-A-Winner | * | * | |
| Please Hold Promotions | * | * | |
| Progressive Distribution Services | * | * | |
| RJ Communications | | * | |
| Sage-Mark | * | * | |
| Scherers Communications | * | * | |
| Semper Barris | * | * | |
| Sitel Corporation | * | * | |
| Smallframe Systems | * | * | |
| SportsTicker | | | * |
| Sprint Telemedia | * | | |
| Talisman Communications | | * | |

Ameritech Information Industries Team
475 North Martingale
Schaumberg, IL 60173
800-451-5283

Amvox
5464 Carpinteria Avenue, #G
Carpinteria, CA 93013
805-684-5979/800-332-6869

Anderson, Dunston & Helene, Inc.
114 Mayfield Avenue
Edison, NJ 08837
201-225-5300/800-824-1000

Apac Telemarketing
O'Hare Aerospace Center
9950 Lawrence Ave.
Schiller Park, IL 60176
708-671-6100/800-822-APAC

## Table A13.1 (continued)

| Supplier | Audiotex service bureau | Audio support service supplier | Syndicated audio information services |
|---|:---:|:---:|:---:|
| Talk2 Corporation | * | * | |
| Tamona | * | * | |
| Target Technologies | * | * | |
| TCS Network Services | * | * | |
| Technico Computer Services | * | * | |
| Technology Unlimited | * | * | |
| Tela | * | * | |
| Tel-Botics | * | * | |
| Telecommunications Marketing | | * | |
| Telecom On-hold Productions | * | * | |
| Telecompute Corporation | * | * | |
| Tele-Disc | * | * | |
| Tele-Kinetics | * | * | |
| Teleline, Inc. | * | * | |
| Telephone Connection of LA | * | * | |
| Telephonetics International | * | * | |
| Telerx Marketing | * | * | |
| Teleshare International USA | * | * | |
| Telesonic | * | * | |
| Teletel | * | * | |
| Television Group | | * | |
| Tel-Info Services, Inc. | * | * | |
| Tel-Med, Inc. | * | * | |
| TeleVoice | * | * | |
| TeleWorld | * | * | |
| TEN | * | * | |

Applied Telematics, Inc.
487 Devon Park Drive, #213
Wayne, PA 19087
215-687-3701/800-272-2441

Associated Press
50 Rockefeller Plaza
New York, NY 10020
212-621-1585

Async
500 Northbridge Road, Suite 870
Atlanta, GA 30350
404-993-3393/800-543-3005

AT&T
55 Corporate Drive
Bridgewater, NJ 08807
914-933-2345/800-243-0900

## Table A13.1 (continued)

| Supplier | Audiotex service bureau | Audio support service supplier | Syndicated audio information services |
|---|---|---|---|
| Tempest Advertising, Inc. | | * | |
| Texas Marketing Communications | * | * | |
| Topaz Telecom Group | * | * | |
| Touch Talk | * | * | |
| Touch Tone Access | * | *+ | |
| Tri Metro | * | * | |
| United Communications International | * | * | |
| United Productions | * | * | |
| USA 800 | * | * | |
| US Audiotex | * | * | |
| USAN | * | * | |
| USA Today | | | * |
| US West Communications | * | | |
| Vocall Communications Corporation | * | * | |
| Voice-FX | * | * | |
| Voice Information Services | * | * | * |
| Voice Interactive Processing | * | * | |
| Voices Plus | | * | |
| Voice Systems & Services | * | * | |
| Voice Xpress, Inc. | * | * | |
| WalkerServer Productions | | * | |
| Walthall Service Bureaus | * | * | |
| Weather Fax, Inc. | * | * | |
| Westwood One/Audiotex | * | * | |

AT&T American Transtech
P.O. Box 44075
Jacksonville, FL 32231-4075
800-241-3354

AT&T Infoworx
55 Corporate Dr.
Bridgewater, NJ 08807
201-336-WORX/800-441-WORX

ATX Audiotex Productions
166 Rockingham Street

Rochester, NY 14620
716-987-5920

AudioCast
22048 Sherman Way, Suite 105
Canoga Park, CA 91303
818-919-9880/800-962-6421

Audio Marketing Systems, Inc.
10207 Venice Boulevard
Los Angeles, CA 90034
213-839-2000

**Table A13.2**

Suppliers of Service Bureau and Support Services

| Supplier | Voice mail | Tele-marketing | Transaction processing | Demographic database service |
|---|---|---|---|---|
| Alert Communications | * | * | * | |
| AA Direct Marketing | | * | * | |
| Amres Telemarketing | | * | | |
| Amvox | * | | | |
| Anderson, Dunston & Helene | | * | | |
| Apac Telemarketing | | * | | |
| ASYNC Corporation | * | | | |
| AT&T Transtech | | * | * | |
| Bellatrix Communications | | * | | |
| CTC | | * | | |
| Cincinatti Bell | * | | | |
| CPM Hull Colvey | | | | * |
| CSS Direct | | | | * |
| Call Center Services | | * | | |
| Call Interactive | | * | * | |
| CCMI/McGraw-Hill | | | | * |
| ComSELL | | * | | |
| CVTC | | * | * | |
| Dial America | | * | | |
| Direct Marketing Technologies | | | | * |
| Donnelley Marketing | | | | * |
| Execucall | * | | | |
| Executive Marketing Services | | | | * |
| First Corporation | | | * | |
| First Data Resources | | * | * | |
| Grolier TeleMarketing, Inc. | | * | | |

Audio Response Services, Inc.
3030 Clarendon Blvd, Suite 201
Arlington, VA 22201
703-247-3482/800-999-1868

Audio-Text Ventures, Inc.
1301 Gulf Life Dr., Suite 200
Jacsonville, FL 32207
904-396-8601

Audio Voice, Inc.
545 8th Ave., Suite 401
New York, NY 10018
212-868-1121/800-348-0500

Audiotext Facilities Management
1744 N. Euclid Avenue
San Diego, CA 92105
619-266-2400

**Table A13.2 (continued)**

| Supplier | Voice mail | Tele-marketing | Transaction processing | Demographic database service |
|---|---|---|---|---|
| ITI | | * | * | |
| Infomedia | | | | * |
| Information 900 Service | | * | | |
| Insystcom Corporation | | * | | |
| International Voice Exchange | * | | | |
| Inquiry Handling Service | | * | | |
| J.C. Penney Telemarketing | | * | * | |
| May Telemarketing | | * | * | |
| MDC Communications | * | | | |
| Metromail | | | | * |
| National Data Corporation | | * | * | |
| National Message Center | * | | | |
| NEP Communications | * | | | |
| NICE/Apex | | * | | |
| North American Selective | | | | * |
| OBS Payment Systems | | | * | |
| Oro Communications Technology | * | | | |
| Phone Base Systems | * | | | |
| RMH Telemarketing | | * | | |
| Scherers Communications | * | * | * | |
| Shaw McLeod | | | | * |
| Sheer Communications | | | | * |
| STARRTEL Voice Mail | * | | | |
| System 800 International | * | | * | |
| Talk2 | * | | | |
| Technology Unlimited | * | | | |
| TCS Network Services | * | | | |
| Technico | * | | | |

Automated Call Processing Corporation
633 Battery Street, #200
San Francisco, CA 94111
415-989-2200/800-888-3862

Audio Communications, Inc.
3140 Polaris, Suite 2
Las Vegas, NV 89102
702-221-6100/800-452-7100

Aviation Data Link, Inc.
28000 A 11 Airport Road

Punta Gorda, FL 33982
813-639-1944/800-237-3188

Barkley Communications, Inc.
222 Cedar Lane, P.O. Box 278
Teaneck, NJ 07666
201-836-9000

Bell Atlantic
Washington, D.C. & Maryland
8251 Greensboro Drive
Mclean, VA 22102
703-448-4620

Table A13.2 (continued)

| Supplier | Voice mail | Tele-marketing | Transaction processing | Demographic database service |
|---|---|---|---|---|
| Tel-Management | * | | | |
| Tele-Disk | * | | | |
| TeleLaison | * | | | |
| Telemarketing West | | * | | |
| Telematch | | | | * |
| Telephone Connection of LA | * | | | |
| Telephone Look-up Service Co. | | | | * |
| Telerx Marketing | | * | | |
| Teleshare | * | | | |
| Telesonic | * | | | |
| Tele-tech Services | | | | * |
| TeleWorld | * | | | |
| Tigon | * | | | |
| Time Communication | * | | | |
| Touch Tone Access | * | | | |
| Transaction Billing Resources | | | * | * |
| U.S. Voice Mail | * | | | |
| USAN | * | | | |
| Voicebank | * | | | |
| Voicecom | * | | | |
| Voicegram | * | | | |
| Voice Exchange Technologies | * | | | |
| Voice Information Processing | * | | | * |
| VoiceMail: One Corporation | * | | | |
| Voice Mail Communications Corp. | * | | | |
| Voicemail International | * | | | |
| Voice Mail Northwest | * | | | |
| Voice Response | | | | * |
| Voice-Tel | * | | | |
| Voice Telemessaging Services | * | | | |
| WATTS Marketing of America | | * | | |
| WISC | * | | | |

Bell Atlantic
Pennsylvania
200 Goddard Boulevard
King of Prussia, PA 19406
215-768-5792

Bellatrix Communications, Inc.
66 Ford Road
Denville, NJ 07834
201-586-0900/800-552-1752

Bell South Advanced Networks
1100 Johnson Ferry Road, #950
Atlanta, GA 30342
404-847-2900

B.F.D. Productions
1210 S. Martin Luther King Blvd.
Las Vegas, NV 89102
702-387-3200

Blair Audiotex Productions
48 Wood Road
Redding, CT 06896
203-938-3704

Call Center Services
302-Knickerbocker Road
Cresskill, NJ 07626
201-567-9314/800-238-CALL

Call Interactive
2301 N. 117th Avenue
Omaha, NE 68164
402-498-7000/800-342-5900

CCMI/McGraw Hill
500 N. Franklin Turnpike
Ramsey, NJ 07446
201-825-3311/800-526-53078

Celebration Computer Systems
9207 County Creek Drive #140
Houston, TX 77036
713-995-2400

Central Telephone Company
8745 West Higgins Road

Chicago, IL 60631
312-399-2897/800-323-2174

Chicago Telemarketing Connection, Inc.
848 West Eastman, Suite 206
Chicago, IL 60622
312-337-5900

Cincinnati Bell Telephone
201 East 4th Street, 102-1050
Cincinnati, OH 45201
513-397-7418

CMI, Inc.
900 Circle 75 Parkway, Suite 780
Atlanta, GA 30339
404-933-4300/800-866-4300

CommSEL
1014 Santiago Drive
Newport Beach, CA 92660
714-646-2440/800-727-2537

CPM Hull Colvey
Toronto, Ontario
Canada

Confer-Call
2801 Youngfield, Suite 240
Golden, CO 80401
303-232-2822/800-252-5150

Creative Advantage
117 Brookridge Estates POB 374
Guilford, CT 06437
203-458-0900

CSS Direct
313 N. 30th Street
Omaha, NE 68131
402-341-3537

Dalcomp, Inc.
The Harborside Financial Center
501 Plaza Three
Jersey City, NJ 07311-3896
201-434-8033

Dana Communications
2 East Broad Street
Hopewell, NJ 08525
609-466-9187

DataDial, Inc.
650 Kenwyn Road
Oakland, CA 94610
415-893-8800

DialAmerica Marketing
960 MacArthur
Mahwah, NJ 07495
800-531-3131

Dial-it Services, Inc.
1949 Stemmons, Suite 110
Dallas, TX 75207
214-747-0747

Dialogue Technologies Corporation
7910 Ralston Road, Suite 6
Arvada, CO 80002
303-431-0400

Diamond Entertainment, Inc.
Route#4, Box 194-A
Sevierville, TN 37862
615-428-1864

Direct Marketing Technologies
Schaumberg, IL
312-517-5600

Direct Response Communications
426 S. Venice Boulevard, Suite 4
Marina Del Rey, CA 90291
213-827-0234

Distinguished Phone Services
33 N. Euclid Avenue
National City, CA 92050
619-263-9040

Donnelley Marketing
1901 South Meyers Road, Suite 700
Oakbrook Terrace, IL 60181-5299
312-495-1211

Dow Jones & Co.
P.O. Box 300
Princeton, NJ 08543-0300
609-520-4900

Edmonton Telephone's Directory Services
10044 108th Street
Edmonton, AB T5J 3S9 Canada
403-441-2000

Execucall
531 N. Wayne Avenue
P.O. Box 15237
Cincinnati, OH 45215
513-563-8666/800-543-3005

Executive Marketing Services
610 N. Washington Street
Naperville, IL
800-367-7311

First Data Resources
10825 Farnam Drive
Omaha, NE 68154
402-399-7798/800-228-9079

First Integrated Resource Strategic
    Technology Corporation
49 Richmondville Avenue
Westport, CT 06880
203-222-8008

Fleetweather, Inc.
1966 Route 52
Hopewell Junction, NY 12533
914-226-8200/800-227-3623

Fourth Media, The
55 Marietta St., Ste 1875
Atlanta, GA 30303
407-577-3904

Gateway Group, The
2423 Susquehanna Road
Roslyn, PA 19001
215-881-2400

Gigaphone, Inc.
1525 Aviation Blvd, Suite A188
Redondo Beach, CA 90278
213-374-4313

GM Productions, Inc.
3110 Roswell Road, Suite 218
Atlanta, GA 30305
404-237-3919

Grolier TeleMarketing, Inc.
Old Sherman Turnpike
Danbury, CT 06816
800-842-0014

GTE California, Inc.
976 Information Access Service
3500 Willow Lane
Thousand Oaks, CA 91361
805-379-6073

GTE Florida
976 Information Access Service
P.O. Box 110, MC9
Tampa, FL 33601
813-228-5000

GTE Southwest
976 Information Access Service
290 E. Carpenter Freeway, Suite 700
Irving, TX 75062
214-717-2101

Hello, Inc.
5637 Princess Anne Road
Virginia Beach, VA 23462
804-490-3216

Hold Company
275 Commerce Drive, Suite 222
Ft Washington, PA 19034
215-643-0700/800-284-HOLD

Hollywood Hotline
P.O. Box 2510
Sparks, NV 89432
702-331-0991

HSN 800/900 Corporation
P.O. Box 9090
Clearwater, FL 34618-9090
813-536-0312/800-274-3283

IdealDial Corporation
2801 Youngfield Street, Suite 355
Golden, CO 80401
303-233-0300

Idelman Telemarketing, Inc.
7415 Dodge Street
Omaha, NE 68114
402-393-8000/800-562-5000

Infoline Technology
445 Hutchinson Avenue, Suite 600
Columbus, OH 43235
800-837-4636

Infomedia Corporation
7700 Leesburg Pike Centre Tower
Falls Church, VA 22043
703-847-0077/800-888-4188

Information 900 Service Corp.
250 West 57th St., Suite 1527-103
New York, NY 10019
212-581-2790

Information Access Service
P.O. Box 540991
Orlando, FL 32854
407-539-1333

Instacom 900 Corporation
180 S 300 W #120
Salt Lake City, UT 84101
801-533-9200

Insystcom Corporation
1812-L Batavia St.
Orange, CA
714-637-8007/800-266-6789

Integrated Data Concepts
P.O. Box 93428
Los Angeles, CA 90093
213-469-3380

Interactive Communications Unlimited
16923 Haas Ave.
Torrance, CA 90504
213-450-3146

International Telemedia Group, Inc.
9255 Sunset Blvd, Penthouse
Los Angeles, CA 90069
213-288-2115

Interactive Telemedia
1438 N. Gower Street, Box 8
Los Angeles, CA 90028
213-462-3321/800-441-4486

International Teleprograms
24 Commerce St., Suite 1225
Newark, NJ 07102
201-624-6020/800-356-5092

International Voice Exchange
136 East South Temple, #1770
Salt Lake City, UT 84111
801-575-6800/800-888-4226

Inquiry Handling Service, Inc.
200 Parkside Drive
San Fernando, CA 91340
800-624-8999

Janes, Preston D. & Sons Studios
316 West 2nd Street, Suite 1202
Los Angeles, CA 90012
213-625-5702

J.C. Penney Telemarketing
100 N. Corporate Drive
Brookfield, WI 53005
800-323-4343

Jingle Phone Productions
1329 W. Irving Park Road
Bensenville, IL 60106
708-860-5565

Kupczk. Kris & Assoc, Inc.
P.O. Box 8159
Calabassa, CA 91372
818-999-0644/800-828-9414

Lip Service
P.O. Box 3138
South Pasadena, CA 91030
818-799-5478

LO*AD Communications
808 N. Spring Street, Suite 705
Los Angeles, CA 90012
213-626-5329/800-255-5623

Marketing Messages
10 Langley Place, P.O. Box 370
Newton Centre, MA 02159
617-527-3023/800-247-9797

Mass Communications
432 Columbia Street, Suite B-9
Cambridge, MA 02141
617-577-7285

May Telemarketing
250 S. 77th Street
Omaha, NE 68114
800-338-2600

MCI Communications
800/900 Services
1133 19th Street N.W.
Washington, D.C. 20036
800-888-0800

MCI Telecommunications
FAX Services
2000 M Street, 8th Floor
Washington, DC 20036
800-888-3FAX

MDC Communications
1052 N. Tustin Avenue
Anaheim, CA 92807
714-637-9473/800-397-5000

MetroNet
360 East 22nd Street
Lombard, IL 60148-4989
708-620-3300/800-MMM-MAIL

Motion Promotions
111 Breckenridge Street, P.O. Box 389
Palmer, MA 01069
413-289-1226

National Audio-Text of the U.S.
4811 Atlantic Boulevard
Jacksonville, FL 32207
904-398-1375/800-277-6556

National Auditex Marketing Co., Inc.
P.O. Box 32088
Baltimore, MD 21208
301-486-0383

National Dial Centers, Inc.
5707 Walnut Street
Philadelphia, PA 19139
215-471-0100

National Message Center, Inc.
8960 Bond Street
Overland Park, KS 66214
913-888-0272

National Phone Services, Inc.
345 N. Canal Street
Chicago, IL 60606
312-559-1111

National Telcom
4 Embarcadero Center, Ste 3590
San Francisco, CA 94111
415-931-3311

NEP Communcations
19729 Henshaw St.
Woodland Hills, CA 91364
818-893-6441

Network Telephone Services
6233 Variel
Woodland Hills, CA 91367
818-992-4300/800-727-6874

New England Telephone
245 State Street
Boston, MA 02109
617-574-1554 (976 services)
617-574-1555 (GAB services)

New York Telephone
Audiotex Services
1095 Avenue of the Americas, #826
New York, NY 10036
212-395-5162

NYNEX Information Resources
100 Church Street
New York, NY 10007
212-513-9048

North American Selective
41 Vreeland Avenue
Totawa, NJ 07512
201-890-0889

OBS Payment Systems
115 Sansome Street
San Francisco, CA 94104
415-391-8555

ORO Communications Technology
338 Wall Street
Princeton, NJ 08540
609-683-4994

On-Hold Productions, Inc.
836 Prospect Street
Glen Rock, NJ 07452
201-444-6488

Pacific Bell
California 900
2600 Camino Ramon, Rm 4W200
San Ramon, CA 94583
415-823-1900/800-344-1341

Pacific Bell
California 976
2600 Camino Ramon, Rm 4W200
San Ramon, CA 94583
415-823-4976/800-344-1341

Pacific Bell
California Call Management
2600 Camino Ramon, RM 4W200
San Ramon, CA 94583
415-867-7708/800-344-1341

Pacific Bell
Voice Mail Services
2600 Camino Ramon, RM 4W200
San Ramon, CA 94583
415-811-7700/800-423-MAIL

Pacific Information Servcies
23309 Paloma Blanca
Malibu, CA 90265
213-456-8554

Pax Modular Systems
8646 Corbin Avenue
Northbridge, CA 91324
818-772-7729/800-888-6562

Perception Electronic Publishing
40 Shawmut Park
Canton, MA 02021
617-821-0320

Phone 800 & 900 Solutions
226 East 54th Street, Suite 306
New York, NY 10022
212-753-2565/800-77-PHONE

Phone Base Systems, Inc.
8620 Westwood Center Drive
Vienna, VA 22182
703-893-8600

Phone Programs
919 Third Avenue
New York, NY 10022
212-371-5450/800-962-4774

Phoneworks
191 Main Street
Hackensack, NJ 07601
201-343-0022

Pick-a-Winner, Inc.
110 110th Avenue NE, Suite 402
Bellevue, WA 98004
206-453-4800

Please Hold Promotions, Inc.
3627 E. Indian School Road
Suite 202B
Phoenix, AZ 85018
602-840-4291/800-825-8237

Progressive Distribution Services
5505 36th Street
Grand Rapids, MI 49512
616-957-5900

RJ Communication Services
7609 Rosdhu Court
Chevy Chase, MD 20856
800-221-1111

RMH Telemarketing
300 E. Lancaster Avenue, Suite 204-D
Wynnewood, PA
215-642-2438/800-367-5733

Sage-Mark, Inc.
1270 East Broadway, Suite 102
Tempe, AZ 85282
602-894-1336/800-727-1336

Scherers Communications
575 Scherers Court
Worthington, OH 43085
614-847-6161/800-828-8255

Semper Barris, Inc.
1-12 West Park Avenue
Long Beach, NY 11561
516-432-6030

Shaw McLeod
Toronto, Ontario, Canada
416-480-0000

Sitel Corporation
5601 N 103rd St.
Omaha, NE 68134
402-498-6810/800-351-3333

Sheer Communications, Inc.
9 Albertson Avenue
Albertson, NY 11507
516-484-3381/800-521-0136

Smallframe Systems
117 Agriculture Building
Embarcadero at Mission
San Francisco, CA 94105
415-421-0900

Smart Phone Corporation
208 West 30th Street, 12th Floor
New York, NY 10001
212-330-0375

SportsTicker
Harborside Financial Center
600 Plaza Two
Jersey City, NJ 07311
201-309-1200

Sprint Gateways
P.O. Box 7910
Shawnee Mission, KS 66207
913-661-8000/800-SELL-900

South Central Bell
976 Services
600 North 19th Street
Birmingham, AL 35203
205-972-4143

Southern Bell
976 Services
675 West Peachtree Street
Atlanta, GA 30375
404-728-7426

Southern New England Telephone
195 Church Street
New Haven, CT 06511
203-771-1185

Southwestern Bell Telephone
Voice Messaging Service
One Bell Center
St Louis, MO 63101
314-235-2011

Southwestern Bell Telephone
976 Services
1 Bell Plaza, 27th Floor
Dallas, TX 75202
214-464-8588

Southwestern Bell Telephone
Gateway Service
1714 Ashland
Houston, TX 77008
713-865-5757

Sprint Gateways
P.O. Box 7910
Shawnee Mission, KS 66207
913-661-8000/800-SELL-900

STARRtel Voice Mail
1760 E. River Road, Suite 118
Tucson, AZ 85718
602-299-3688

Talisman Communications Corp.
420 Lexington Avenue
New York, NY 10017
212-697-2220/800-TALISMAN

Talk2 Corporation
2325 Ulmerton Road, Suite 16
Clearwater, FL 34622
813-572-8255

Target Technologies, Inc.
16 Knight Street
Norwalk, CT 06851
203-866-6010

Technico Computer Services
545 8th Avenue, Suite 401
New York, NY 10012
212-502-0696

Technology Unlimited
1179 Andover Park West
Seattle, WA 98188
206-575-8644

TCS Network Services
220 Montgomery St., # 484
San Francisco, CA 94104
415-956-0144

Tela, Inc.
190 East 9th Avenue, Suite 600
Denver, CO 80203
303-733-4121

Telecom On-Hold Productions
Blake, Suite 1C

Denver, CO 80202
303-292-3303/800-289-8677

Tele-Disc, Inc.
33 Great Neck Road
Great Neck, NY 11021
516-466-0404

Tele-Kinetics, Inc.
3080 Olcott Street, Suite 135C
Santa Clara, CA 95054
408-727-1979

Tel-Botics
12850 S.W. 4th Court
Pembroke Pines, FL 33027
305-931-7599

Telecompute Corporation
1275 K Street N.W., Suite G-9
Washington, D.C. 20005
202-789-1111/800-USA-VOICE

Telecom*USA Information Resources
500 2nd Avenue S.E.
Cedar Rapids, IA 52401
319-366-6600/800-728-7000

Telecommunications International
6399 Wilshire Blvd, Penthouse
Los Angeles, CA 90048
213-653-3000/800-992-7000

Tel-Info Services, Ltd.
314 West 53rd Street
New York, NY 10019
212-246-7676

Tel-Management Inc.
2337 Lemoine Avenue
Fort Lee, NJ 07024
201-224-6510

TeleMatch
6883 Commercial Dr.
Springfield, VA 22159
703-658-8300/800-523-7346

Telephone Announcement Systems
187 Gibralter Road
Horsham, PA 19044
215-443-0600

Telephone Connection of Los Angeles
2554 Lincoln Boulevard, Suite 137
Marina Del Rey, CA 90291
213-827-8787

Telephone Entertainment Network
630 Ninth Avenue
New York, NY 10036
212-757-0702

Teleline
5950 Wilshire Boulevard, 2nd Floor
Los Angeles, CA 90036
213-930-2260

Telephonetics International, Inc.
12311 Taft Street
Pembroke Pines, FL 33026
305-432-6288/800-4-HOLD ON

Telerx Marketing, Inc.
901 Bethlehem Pike
Spring House, PA 19477
215-641-1616/800-438-3232

Teleshare International USA
6684 Gunpark Drive, Suite 2000
Boulder, CO 80301
303-530-3848

Telesonic
120 Admiral Cochrane Drive
Annapolis, MD 21401
301-841-6920

Telecom*USA Information Resources
500 2nd Avenue S.E.
Cedar Rapids, IA 52406-3162
319-366-6600/800-728-7000

TeleLiaison, Inc.
3501 Rue Ashby
Villa St. Laurent, PQ H4R 2K3
Canada

Telephone Entertainment Network
630 Ninth Avenue
New York, NY 10036
212-757-0702

Telephonetics International
12311 Taft Street
Pembroke Pines, FL 33026
305-432-6288/800-446-5366

Teleline, Inc.
5950 Wilshire Boulevard, 2nd Floor
Los Angeles, CA 90036
213-930-2260/800-842-2647

Telemarketing Company
5300 W. Lawrence Avenue
Chicago, IL 60630
312-635-1500

Telemarketing West
3230 East Imperial Highway, Suite 202
Brea, CA 92621
800-424-9378

Telematch
6883 Commercial Drive
Springfield, VA 22159
703-658-8300/800-523-7346

Telesphere International, Inc
Two Mid-Atlantic Plaza #500
Oakbrook Terrace, IL 60181
312-954-7700

Tele-Tech Services
P.O. Box 757
McAfee, NJ 07428
800-433-6181

Teletel, Inc.
100 Wilshire Boulevard
Santa Monica, CA 90401
213-458-6333

Teletext, Inc.
12311 Taft Street
Pembroke Pines, FL 33026
305-436-1000/800-446-5366

TeleVoice, Inc.
11767 Katy Freeway
Houston, TX 77079
713-496-7266

Television Group, Inc.
1717 West 6th Street, Suite 260
Austin, TX 78703
512-476-1054

TeleWorld, Inc.
3730 North 26th Street
Boulder, CO 80302
303-447-9489

Tel-Med, Inc.
952 S. Mount Vernon Avenue,
P.O. Box 1768
Colton, CA 92324
714-825-6034

Tempest Advertising, Inc.
575 Madison Avenue, Suite 1006
New York, NY 10022
212-605-0445

Texas Marketing Communications
5600 Colleyville Blvd., Suite A
Colleyville, TX 76034
817-581-9550

The Hold Company, Inc.
275 Commerce Dr., Suite 222
Fort Washington, PA 19034
215-643-0700/800-284-HOLD

The 9 Call Corporation
One Kendall Square, Bldg.300
Cambridge, MA 02139
617-577-8855

The 900 Connection, Inc.
575 Lexington Avenue, Suite 2601
New York, NY 10022

Tigon
17080 Dallas Parkway
Dallas, TX 75248
214-733-2700/800-962-2330

Time Communications
1600 Laperriere Ave.
Ottawa, ON K1Z 8P5
Canada
613-725-9111

Topaz Telecom Group Ltd.
350 Bay Street, Suite 301
Toronto, Ontario M5H 2S6
416-362-6200

Touch Talk
1800 N. Meridian, Suite 401
Indianapolis, IN 46202
317-921-0247

Touch Tone Acces
9 Whippany Road

Whippany, NJ 07981
201-884-0888

Transaction Billing Resources
24 Village Court
Hazlet, NJ 07730
201-888-0088

United Communications International
16530 Ventura Boulevard, 6th Floor
Encino, CA 91436
818-784-1058

United Telephone Company of Indiana
P.O. Box 391
Warsaw, IN 46580
219-267-1853

United Telephone Company of Florida
P.O. Box 5000
Altamonte Springs, FL 32716
407-889-6478

USA 800, Inc.
6608 Raytown Road
Kansas City, MO 64133
816-358-1303/800-872-9287

US Audiotex
18 Crow Canyon Court, Suite 100
San Ramon, CA 94583
415-838-7996

United Productions, Inc.
2300 West Sahara Suite 820, Box 18
Las Vegas, NV 89102
702-871-6599/800-222-6242

USAN, Inc.
300 Northwoods Parkway, #140
Norcross, GA 30071
404-729-1449

USA Today Talking Services
1000 Wilson Boulevard
Rooslyn, VA 22209
212-288-8873

U.S. Voice Mail
400 Renaissance Center, #500
Detroit, MI 48243
313-259-5080

U.S. West Communications
1801 California Street, Room 1620
Denver, CO 80202
303-896-9488/800-777-4772

VocCall Communications
60 Hudson St., Ste 307
New York, NY 10013
212-233-1222

Voice Exchange Technologies
1901 Congressional Drive, Suite 12
St Louis, MO 63146
314-298-1751

Voice Information Processing
660 Village Trace, Bldg. 18
Marietta, GA 30047
404-953-8123

Voice Information Services
1949 Stemmons #110
Dallas, TX 75207
214-747-0747

Voicebank
140 Valley Drive
Brisbane, CA 94005
415-467-2770/800-888-6423

Voice-FX Corporation
153 Clemson Road
Bryn Mawr, PA 19010
215-741-1864

Voice-Gram, Inc.
2805 Eastern Boulevard
York, PA 17402
717-755-0914

Voice Interactive Processing
1680 38th Street, Suite 400
Boulder, CO 80301
303-442-7800/800-688-2128

Voice Mail Communications Corp.
5218 East Colfax Avenue
Denver, CO 80220
303-321-3010

Voice Mail Northwest, Inc.
919 Southwest Taylor, Ste 400
Portland, OR 97205
503-224-6505

VoiceMail: One Corporation
50 University Avenue
Rochester, NY 14605
716-232-7350

Voicemail International
2953 Bunker Hill Road
Santa Clara, CA 95054
408-980-4000

Voice Response, Inc.
1910 East Kimberly Road
Davenport, IA 52807
319-355-5381/800-331-1510

Voices Plus
1020 Ventura Boulevard, Suite 90
Studio City, CA 91604
213-969-2462

Voice-Tel
70 W. Streetsboro Street
Hudson, OH 44236
800-247-4237

Voice Telemessaging Services, Inc.
1350 Bayshore Highway, #510
Burlingame, CA 94010
415-375-8551/800-245-8551

Walker Sever Productions
7516-A Avenue H
Lubbock, TX 79404
806-745-1430/800-533-3230

WATS Marketing of America
3250 North 93rd St.
Omaha, NE 68134
402-572-5512/800-351-1000

Westwood One/Audiotex
1700 Broadway, 3rd Floor
New York, NY 10019
212-237-2640

# Appendix 14
## Voice-Processing Product Suppliers for Individuals With Disabilities

Adaptive Communication Systems, Inc.
354 Hookstown Grade Road
Clinton, PA 15026
412-264-2288

Adhoc Reading Systems, Inc.
28 Brunswick Woods Drive
East Brunswick, NJ 08816
201-254-7300

AICOM Company
2375 Zanker Road, Suite 205
San Jose, CA 95131
408-922-0855

American Printing House for the Blind
1839 Frankfurt Avenue, P.O. Box 6085
Louisville, KY 40206
502-895-2405

Arkenstone, Inc.
540 Wedell Drive, Suite 1
Sunnyvale, CA 94089
408-752-2200/800-745-4443

Artic Technologies
55 Park Street, #2
Troy, MI 48083
313-588-7370

Arts Computer Products, Inc.
145 Tremont Street, Suite 407
Boston, MA 02111
617-482-8248

Asahel Engineering
East 246th Main
Pullman, WA 99163
509-334-2226

Blazie Engineering
3660 Mill Green Road
Street, MD 21154
301-879-4944

Institute on Applied Rehabilitation
    Technology
Boston Children's Hospital
300 Longwood Avenue
Boston, MA 02115
617-735-6466

Canon, U.S.A, Inc.
1 Canon Plaza
Lake Success, NY 11042
516-488-6700

Computer Aids Corporation
124 West Washington Boulevard
Fort Wayne, IN 46802
219-422-2424

Computer Conversations, Inc.
6297 Worthington Road, S.W.
Alexandria, OH 43001
614-924-3325

CTech
P.O. Box 30, 2 North William Street
Pearl River, NY 10965
914-735-7907

Assistive Technology Group
Digital Equipment Corporation

30 Forbes Road
Northboro, MA 01532-2595

Electronic Visual Aids Specialists
16 David Avenue, P.O. Box 371
Westerly, RI 02891
401-596-3155/800-872-3827

Enabling Technologies
3102 S.E. Jay Street
Stuart, FL 34997
407-283-4817

Grassroots Computing
P.O. Box 460
Berkeley, CA 94701
415-644-1855

## Table A14.1

Voice processing product suppliers for individuals with disabilities

| Supplier | Speech Output Systems | Speech Input Systems | Reading Machine for the Blind | Talking Calculators |
|---|---|---|---|---|
| Adaptive Communication Systems, Inc. | * | | | |
| Adhoc Reading Systems, Inc. | | | * | |
| Aicom Company | * | | | |
| American Printing House for the Blind | * | | | |
| Arkenstone, Inc. | | | * | |
| Asahel Engineering | | | * | |
| Arts Computer Products, Inc. | * | | | |
| Automated Functions, Inc. | * | | | |
| Blazie Engineering | * | | | |
| Boston Children's Hospital | * | | | |

## Table A14.1 (continued)

| Supplier | Speech Output Systems | Speech Input Systems | Reading Machine for the Blind | Talking Calculators |
|---|---|---|---|---|
| Canon USA, Inc. | | | | * |
| Computer Aids Corporation | * | | | |
| Computer Conversations, Inc. | * | | | |
| CTech | * | | | |
| Digital Equipment Corporation | * | | | |
| Electronic Visual Aids Specialists | * | | | |
| Enabling Technologies | * | | | |
| Grassroots Computing | * | | | |
| GW Micro | * | | | |
| Henter-Joyce, Inc | * | | | |
| HFK Software | * | | | |
| HumanWare, Inc. | * | | | |
| IBM NSCPWD | * | * | | |
| Interface Systems International | | | | |
| Kansys, Inc. | * | | | |
| Level One Technologies, Inc. | | | * | |
| MTI, Inc. | | * | | |
| Omnichron | * | | | |

**Table A14.1 (continued)**

| Supplier | Speech Output Systems | Speech Input Systems | Reading Machine for the Blind | Talking Calculators |
|---|:---:|:---:|:---:|:---:|
| Personal Data Systems, Inc. | * | | | |
| Power VAR | * | * | | |
| Prab Command, Inc. | | * | | |
| Prentke-Romich Company | * | | | |
| Raised Dot Computing | * | | | |
| Robotron Access Products, Inc. | * | | | |
| Sentient Systems Technology, Inc. | * | | | |
| Sharp Electronics Corporation | | | | * |
| Supersoft | | * | | |
| Syn-Talk Systems & Services | * | | | |
| Syntha-Voice Computers, Inc. | * | | | |
| TARMAC, Inc. | * | | | |
| Telesensory Systems, Inc. | * | | | |
| Totec Company, Ltd. | * | | * | |
| Transceptor Technologies, Inc. | * | | | |
| Truvel Corporation | * | | | |
| Visuaide 2000, Inc. | * | | | |
| Words+, Inc. | * | | | |
| Xerox Imaging Systems | * | | | |

GW Micro
310 Racquet Drive
Fort Wayne, IN 46825
219-483-3625

Henter-Joyce, Inc.
7901 4th Street North, Suite 211
St. Petersburg, FL 33702
813-576-5658

HFK Software
68 Wells Road
Lincoln, MA 01773
617-259-0059

HumanWare, Inc.
Horseshoe Bar Plaza
6140 Horseshoe Bar Road, Suite P
Loomis, CA 95650
916-652-7253/800-722-3393

IBM National Support Center for Persons with
    Disabilities
P.O. Box 2150
Atlanta, GA 30055
404-988-2733/800-426-2133

Interface Systems International
P.O. Box 20415
Portland, OR 97220
503-256-3214

Kansys, Inc.
1016 Ohio Street
Lawrence, KS 66044
913-842-4016

Level One Technologies, Inc.
Suite 1610, 5201 Leesburg Pike
Falls Church, VA 22041
703-671-7500

MTI, Inc.
14711 NE 29th Place, Suite 245
Bellevue, WA 98007
206-881-1789

Omnichron
1438 Oxford Avenue

Berkeley, CA 94709
415-540-6455

Personal Data Systems, Inc.
100 W. Rincon, Suite 207
Campbell, CA 95008
408-866-1126

Power VAR
2691 Dow Avenue, Suite F
Tustin, CA 92680
714-544-9941

Prab Command, Inc.
5140 Sprinkle Road
Kalamazoo, MI 49002
616-383-4400

Prentke-Romich Company
1022 Heyl Road
Wooster, OH 44691
216-262-1984

Raised Dot Computing
408 South Baldwin Street
Madison, WI 53703
608-257-9595

Robotron Access Products, Inc.
1201 Braddock Place #308
Alexandria, VA 22314
703-683-5818/800-835-1031

Sentient Systems Technology, Inc.
5001 Baum Boulevard
Pittsburgh, PA 15213
412-682-0144

Sharp Electronics Corporation
Sharp Plaza
Mahwah, NJ 07430
201-529-8200

Supersoft
P.O. Box 1628
Champaign, IL 61820
217-359-2112

Syn-Talk Systems and Services
70 Estero Avenue
San Francisco, CA 94127
415-334-0586

Syntha-Voice Computers, Inc.
1037A Levick Street
Philadelphia, PA 19111
416-578-0565/800-263-4540

TARMAC, Inc.
71 Norh Market Street
Asheville, NC 28801
704-254-6361

Telesensory Systems, Inc.
455 North Bernardo Avenue
Mountain View, CA 94043-5274
415-960-0920

Totec Company, Ltd.
5201 Leesburg Pike, Suite 1610
Falls Church, VA 22041
703-998-6177

Transcepter Technologies, Inc.
1327 Jones, Suite 105
Ann Arbor, MI 48105
313-996-1899

Truvel Corporation
520 Herndon Parkway
Herndon, VA 22070
703-742-9500

Visuaides 2000, Inc.
955 D'Assigny, Suite 143
Longuenal, Quebec J4K 5C3

Words + , Inc.
P.O. Box 1229
Lancaster, CA 93534
805-949-8331

Xerox Imaging Systems
9 Centennial Drive
Peabody, MA 01960
508-977-2000/800-343-0311

# Appendix 15

## Overseas Product and Service Suppliers and Telephone Companies

AEG Olympia AG
Buckestrasses 1-5
D-7750 Konstanz
Federal Republic of Germany
49-75-31-86-21-96

Aerotel Ltd.
8 Bezalel Street
Ramat-Gan 52521 Israel
972-3-751-7820

AILSS
c/o D J Communications Ltd.
15 Ryecroft Lane
Worsley, Manchester M28 4PN U.K.
061-832-0574

Applied Microsystems Technology Ltd.
249-251 Cricklewod Broadway
London NW2 6NX U.K.
01-450-3222

Asia Link
1st Floor, 57 Wyndham Street, Central
Hong Kong

ATIEP
Longcroft House
Victoria Avenue

Bishopsgate, London EC1M 4NS, U.K.
44 71 283 3244

Bell Audiotex
Bell House, 31-33 Ansleigh Place
London W11 6DW, U.K.
44 71 221 3141

Brite Voice Systems Group
Croosford Court, Dane Road Sale
Cheshire M33 1BZ, U.K.
44 061 976 4550

British Telecom, Premium Services
Intel House, 24 Southwalk Bridge Road
London SE1 9HJ U.K.
44-1-928-8686

Broadsystem Ltd.
Elephant House
London, SE1 9HJ U.K.
44-1-485-5964

BT Callstream
Tenter House
Moorfields
London, EC2Y 9TH, U.K.
0800 282 282

Cablecom Productions
35 Hay's Mews
Berkeley Square
London, W1X 7RQ U.K.
071 409 1005

Esselte Voice AB
Box 1810
S-171 22 Solna, Sweden
46 8 705 1700

Finland Posts and Telecommunications
P.O. Box 140
Helsinki SF 00511, Finland
358-0704-2509

France Telecom
36 rue du Commandent Mouchette
Paris
Codex 14 75675, 33-1-45-64-22-22

Global Communications Ltd.
211 Picadilly
London W1V 9LD, U.K.
44-1-548-9959

GPT
Sopers Lane
Poole, Dorset, U.K. BH17 7BQ

Halycon Integrated Systems
292A Burdett Road
London ECTN 8AT U.K.
44-1-515-8703

High-Track Communications Ltd.
4 Highbury Drive
London N5 1QZ U.K.
44-1-831-3755

Infovox AB
P.O. Box 2503
S 171 02 Solna, Sweden
46-8-735-8090

Innovative Communications Europe, Ltd.
19 Garard Street
London, W1V 7LA
44 71 734 3345

IPC Telemarketing
59 Uppr Ground

London SE1 9PG
44 71 261 6000

ITCA
c/o Telephone Technology PLC
Wellington Park House, Thirsk Row
Leeds LS1 4DP, U.K.
0532-425566

JW Nijholt BV
Van Riemsdykweg
3088 BD Rotterdam, Netherlands
31 10 4280466

JW Nijholt AS
Lille Grensen 3
0159 Oslo 1, Norway
47 2 416100

JW Nijholt AB
St Eriksgaten 121A
133 43 Stockholm, Sweden
46 8 341094

JW Nijholt Ltd.
3rd Floor, Blackfriars House
St Mary's Parsonage, Manchester, M3 1RE,
    U.K.
44 61 832 3406

KTAS ServiceBureauet
Norregade 21
1199 Copenhagen K, Denmark
45 33 99 20 38

LCM Group AB
Box 1124
183 11 Taby, Sweden
46 8 638 08 00

Legion Telecom Ltd.
4 Greenland Place
London NW1 0AP, U.K.
44 71 757 7786

Le Nouvel Observateur
14 rue Dussoubs
Paris, 75002 France
33-1-40-28-35-00

Lernout & Hauspie Speech Products
Rozendaal Straat, 14
Ieper 8900, Belgium
32-57-21-95-00

Livewire Communications, Ltd.
Warrick House, Station Court, Station Road
Great Shelford, Cambs CB2 5LR U.K.
44 223 845588

Marconi Speech & Information Systems
Air Speed Road
The Airport
Portsmouth, Hants PO3 5RE, U.K.
44-705-661 222

Mercury Communications Ltd.
New Mercury House, 26 Red Lion Square
London WC1R 4HQ, U.K.
44 71 528 2552

Newbridge Information Systems
Coldra Woods, Chepstow Road
Newport, Gwent, U.K. NP6 1JB

Nordisk Telelnfo
Vestregate 6
4800 Arendal, Norway
47 41 27922

On-Street Marketing, Ltd.
Commerce House, Vicarage Lane
Water Orton, Birmingham B46 1RR U.K.
44-21-749 3082

On-Street Marketing AB
Skomakaregaten 2
211 34 Malmo, Sweden
46 40 23 60 70

PTT Telecom Netherlands BV
IECT Room AA441 P.O. Box 30100
The Hague, 2500GA Netherlands
31-70-43643

Periphonics Voice Processing Systems
Albany Court, Albany Park
Camberley, Surrey, GU 15 2XA U.K.
0276-692-020

Progressive Tele-Link, Ltd.
Suite A, Third Floor, St. Augustines Court
1 St. Augustines Place
Bristol BS1 4XP, U.K.
0272 251654

Puerto Rico Telephone Company
P.O. Box 998
San Juan 00936 Puerto Rico

Racal - Vodat Ltd.
1 Pentagle
Newbury, Berkshire, U.K.
44-635-33251

RCP Telemedia
1 Suffolk Road
Kowloon Tong, Hong Kong
852 3383641

Regie des Telegraphes et des Telephones
rue des Palais 42
1210 Brussels, Belgium
32-2-213-45-30

Spectel
21 Stillorgan Industrial Park
Stillorgan, County Dublin, Ireland
353 1 953116

Storacall Voice Systems
Unit 1, Sky Business Centre, Eversley Way
Thorpe Nr. Egham, Surrey TW20 8RF U.K.
0784-71155

Swedish Telcom
Box 4548
203 20 Malmo, Sweden
46 40 25 29 28

Swedish Telecommunications
Marbactagaton II
Forsta 12386 Sweden
46-8-7137

Tekmark
50 Hanscrecent
London SW1 X0NA, U.K.
44 71 581 1805

Telecom Australia
199 William Street
Melbourne Victoria 3 Australia
613-606-8425

Telecom Communications PLC
Telecom House, 37 Farrington Road
London, EC1M 3JB, U.K.
44 71 696 8224

Telecom Eireann Headquarters
St. Stephen's Green West
Dublin 2 Ireland (Republic)
353-1-714444

Telecom Express Ltd.
211 Piccadily
London W1V 9LD U.K.
44-1-548-9950

Telecom Information
Royal Oak House, Pringe Street
Bristol BS1 4QE, U.K.
44-0272-293898

Telefonica Servicios
P. Castellana 128
Madrid 28010 Spain
34-1-411-1109

Telemedia
18 avenue des Champs-Elysees
75008, Paris, France
33 1 42 01 01 01

Telenetwork Belgium BVBA
Drkpersstraat 5-7
1000 Brussels, Belgium
32 2 2230790

Telenetwork Denmark A/S
Stenlose Centeret 69
3660 Stenlose, Denmark
45 173333

Telenetwork Finland Oy
Kaisaniemenkatu 2b
00100, Helsinki, Finland
358 0 6221783

Telenetwork International International
    Holding BV
Albert Plesmanweg 57
3088 GB Rotterdam, Holland
31 10 4951066

Telenetwork Norway AS
Grensen 9
0159 Oslo 1, Norway
47 2 425616

Telenetwork Sweden AB
Grev Turegatan 19
114 38 Stockholm, Sweden
46 8 6601373

Telenetwork Switzerland Ltd.
Robert-Zund-Strasse 2
P.O. Box 4865 CH-6002
Lucerne, Switzerland
41 41 23 74 40

Telenetwork UK, Ltd.
Crown House, 72 Hammersmith Road
London, W14 8YE, U.K.
44 71 371 2294

Telephone Information Services
24-30 West Smithfield
London, ECIA 9DL, U.K.
44-71-975-9000

Telephone Information & Communication Ltd.
16 Hatton Garden 2nd Floor
London, EI4 7DQ, U.K.
44-1-242-1002

Telephone Publishing Sverige AB
Box 17160
20010 Malmo, Sweden
46 40 12 80 40

Telsis Ltd.
Barnes Wallis Road, Segensworth East
Fareham, Hants, P015 5TT, U.K.
44 489-885877

Telsis Pty, Ltd.
119 Willoghby Road
Crows Nest, NSW 2065, Australia

Telspec Ltd.
Lancaster Parker Road, Rochester Airport
Rochester, Kent, ME1 3QU, U.K.
44-634-687133

TISL
TISL House, St. John's Rd.
Isleworth, Middlesex, TW7 6NL, U.K.
44-1-847-3003

Triton Telecomm
45 Kings Terrace
London, NW1 0JR, U.K.
44-71 911 6002

Vanderhoof plc
Rowley Drive
Coventry CV3 4FG, U.K.
44-203-304367

Vodata Ltd.
1 Pentangle, Park Street
Newbury, Berkshire, RG13 1EA, U.K.
44 635 503342

Voice Data Systems B.V.
Newtonlaan 211
Utrecht 3584 BH Netherlands

Voice Equipment AB
Pyramidbacken 1
141 72, Huddinge, Sweden
46 8 680 0100

Voice Systems International, Ltd.
Innovation Centre
Cambridge Science Pk., Milton Rd.,
    Cambridge, CB4 4GF, U.K.
44-223-420327

# Appendix 16

## Voice-Processing Associations, Publications, and Conferences

America's Carriers Telecommunications
 Association (ACTA)
240 Spring Wind Way
Casselberry, FL 32707
407-695-7919

American Facsimile Association
100 North 17th Street, 15th Floor
Philadelphia, PA 19103
215-568-8336

American Telemarketing Association (ATA)
606 North Larchmont Boulevard, Suite 4B
Los Angeles, CA 90004
213-463-2330/800-441-3335

American Voice Input Output Society
 (AVIOS)
4010 Moorpark Avenue
Suite 105K
San Jose, CA 95117
408-248-1353

Association of Telemessaging Services
 International (ATSI)
1150 South Washington Street, Suite 150
Alexandria, VA 22314
703-684-0016

Association of Telephone Information &
 Entertainment Providers Ltd.
Longcroft House, Victoria Avenue, Bishopgate
London, EC2M 4NS, England
44-71-283-3244

Association Francaise de Telematique
 (AFTEL)
3 rue Bellini
92806 Puteaux Cedex, France
33-1-47-73-6561

Association of Information Providers of New
 York
485 Madison Avenue 15th Floor
New York, NY 10022
212-935-6020

Association of Telemessaging Services
 International (ATSI)
320 King Street, Suite 500
Alexandria, VA 22314
703-684-0016

Canadian Association of Message Exchanges
 (CAM-X)
1 Director Court, Suite 103
Woodbridge, Ontario L4L 4S5 Canada

Communications Managers Association
40 Morristown Road
Bernardsville, NJ 07924
908-766-3824

Electronic Funds Transfer Association (EFTA)
1421 Prince Street, Suite 310
Alexandria, VA 22314
703-549-9800

Exchange Carriers Standards Association
  (ECSA)
5430 Grosvenor Lane, Suite 200
Bethesda, MD 20814
301-564-4505

Information Industry Association (IIA)
555 New Jersey Avenue N.W., #800
Washington, D.C. 20001
202-639-8262/800-346-6561

Information Providers Action Committee
  (IPAC)
2810 Sunday Trail Road
Los Angeles, CA 90068
213-876-5162

Information Providers of Illinois
345 N. Wells Street
Chicago, IL 60610
312-559-1111

International Communications Association
  (ICA)
12750 Merit Drive, Suite 710 LB89
Dallas, TX 75251
214-233-3889/800-422-4636

International Teleconferencing Association
  (ITA)
1150 Connecticut Avenue N.W. Suite 1050
Washington, D.C. 20036
202-833-2549

International Telecommunications Union
  (ITU)
Place des Nations CH-1211
Geneva, 20 Switzerland
41-22-730-56-89

International Telemedia Association (ITA),
  Inc.
1100 Circle 75 Parkway, Suite 800

Atlanta, GA 30339
404-933-1559

Mid-Atlantic Audiotex Association
2000 L Street N.W., Suite 200
Washington, D.C. 20036
202-466-3810

National Association of Regulatory Utilities
  Commissions (NARUC)
P.O. Box 684
Washington, D.C. 20044
202-898-2200

National Association for Information Providers
  (NAIP)
1150 Connecticut Avenue N.W., Suite 1050
Washington, D.C. 20036
202-833-2545

Newspaper Voice Network
c/o The Baltimore Sun
501 North Calvert Street
Baltimore, MD 21278
410-332-6644

North American Telecommunications
  Assocation (NATA)
2000 M Street N.W., Suite 550
Washington, D.C. 20036
202-296-9800/800-538-6282

Operator Service Providers of America
  (OSPA)
1776 K Street N.W.
Washington, D.C. 20006
202-429-7040

Tele-Communications Association (TCA)
858 South Oak Park Road, #102
Covina, CA 91724
818-967-9411

Telecommunications Industry Association
  (TCA)
2001 Pennsylvania Avenue N.W., Suite 800
Washington, D.C. 20006
202-457-4912

United States Telephone Association (USTA)
900 19th Street N.W., Suite 800
Washington, D.C. 20006
202-835-3100

Voice Mail Association of Europe
Swiss PTT—Telecom TX
3030 Bern, Switzerland
41-31-627205

Messaging
Information Publishing Corporation
P.O. Box 42382
Houston, TX 77242
713-974-6637

PACE
Information Publishing Corporation
P.O. Box 42375
Houston, TX 77242
713-974-6637

SPEECH TECH
Media Dimensions, Inc.
42 East 23rd Street
New York, NY 10010
212-533-7481

Talking Yellow Pages & Advertiser-Supported
    Conference
Audiotex Group, The
P.O. Box 107,
Point Pleasant, PA 18950
800-365-VOICE

Telecom Developers
Inbound Outbound & Teleconnect
12 West 21 Street
New York, NY 10010
212-691-8215

UNICOM
NATA
299 M Street N.W., Suite 550
Washington, D.C. 20036-3367
202-296-9800/800-538-6282

VOICE
Information Publishing Corporation
P.O. Box 42382
Houston, TX 77242
713-974-6637

VoicePower
VoicePower, Inc.
P.O. Box 313, Don Mills
Ontario, Canada M3C 2S7
416-449-5109

ASR News (Newsletter)
Voice Information Associates
P.O. Box 625
Lexington, MA 02173
617-861-6680

The Audiotex Directory and Buyer's Guide
P.O. Box 25961
Los Angeles, CA 90025
213-479-0654

Inbound Outbound Magazine
12 West 21 Street
New York, NY 10010
212-691-8215

Info II (Newsletter)
InfoText Publishing, Inc.
34700 Coast Highway, #309
Capistrano Beach, CA 92624
714-493-2434

InfoText Magazine
34700 Coast Highway
Suite 309
Capistrano Beach, CA 92624
714-493-2434

Phone + Magazine
Taurus Publishing, Inc.
13402 N. Scottsdale Road, Suite B-185
Scottsdale, AZ 85254-4056
602-483-0014

Speech Technology Magazine
Media Dimensions, Inc.
42 East 23rd Street
New York, NY 10010
212-533-7481

Teleconnect Magazine
12 West 21 Street
New York, NY 10010
212-691-8215

Voice In Europe
Satin Information Services, Ltd.
The Gazebo, Grundisburgh Road.
Woodbridge, Suffolk, England IP13 6HX
44-394383755

Voice News (Newsletter)
Stoneridge Technical Services
P.O. Box 1891
Rockville, MD 20850
301-424-0114

Voice Processing Magazine
Information Publishing Corporation
P.O. Box 42382
Houston, TX 77242
713-974-6637

Voice Processing News (Newsletter)
Probe Research
10 Madison Avenue
Morristown, NJ 07960
201-285-1365

World Telemedia (Magazine)
Triton Telecom Ltd.
45 Kings Terrace
London NW1 0JR England
44-71 911 6020

Dataquest
1290 Ridder Park Drive
San Jose, CA 95131
408-437-8000

Frost & Sullivan, Inc.
106 Fulton Street
New York, NY 10038
212-233-1080

The Gartner Group
72 Cummings Point Road
Stamford, CT 06904
203-964-0096

International Data Corp. (IDC)
P.O. Box 955
Five Speen Street
Framingham, MA 01701

International Research Development (IRD)
6 Trowitt Street
Norwalk, CT 06855
203-866-7800

Link Resources Corporation
79 Fifth Avenue
New York, NY 10003
212-627-1500

Market Intelligence Research Corporation
(MIRC)
2525 Charleston Road
Mountain View, CA 94043
415-961-9000

Strategic Telemedia
P.O. Box 107, Prince Street Station
New York, NY 10012
212-941-7537/800-365-VOICE

Robins Press
205 Third Avenue, Suite 8L
New York, NY 10003
212-614-9842

Tern Systems
168 Stone Root Lane
Concord, MA 01742
508-369-8146

The Yankee Group
200 Portland Street
Boston, MA 02139
617-367-1000

Vanguard Communications Corp.
100 American Road
Morris Plains, NJ 07950
201-605-8000

Venture Development Corporation
One Apple Hill
P.O. Box 9000
Natick, MA 01760

Voice Information Associates
P.O. Box 625
Lexington, MA 02173
617-861-6680

# Appendix 17
# Regulatory Agencies

## Federal

FCC - Common Carrier Bureau
Policy & Program Planning Division
1919 M Street, Room 544
Washington, D.C. 20554
202-632-9342

FCC - Informal Complaints and Public Inquiry
Branch
2025 M Street N.W., Room 6202

Washington D.C. 20554
202-632-7553

National Telecommunications & Information
Administration (NTIA)
14th & Constitution Avenue N.W., OPAD,
Room 4725
Washington D.C. 20230
202-377-1880

## State

Alabama Public Service Commission
P.O. Box 991
Montgomery, AL 36101
205-242-5209

Alaska Public Utilities Commission
1016 West 6th Avenue, Suite 400
Anchorage, AK 99501
907-276-6222

Arizona Corporation Commission
1200 West Washington Street
Phoenix, AZ 85007
602-542-4251/800-222-7000

Arkansas Public Service Commission
1000 Center P.O. Box C-400
Little Rock, AR77203
501-682-2051

California Public Utilites Commission
505 Van Ness
San Francisco, CA 94102
415-557-0647

Colorado Public Utilities Commission
Logan Tower 1580 Logan, OL2
Denver, CO 80203
303-894-2000

Connecticut Department of Public Utility
Control
One Central Park Plaza
New Britain, CT 06051
203-827-1553

Delaware Public Service Commission
1560 South DuPont Highway
Dover, DE 19003
302-739-4247

District of Columbia Public Service
Commission
450 5th Street N.W.
Washington, D.C. 20001
202-626-5100

Florida Public Service Commission
101 East Gaines Street
Tallahassee, FL 32399
904-488-1234

Georgia Public Service Commission
244 Washington Street S.W.
Atlanta, GA 30334
404-656-4501

Hawaii Public Utilities Commission
465 S. King Street, 1st Floor
Honolulu, HI 96813
808-548-3990

Idaho Public Utilities Commission
State House
Boise, ID 83720
208-334-0300

Illinois Commerce Commission
527 East Capitol Avenue, P.O. Box 19280
Springfield, IL 62794
217-782-5778

Indiana Public Service Commission
913 State Office Building
Indianapolis, IN 46204
317-232-2701

Iowa Utilities Board
Lucas State Office Building
Des Moines, IA 50319
515-281-5979

Kansas Corporation Commission
Docking State Office Building
Topeka, KS 66612
913-271-3100

Kentucky Public Service Commission
730 Schenkel Lane, P.O. Box 615
Frankfort, KY 40602
502-564-3040

Louisianna Public Service Commission
P.O. Box 91154
One American Place, Suite 1630
Baton Rouge, LA 70825
504-342-4427

Maine Public Utilities Commission
242 State Street, State House Station 18
Augusta, ME 04333
207-289-3831

Maryland Public Service Commission
231 East Baltimore Street
Baltimore, MD 21202
410-333-6000

Massachuseets Department of Public Utilities
100 Cambridge Street
Boston, MA 02202
617-727-3500

Michigan Public Service Commission
6545 Mercantile Way, P.O. Box 30221
Lansing, MI 48909
517-334-6445

Minnesota Public Utilities Commission
780 American Center Building
150 East Kellogg Boulevard
St. Paul, MN 55101
612-296-7124

Mississippi Public Service Commission
Walter Sillers State Office Building
P.O. Box 1174
Jackson, MS 39215
601-961-5400

Missouri Public Service Commission
Truman State Office Building, P.O. Box 360
Jefferson City, MO 65102
314-751-3234

Montana Public Service Commission
2701 Prospect Avenue
Helena, MT 59620
406-444-6188

Nebraska Public Service Commission
300 The Atrium, P.O. Box 94927
Lincoln, NE 68509
402-471-3101

Nevada Public Service Commission
727 Fairview Drive
Carson City, NV 89710
702-687-6001

New Hampshire Public Utilities Commission
8 Old Suncook Road, Building 1
Concord, NH 03301
603-271-2431

New Jersey Board of Public Utilities
2 Gateway Center
Newark, NJ 07102
201-648-2026

New Mexico State Corporation Commission
P.O. Drawer 1269
Santa Fe, NM 87504
505-827-4500

New York Public Service Commission
Empire State Plaza, 400 Broome Street
Albany, NY 12223
518-474-4364

North Carolina Utilities Commission
P.O. Box 29510
Raleigh, NC 27626
919-733-4249

North Dakota Public Service Commission
State Capital
Bismark, ND 58505
701-224-2400

Ohio Public Utilities Commission
180 East Broad Street
Columbus, OH 43266
614-466-3016

Oklahoma Corporation Commission
500 Jim Thorpe Office Building

Oklahoma City, OK 73105
402-521-4467

Oregon Public Utility Commissioner
300 Labor & Industry Building
Room 330
Salem, OR 97310
503-378-6611

Pennsylvania Public Utility Commission
P.O. Box 3265
Harrisburgh, PA 17120
717-787-2740

Rhode Island Public Utilities Commission
100 Orange Street
Providence, RI 02903
401-277-3500

South Carolina Public Utilities Commission
P.O. Drawer 11649, 111 Doctors Circle
Columbia, SC 29211
803-737-5100

South Dakota Public Utilities Commission
Capital Building, 500 East Capital Avenue
Pierre, SD 57501
605-773-3201

Tennessee Public Service Commission
460 James Robertson Parkway
Nashville, TN 37219
615-741-7489

Texas Public Utilities Commission
7800 Shoal Creek Boulevard South #400S
Austin, TX 78757
512-458-0100

Utah Public Service Commission
160 East 300 South, 4th Floor
Heber M. Wells Building
Salt Lake City, UT 84145
801-530-6716

Vermont Public Service Board
City Center Building, 89 Main Street
Montpelier, VT 05602
802-828-2358

Virginia State Corporation Commission
P.O. Box 1197, Jefferson Building
Richmond, VA 23209
804-786-3420

Washington Utilities and Transportation
  Commission
1300 S. Evergreen Park S.W.
Olympia, WA 98504
206-753-6423

West Virginia State Utilities Commission
P.O. Box 812, 201 Brooks Street

Charleston, WV 25323
304-340-0300

Wisconsin Public Service Commission
P.O. Box 7854, 4802 477 Hill Farms State
  Office Building
Madison, WI 53707
608-266-2001

Wyoming Public Service Commission
700 West 21st Street
Cheyenne, WY 82002
307-777-7427

# *Appendix 18*
# *LATA Numbers*

Table A18.1 provides LATA numbers that exist for U. S. telephone companies.

**Table A18.1**
LATA Numbers

| AMERITECH | | | |
|---|---|---|---|
| *State* Operating Telco | *LATA No.* | *LATA name* | *NPAs* |
| *Illinois* | 336 | Indianapolis (IN) | 217, 219*, 317* |
| Illinois Bell | 354 | Southwest (WI) | 608*, 815 |
| GTE North of | 356 | Southeast (WI) | 414*, 815 |
| IL | 358 | Chicago | 219, 312, 414*, 708, 815 |
| Contel of IL | 360 | Rockford | 608*, 815 |
| | 362 | Cairo | 618 |
| | 364 | Sterling | 815 |
| | 366 | Forrest | 217, 309, 815 |
| | 368 | Peoria | 309, 815 |
| | 370 | Champaign | 217 |
| | 374 | Springfield | 217 |
| | 376 | Quincy | 217 |
| | 520 | St. Louis (MO) | 314*, 618 |
| | 634 | Davenport (IA) | 309, 319*, 608*, 815, 816* |
| | 938 | Terra Haute (IN) | 217, 812* |
| | 976 | Mattoon | 217 |
| | 977 | Galesburg | 217, 309 |
| | 978 | Olney | 618 |
| *Indiana* | 330 | Evansville | 812 |
| Indiana Bell | 332 | South Bend | 219 |
| GTE North of | 334 | Auburn/Huntington | 219, 419* |
| IN | 336 | Indianapolis | 217*, 219, 317 |
| United Tel. of | 338 | Bloomington | 812 |
| IN | 358 | Chicago (IL) | 219, 312*, 414*, 708*, 815 |
| | 462 | Louisville (KY) | 502*, 812 |
| | 922 | Cincinnati (OH) | 513*, 606*, 812 |
| | 937 | Richmond | 317, 513* |
| | 938 | Terre Haute | 217*, 812 |

* Area code (NPA) that primarily services an adjacent state. Each state includes only up to the three telephone companies with more than 100,000 access lines. Some states may have fewer than three telephone companies with more than 100,000 access lines.

## Table A18.1 (continued)

| AMERITECH | | | |
|---|---|---|---|
| *State*<br><br>Operating Telco | *LATA No.* | *LATA name* | *NPAs* |
| *Michigan* | 326 | Toledo (OH) | 313, 317*, 419* |
| Michigan Bell | 340 | Detroit | 313, 517 |
| GTE North of | 342 | Upper Peninsula | 715, 906 |
| MI | 344 | Saginaw | 517 |
| | 346 | Lansing | 517 |
| | 348 | Grand Rapids | 517, 616 |
| | 350 | Northeast (WI) | 414*, 715* |
| *Ohio* | 320 | Cleveland | 216 |
| Ohio Bell | 322 | Youngstown | 216, 412 |
| GTE of North | 324 | Columbus | 614 |
| OH | 325 | Akron | 216 |
| Cincinnati Bell | 326 | Toledo | 313*, 419 |
| | 328 | Dayton | 513 |
| | 334 | Auburn/Huntington (IN) | 219*, 419 |
| | 340 | Detroit (MI) | 313*, 517 |
| | 922 | Cincinnati | 513, 606*, 812* |
| | 923 | Mansfield | 216, 419, 513, 614 |
| | 937 | Richmond (IN) | 317*, 513 |
| *Wisconsin* | 342 | Upper Peninsula (MI) | 715, 906* |
| Wisconsin Bell | 350 | Northeast | 414, 715 |
| GTE of North | 352 | Northwest | 612, 715 |
| WI | 354 | Southwest | 608, 815 |
| | 356 | Southeast | 414, 815 |
| | 358 | Chicago (IL) | 219*, 312*, 414, 708*, 815* |
| | 360 | Rockford (IL) | 608, 815* |
| | 624 | Duluth (MN) | 218*, 715 |
| | 634 | Davenport (IA) | 309*, 319*, 608, 815*, 816* |

Table A18.1 (continued)

| BELL ATLANTIC | | | |
|---|---|---|---|
| *State* | | | |
| Operating Telco | *LATA No.* | *LATA name* | *NPAs* |
| *Delaware* | 228 | Philadelphia | 215*, 302 |
| Diamond State Tel. | 236 | Washington D.C. | 202*, 301, 703* |
| *Maryland* | 238 | Baltimore | 301, 410 |
| C&P | 240 | Hagerstown | 301, 304, 717, 814 |
| | 242 | Salisbury | 301 |
| *New Jersey* | 220 | Atlantic Coast | 609 |
| New Jersey Bell | 222 | Delaware Valley | 609 |
| United Tel of NJ | 224 | North Jersey | 201, 908 |
| | 232 | Northeast (PA) | 215*, 717*, 814* |
| *Pennsylvania* | 133 | Poughkeepsie | 717, 914 |
| Bell of PA | 138 | Binghamton | 607, 717 |
| GTE North of PA | 140 | Buffalo | 716, 814 |
| United Tel of PA | 224 | North Jersey | 201*, 908 |
| | 226 | Capital | 215, 717, 814 |
| | 228 | Philadelphia | 215, 302 |
| | 230 | Altoona | 814 |
| | 232 | Northeast | 215, 717, 814 |
| | 234 | Pittsburgh | 412 |
| | 256 | Clarksburgh (WV) | 304*, 412 |
| | 924 | Erie | 814 |

## Table A18.1 (continued)

| BELL ATLANTIC | | | |
|---|---|---|---|
| *State*<br><br>Operating Telco | *LATA No.* | *LATA name* | *NPAs* |
| *Virginia* | 236 | Washington D.C. | 202*, 301*, 703 |
| C&P | 244 | Roanoke | 615*, 703 |
| Contel of VA | 246 | Culpepper | 703 |
| Central Tel of VA | 248 | Richmond | 804 |
| | 250 | Lynchburgh | 804, 919* |
| | 252 | Norfolk | 804, 919* |
| | 254 | Charleston (WV) | 304*, 703 |
| | 466 | Winchester (KY) | 606*, 615* |
| | 927 | Harrisburg | 703 |
| | 928 | Charlottesville | 804 |
| | 929 | Edinburg | 703 |
| | 932 | Bluefield (WV) | 304*, 703 |
| | 951 | Rocky Mount (NC) | 804, 919* |
| | 956 | Bristol (TN) | 615*, 703 |
| *West Virginia* | 240 | Hagerstown (MD) | 301*, 304, 717*, 814* |
| C&P | 254 | Charleston | 304, 703* |
| | 256 | Clarksburg | 304, 412 |
| | 932 | Bluefield | 304, 703* |
| *Washington D.C.* | 236 | Washington D.C. | 202, 301*, 703* |

## Table A18.1 (continued)

| BELL SOUTH | | | |
|---|---|---|---|
| *State* <br><br> Operating Telco | *LATA No.* | *LATA name* | *NPAs* |
| *Alabama* | 438 | Atlanta (GA) | 205*, 904 |
| South Central | 448 | Pensacola (FL) | 205, 904* |
| Bell | 470 | Nashville (TN) | 205*, 502*, 615* |
| *GTE of the South* | 476 | Birmingham | 205 |
| | 477 | Huntsville | 205, 601 |
| | 478 | Montgomery | 205, 912* |
| | 480 | Mobile | 205, 601*, 904* |
| | 482 | Jackson (MS) | 205, 318*, 504*, 601*, 901* |
| *Florida* | 448 | Pensacola | 205*, 904 |
| Southern Bell | 450 | Panama City | 904, 912 |
| GTE of Florida | 452 | Jacksonville | 904 |
| United Tel of FL | 454 | Gainsville | 904 |
| | 456 | Daytona Beach | 904 |
| | 458 | Orlando | 407, 904 |
| | 460 | Southeast | 305, 407 |
| | 480 | Mobile (AL) | 204*, 601*, 904 |
| | 939 | Fort Meyers | 813 |
| | 952 | Tampa | 813 |
| | 953 | Tallahassee | 904 |

## Table A18.1 (continued)

| BELL SOUTH | | | |
|---|---|---|---|
| *State* Operating Telco | *LATA No.* | *LATA name* | *NPAs* |
| *Georgia* Southern Bell GTE of the South | 438 | Atlanta | 812 |
| | 440 | Savannah | 502, 812 |
| | 442 | Augusta | 502, 615*, 901 |
| | 444 | Albany | 606, 615* |
| | 446 | Macon | 502, 601*, 901* |
| | 450 | Panama City (FL) | 205*, 502, 615 |
| | 472 | Chattanooga (TN) | 606, 615*, 704* |
| | 478 | Knoxville (TN) | 513*, 606, 812* |
| *Kentucky* South Central Bell GTE of the South | 330 | Evansville (IN) | 812* |
| | 462 | Louisville | 502, 812 |
| | 464 | Owensboro | 502, 615*, 901* |
| | 466 | Winchester | 606, 615* |
| | 468 | Memphis (TN) | 502, 601*, 901* |
| | 470 | Nashville (TN) | 205*, 502, 615 |
| | 474 | Knoxville (TN) | 606, 615*, 704* |
| | 922 | Cincinnati (OH) | 513*, 606, 812* |

## Table A18.1 (continued)

| BELL SOUTH | | | |
|---|---|---|---|
| *State* <br><br> Operating Telco | *LATA No.* | *LATA name* | *NPAs* |
| *Louisiana* <br> South Central Bell | 482 | Jackson (MS) | 205*, 318, 504, 601*, 901* |
| | 486 | Shreveport | 318, 501* |
| | 488 | Lafayette | 318 |
| | 490 | New Orleans | 504, 601* |
| | 492 | Baton Rouge | 504 |
| | 530 | Pine Bluff (AR) | 308*, 501* |
| *Mississippi* <br> South Central Bell | 468 | Memphis (TN) | 502*, 601, 901* |
| | 477 | Huntsville | 205*, 601 |
| | 480 | Mobile (AL) | 205*, 601, 904* |
| | 482 | Jackson (MS) | 205*,318*, 504*, 601, 901* |
| | 484 | Biloxi | 504*, 601 |
| | 490 | New Orleans | 504*, 601 |
| *North Carolina* <br> Southern Bell <br> Carolina Tel & <br> Tel <br> Central Tel | 250 | Lynchburg (VA) | 804*, 919 |
| | 420 | Asheville | 704 |
| | 422 | Charlotte | 704, 803* |
| | 424 | Greensboro | 919 |
| | 426 | Raleigh | 919 |
| | 428 | Wilmington | 803*, 919 |
| | 430 | Greenville | 704, 803 |
| | 472 | Chattanooga (TN) | 205*, 404*, 615* |
| | 949 | Fayetteville | 919 |
| | 951 | Rocky Mount | 804*, 919 |

## Table A18.1 (continued)

| BELL SOUTH | | | |
|---|---|---|---|
| *State* | | | |
| Operating Telco | *LATA No.* | *LATA name* | *NPAs* |
| *South Carolina* | 422 | Charlotte (NC) | 704*, 803 |
| Southern Bell | 428 | Wilmington (NC) | 803, 919* |
| GTE of the South | | | |
| | 430 | Greenville | 704*, 803 |
| | 432 | Florence | 803 |
| | 434 | Columbia | 803 |
| | 436 | Charleston | 803 |
| | 440 | Savannah (GA) | 803, 912* |
| | 442 | Augusta (GA) | 404*, 803, 912* |
| *Tennessee* | 244 | Roanoke (VA) | 615, 703* |
| South Central Bell | 464 | Owenboro (KY) | 502*, 615, 901 |
| United Interstate | 468 | Memphis | 502*, 601, 901 |
| Mountain | 470 | Nashville | 205*, 502*, 615 |
| Telephone | 472 | Chattanooga | 205*, 404*, 615 |
| | 474 | Knoxville | 606*, 615, 704* |
| | 482 | Jackson (MS) | 205*, 318*, 504*, 601*, 901 |
| | 528 | Little Rock (AR) | 314*, 501*, 901, 918* |
| | 956 | Bristol | 615, 703* |

## Table A18.1 (continued)

| NYNEX | | | |
|---|---|---|---|
| *State*<br>Operating Telco | *LATA No.* | *LATA name* | *NPAs* |
| *Connecticut*<br>Southern NE Tel | 132<br>920 | New York Metro (NY)<br>Connecticut | 203, 212, 516, 718, 914, 917<br>203 |
| *Maine*<br>New England Tel | 120 | Maine | 207 |
| *Massachusetts*<br>New England Tel | 126<br><br>128 | West Massachusetts<br>East Massachusetts | 413<br><br>508, 617 |
| *New Hampshire*<br>New England Tel | 122 | New Hampshire | 603 |
| *New York*<br>New York Tel<br>Rochester Tel<br>Contel of NY | 132<br><br>133<br>134<br>136<br>138<br>140<br>921<br>974 | New York Metro<br><br>Poughkeepsie<br>Albany<br>Syracuse<br>Binghamton<br>Buffalo<br>Fishers Island<br>Rochester | 203, 212, 516, 718, 914, 917<br>   (917 effective 1993)<br>717, 914<br>413, 518<br>315, 607<br>617, 717<br>716, 814<br>516<br>716 |
| *Rhode Island*<br>New England Tel | 130 | Rhode Island | 401 |
| *Vermont*<br>New England Tel | 124 | Vermont | 802 |

Table A18.1 (continued)

| PACIFIC TELESIS GROUP | | | |
|---|---|---|---|
| *State*<br><br>Operating Telco | *LATA No.* | *LATA name* | *NPAs* |
| *California*<br>Pacific Bell<br>GTE of CA<br>Contel of CA | 666<br>670<br>722<br>724<br>726<br>728<br>730<br><br>732<br>734<br>736<br>738<br>740<br>973 | Phoenix (AZ)<br>Eugene (OR)<br>San Francisco<br>Chico<br>Sacramento<br>Fresno<br>Los Angeles<br><br>San Diego<br>Bakersfield<br>Monterey<br>Stockton<br>San Luis Obispo<br>California | 602*, 619, 801*<br>503*, 916<br>408, 415, 510, 707<br>916<br>916<br>209<br>213, 310, 602*, 619, 714, 805, 818<br>619<br>805<br>408<br>209<br>805<br>619 |
| *Nevada*<br>Contel of Nevada<br>Nevada Bell | 652<br>660<br>720<br>721 | Idaho (IA)<br>Salt Lake City (UT)<br>Reno<br>Pahrump | 208*, 307*, 503*, 702, 801*<br>602*, 702, 801*<br>503*, 702, 916*<br>702 |

Table A18.1 (continued)

| SOUTHWESTERN BELL | | | |
|---|---|---|---|
| State<br><br>Operating Telco | LATA<br>No. | LATA name | NPAs |
| Arkansas<br>Southwestern<br>Bell | 468<br>486<br>522<br>526<br>528<br>530<br>554 | Memphis (TN)<br>Shreveport (LA)<br>Springfield (MO)<br>Fort Smith<br>Little Rock<br>Pine Bluff<br>Longview (TX) | 502*, 606, 901*<br>318*, 501<br>417*, 501, 918*<br>417*, 501, 918*<br>501, 918*<br>318*, 501<br>501, 903 |
| Kansas<br>Southwestern<br>Bell | 524<br>532<br>534<br>538<br>646<br>958 | Kansas City (MO)<br>Wichita<br>Topeka<br>Tulsa (OK)<br>Grand Island (NE)<br>Lincoln (NE) | 712*, 816*, 913<br>316, 405*, 417*, 719*, 918*<br>308*, 402*, 719*, 913<br>316, 918*<br>303*, 307*, 308*, 605*, 913*<br>402*, 913 |
| Missouri<br>Southwestern<br>Bell<br>United Tel. of<br>MO<br>Contel of MO | 520<br>521<br>522<br>524<br>526<br>528<br>532<br>632<br>634<br>644 | St. Louis<br>Westphalia<br>Springfield<br>Kansas City<br>Fort Smith (AR)<br>Little Rock (AR)<br>Wichita (KS)<br>Des Moines (IA)<br>Davenport (IA)<br>Omaha (NE) | 314, 618*<br>314<br>417, 501*, 918*<br>712*, 816, 913*<br>417, 501*, 918*<br>501*, 918*<br>316*, 417, 719*, 918*, 405<br>507*, 515*, 816<br>309*, 319*, 608*, 815*, 816<br>402*, 605*, 712*, 816 |
| Oklahoma<br>Southwestern<br>Bell<br>GTE Southwest | 522<br>526<br>528<br>532<br>536<br>538<br>546 | Springfield (MO)<br>Fort Smith (AR)<br>Little Rock (AR)<br>Wichita (KS)<br>Oklahoma City<br>Tulsa<br>Amarillo (TX) | 417*, 501*, 918<br>501*, 918<br>501*, 918<br>316*, 405, 417*, 719*, 918<br>405, 806*<br>918<br>405, 505*, 719*, 806* |

## Table A18.1 (continued)

| SOUTHWESTERN BELL | | | |
|---|---|---|---|
| *State* <br><br> Operating Telco | *LATA No.* | *LATA name* | *NPAs* |
| *Texas* | 486 | Shreveport (LA) | 501*, 318 |
| Southwestern | 540 | El Paso | 505*, 915 |
| Bell | 542 | Midland | 915 |
| Contel of Texas | 544 | Lubbock | 806 |
| | 546 | Amarillo | 405*, 505*, 719*, 806 |
| | 548 | Wichita Falls | 817 |
| | 550 | Abilene | 915 |
| | 552 | Dallas | 214, 817, 903 |
| | 554 | Longview | 501*, 903 |
| | 556 | Waco | 817 |
| | 558 | Austin | 512 |
| | 560 | Houston | 409, 713 |
| | 562 | Beaumont | 409 |
| | 564 | Corpus Christi | 512 |
| | 566 | San Antonio | 512 |
| | 568 | Brownsville | 512 |
| | 570 | Hearne | 409 |
| | 664 | New Mexico (NM) | 505*, 915 |
| | 961 | San Angelo | 915 |

**Table A18.1 (continued)**

## US WEST

| State<br><br>Operating Telco | LATA<br>No. | LATA name | NPAs |
|---|---|---|---|
| *Arizona*<br>US West<br>Communications | 660<br>666<br>668<br>730<br><br>980 | Salt Lake City<br>Phoenix<br>Tucson<br>Los Angeles (CA)<br><br>Navajo (UT) | 602, 702*, 801*, 303<br>602, 619*, 801*<br>505*, 602<br>213*, 602, 619*, 714*, 805*,<br>818*, 310<br>602 |
| *Colorado*<br>US West<br>Communications | 532<br>534<br>646<br>654<br>656<br>658<br>660 | Wichita (KS)<br>Topeka (KS)<br>Grand Island (NE)<br>Wyoming (WY)<br>Denver<br>Colorado Springs<br>Salt Lake City | 316*, 405*, 417*, 719, 918*<br>402, 719, 913*, 308<br>303, 307*, 308*, 605*, 913*<br>208*, 303, 307*, 308*, 406*<br>605, 801*<br>719<br>602*, 702*, 801*, 303 |
| *Idaho*<br>US West<br>Communications | 648<br>652<br>654<br><br>676<br>960 | Great Falls (MT)<br>Idaho<br>Wyoming (WY)<br><br>Spokane (WA)<br>Coeur D'Alene | 208, 406*<br>208, 307*, 503*, 702*, 801*<br>208, 303*, 307*, 308*, 406*,<br>605*, 801*<br>208, 503*, 509<br>208, 406*, 509* |

**Table A18.1** (continued)

| US WEST | | | |
|---|---|---|---|
| *State*<br><br>Operating<br>Company | *LATA*<br>*No.* | *LATA name* | *NPAs* |
| *Iowa* | 524 | Kansas City (MO) | 712, 816*, 913 |
| US West | 620 | Rochester (MN) | 319, 507*, 515, 605*, 712 |
| Comm. | 630 | Sioux City | 402*, 507*, 605*, 712 |
| GTE North | 632 | Des Moines | 507*, 515, 816* |
| | 634 | Davenport | 309*, 319, 608*, 815*, 816* |
| | 635 | Cedar Rapids | 319, 507* |
| | 640 | South Dakota (SD) | 307*, 308*, 402*, 507*, 406,<br>605*, 701*, 712, 816* |
| | 644 | Omaha (NE) | 402*, 605*, 712, 816* |
| | 646 | Grand Island (NE) | 303*, 307*, 308*, 605*, 913* |
| *Minnesota* | 352 | Northwest (WI) | 612, 715* |
| US West | 620 | Rochester | 319*, 507, 515*, 605*, 712* |
| Comm. | 624 | Duluth | 218, 715* |
| | 626 | St. Cloud | 605*, 612, 218 |
| | 628 | Minneapolis | 612 |
| | 630 | Sioux City (IA) | 402*, 507, 605*, 712* |
| | 632 | Des Moines (IA) | 507, 515*, 816* |
| | 635 | Cedar Rapids (IA) | 319*, 507 |
| | 636 | Fargo (ND) | 218, 605*, 701* |
| | 640 | South Dakota (SD) | 307*, 308*, 402*, 507, 605*,<br>701*, 712*, 406 |

## Table A18.1 (continued)

| US WEST | | | |
|---|---|---|---|
| *State*<br><br>Operating<br>Company | *LATA<br>No.* | *LATA name* | *NPAs* |
| *Montana*<br>US West<br>Communications | 638<br>648<br>650<br>654<br><br>960<br>963 | Bismarck (ND)<br>Great Falls<br>Billings<br>Wyoming (WY)<br><br>Coeur D'Alene (ID)<br>Montana | 406, 605*, 701*<br>208*, 406<br>307*, 406, 701*<br>208*, 303*, 307*, 308*, 406,<br>605*, 801*<br>208*, 406, 509*<br>406 |
| *Nebraska*<br>US West<br>Communications | 534<br>630<br>640<br><br>644<br>646<br>958 | Topeka (KS)<br>Sioux City (SD)<br>South Dakota (SD)<br><br>Omaha<br>Grand Island<br>Lincoln | 308, 402, 719*, 913*<br>402, 507*, 605*, 712*<br>307*, 308, 402, 507*, 605*<br>701*, 712*, 406<br>402, 605*, 712*, 816*<br>303*, 307*, 308, 605*, 913*<br>402, 913* |
| *North Dakota*<br>US West<br>Communications | 636<br>638<br>640<br><br>650 | Fargo<br>Bismarck<br>South Dakota (SD)<br><br>Billings (MT) | 218*, 605*, 701<br>406*, 605*, 701<br>307*, 308, 402, 507*, 605*,<br>701*, 712*, 406<br>307*, 406*, 701 |
| *New Mexico*<br>US West<br>Communications | 540<br>664<br>668 | El Paso (TX)<br>New Mexico<br>Tucson (AZ) | 505, 915*<br>505, 915*<br>505, 602* |

**Table A18.1 (continued)**

| US WEST | | | |
|---|---|---|---|
| *State*<br><br>Operating<br>Company | *LATA<br>No.* | *LATA name* | *NPAs* |
| *Oregon*<br>US West<br>Communications | 652<br>670<br>672<br>720 | Idaho (ID)<br>Eugene<br>Portland<br>Reno | 208*, 307*, 503, 702*, 801*<br>503, 916*<br>206*, 503, 509*<br>503, 702*, 916* |
| *South Dakota*<br>US West<br>Communications | 620<br>626<br>630<br>636<br>638<br>640<br><br>644<br>646<br><br>654 | Rochester (MN)<br>St. Cloud (MN)<br>Sioux City (IA)<br>Fargo (ND)<br>Bismarck (ND)<br>South Dakota<br><br>Omaha (NE)<br>Grand Island<br>(NE)<br>Wyoming (WY) | 319*, 507*, 515*, 605, 712*<br>605, 612*, 218<br>402*, 507*, 605, 712*<br>218*, 605, 701*<br>406*, 605, 701*<br>307*, 308*, 402*, 507*, 605, 712*,<br>406, 701<br>402*, 605, 712*, 816*<br>303*, 307*, 308*, 605, 913*<br><br>208*, 303*, 307*, 308*, 406*, 605,<br>801 |

**Table A18.1 (continued)**

| US WEST | | | |
|---|---|---|---|
| *State* <br><br> Operating Company | *LATA No.* | *LATA name* | *NPAs* |
| *Utah* <br> US West <br> Communications | 652 <br> 654 <br><br> 660 <br> 981 | Idaho (ID) <br> Wyoming (WY) <br><br> Utah <br> Navajoa | 208\*, 307\*, 503\*, 702\*, 801 <br> 208\*, 303\*, 307\*, 308\*, 406\*, <br> 605\*, <br> 801 <br> 602\*, 702\*, 801 <br> 801\* |
| *Washington* <br> US West <br> Communications | 960 <br> 672 <br> 674 <br> 676 | Cour D'Alene <br> Portland (OR) <br> Seattle <br> Spokane | 208, 406, 509 <br> 206, 503\*, 509 <br> 206 <br> 208\*, 503\*, 509 |
| *Wyoming* <br> US West <br> Communications | 640 <br><br> 646 <br><br> 650 <br> 652 <br> 654 | South Dakota (SD) <br><br> Grand Island (NE) <br><br> Billings (MT) <br> Idaho (ID) <br> Wyoming | 307, 308\*, 402\*, 507\* <br> 605\*, 701\*, 712\* <br> 303\*, 307, 308, 605\*, <br> 913 <br> 307, 406\*, 701\* <br> 208\*, 307, 503\*, 702\*, 801\* <br> 208\*, 303\*, 307, 308\*, 406\*, <br> 605\*, 801\* |

Table A18.1 (continued)

| US WEST | | | |
|---|---|---|---|
| *State* <br><br> Operating <br> Company | *LATA No.* | *LATA name* | *NPAs* |
| *Oregon* <br> US West <br> Communications | 652 <br> 670 <br> 672 <br> 720 | Idaho (ID) <br> Eugene <br> Portland <br> Reno | 208*, 307*, 503, 702*, 801* <br> 503, 916* <br> 206*, 503, 509* <br> 503, 702*, 916* |
| *South Dakota* <br> US West <br> Communications | 620 <br> 626 <br> 630 <br> 636 <br> 638 <br> 640 <br><br> 644 <br> 646 <br> 654 | Rochester (MN) <br> St. Cloud (MN) <br> Sioux City (IA) <br> Fargo (ND) <br> Bismarck (ND) <br> South Dakota <br><br> Omaha (NE) <br> Grand Island (NE) <br> Wyoming (WY) | 319*, 507*, 515*, 605, 712* <br> 605, 612*, 218 <br> 402*, 507*, 605, 712* <br> 218*, 605, 701* <br> 406*, 605, 701* <br> 307*, 308*, 402*, 507*, 605, <br> 712*, 406, 701 <br> 402*, 605, 712*, 816* <br> 303*, 307*, 308*, 605, 913* <br> 208*, 303*, 307*, 308*, 406*, <br> 605, 801 |

# Appendix 19
## Terminology

PRICES are end-user list prices.

The SCRIPT is a specific voice response application which consists of pre-defined voice instructions or information (PROMPTS), and responses to caller DTMF input.

PROMPTS are pre-recorded voice instructions or information for the CALLER to hear.

CALLER is the individual who calls into the voice response system. USER is the person who programs a SCRIPT.

MESSAGE is the audio left by a CALLER, when he or she is asked to record a message on the system.

INTERACTIVE VOICE RESPONSE systems are voice response systems which provide real-time access to dynamic databases, and permit the caller to order something, leave information, or obtain specific account information.

VOICE MAIL and AUTO ATTENDANT systems are voice processing systems generally used to provide an automation of the switchboard function. Included are freestanding automated attendant systems, freestanding voice mail systems, and combined auto attendant and voice mail systems.

INFORMATION PROVIDER systems are interactive voice response systems used to provide "public" information to a caller.

OUTBOUND CALL PROCESSING systems are used for automatic and semiautomatic out-dialing of calls. They also provide the capability of obtaining responses from the called party.

SUBSYSTEM VOICE COMPONENTS are not complete voice processing systems, but rather subsystems of a voice processing system or product and systems development tools. Included are such items as voice recognizers, text-to-speech devices, telephonic interfaces, voice application generation tool kits, speech signal analyzers, and interactive voice and data terminal (IVDTs).

PASSIVE INTERCEPT systems provide a particular message when a caller reaches them. Telephone company number intercepts are an example of a PASSIVE INTERCEPT system.

REVENUE is the end-user amount paid for a product or service. Because multiple channels of distribution (OEMs, interconnect dealers, and wholesale distributors) exist, this is the only way to obtain a realistic measure of the market size and avoid double counting.

# *Glossary*

| | |
|---|---|
| Abandoned calls: | Calls where the calling or called party hangs up before being connected with a telephone service representative. |
| AGTK: | Application generator toolkit. A set of tools that are used to implement and modify a voice-processing application. It includes software to create the script and packages for the creation and editing of prompts. |
| AMIS: | Audio message interchange standard. A standard recommended by a special voice-mail industry project group that defines the way in which messages are sent from one voice-mail system to another. |
| *Audiotex*: | A generic term used to refer to callers obtaining voice information over the telephone interactively. It was coined from the term *videotex*, which refers to interactive video services. The information obtained is usually of a public nature. |
| ACD: | Automatic call distributor. A system for the distribution of calls to telephone service representatives in a logical fashion that depends upon the real-time traffic load or which TSRs have been idle the longest. |
| ACD Group: | Also known as an ACD Split, ACD Gate, or ACD Queue. A group of telephone service representives that are grouped as a functional unit to handle certain types of calls. |
| ACS: | Automatic call sequencer. A system that answers the telephone, plays a greeting to the caller, and places the caller on hold. It provides information to the TSRs about which calls have been hold the longest. An ACS does not perform any call switching. |
| Backhaul: | Routing of a call to a remote site for live operator services. |
| BISYNC: | Binary synchronous transmission. A byte-oriented, half-duplex, synchronous protocol originated by IBM in 1964. |

| | |
|---|---|
| Branding: | Identifying the OSP to the caller. |
| BRI: | Basic rate interface. This is also called the 2B + D interface. Each B (bearer) channel is a 64-kb/s channel and the D (data) channel is a 16-kp/s. The bearer channel typically carries the information and the data channel is typically used for monitoring and control. BRI is an ISDN term. |
| BSE: | Basic service elements. These are the technical telephone system features such as ANI, DID trunks, call forwarding, stutter dial tone, suppressed ringing, and directory database access. |
| Call progress: | The status of the telephone line; ringing, busy, ring/no-answer, answering machine, telephone company intercept, message, and the like. |
| Call setup time: | The amount of time required to establish a call between the caller and called party. It includes dialing, wait time, the time to move through the central offices and long-distance network, ringing, and answer. |
| Carterfone decision: | A decision by the FCC in 1968, which said devices not supplied by the telephone company could be connected to the United States public telephone network—"if they were privately beneficial, but not publicly harmful." This was a landmark decision that allowed companies other than the telephone company to provide equipment that would connect with the public telephone network and was the beginning of an entire industry. |
| CCS: | One hundred call seconds. This is the U.S. standard unit for measuring telephone traffic. It is calculated by dividing the number of seconds of telephone traffic by 100. |
| CEI: | Comparatively efficient interconnect. The telephone companies providing interconnection opportunities to BSEs to enhanced service providers on an equal basis. The principles that define CEI include availability of BSEs, pricing, installation, interfaces, and common end-user access. |
| Channel bank: | A device that converts a T-1 signal into 24 analog signals. |
| CICS: | Customer information control system. A programming environment provided by IBM for transaction processing. |
| CPE: | Customer premise equipment. Equipment that a customer owns or leases. |
| CSU: | Channel service unit. A device used to connect a digital telephone interface to another device that can utilize a digital signal. Functions performed include line conditioning and line equalization. |
| DS0: | Digital service, level 0. The 64-kb/s standard for a single voice channel. A U.S./Canadian DS-1 (T-1) system is made up of 24 DS0 channels. |

| | |
|---|---|
| DS1: | Digital service, level 1. In the U.S. and Canada, the bit rate is 1.544 Mb/s. In Europe, and other parts of the world, the bit rate is 2.048 Mb/s, which permits 30 DS0 channels. |
| DTMF: | Dual-tone multifrequency (also known as touch-tone). Each tone is composed of a pair of audible tones—one high frequency and the other a lower frequency. |
| Dynamic port alloca- tion: | For a voice-processing system running multiple applications, automatic allocation of ports based on the traffic being used by each application. |
| Erlang(E): | The internationally accepted and dimensionless unit of traffic intensity. 1 E is the intensity of traffic in a resource that is continuously occupied. 1 E would equal 1 call-hour per hour or 1 call-minute per munute. |
| FDM: | Freqency division multiplexing is a switching system in which each channel is separated by frequency. Analog signals are frequency modulated at a different frequency for each channel and are connected with a single transmission facility. |
| GAB: | Group access bridging. A service for bridging of multiple calls to create a conference call. |
| Glare: | A telephone network condition that occurs when both ends of a telephone line are seized simultaneously for different pur- poses. |
| Hook flash: | A quick depression and release of the switch on the telephone instrument. It is used for special signaling functions such as call transfer or call waiting transfer. |
| Inband sig- naling: | Signaling on the same physical circuit that is utilized for voice. This is typically specific tones or break of the line. |
| Interflow: | The overflow of calls from one ACD to another ACD or to other destinations, such as a night answering position or a voice mail system. |
| InterLATA: | Telephone communication from one LATA to another. |
| Intraflow: | The overflow of calls from one ACD group to another ACD group. |
| IntraLATA: | Telephone communication within the same LATA. |
| ISDN: | Integrated services digital network. An international standard that defines end-to-end transmission of voice data and signaling. |
| IXC: | Interexchange carrier. Telephone carriers that provide trans- mission services from one LEC to the next. |
| LATA: | Local access transport area. A geographical area within which a local telephone company operates. |
| Least cost routing: | Determines the lowest cost telephone line to use for a call to a particular destination. |
| LEC: | Local exchange carrier. The local telephone company, which could be either a *Bell Operating Company* (BOC) or an inde- pendent, that provides the local transmission services. |

| | |
|---|---|
| Local loop: | The wires that run from the subscriber's telephone set, PBX, or key telephone system to the telephone company's central office. |
| MFJ: | The modified final judgement is the federal court ruling that established the rules and regulations concerning the deregulation and divestiture of AT&T and the Bell system. |
| MF: | Multifrequency signaling. A dual-tone signaling scheme that is similar to DTMF but with different tone frequencies. MF existed before DTMF and was used for signaling within and between telephone switches. |
| NPA: | Numbering plan area. The area code number. Within any of the 200 area codes that exist in the United States, Canada, Bermuda, the Caribbean, Northwestern Mexico, Alaska and Hawaii, no two telephone lines may have the same seven-digit telephone number. The three-digit NPA is NXX, where N is any digit 2 to 9 and X is any digit. Until the mid 1980s, the middle digit had been restricted to being either a 0 or a 1. The number of area codes that were available with this scheme were nearly depleted, hence the change in the numbering scheme. |
| NXX: | A three-digit code which identifies the local telephone exchange. N is any digit 2 to 9 and X is any digit. Until the mid 1980s, this code was NNX. With this numbering plan, area codes and local exchange numbers were always different. The telephone company has solved the problem of confusing local exchange numbers with area codes by forcing callers to dial "1" for a long-distance number within their own area code. |
| Off-hook: | The telephone headset is lifted from its cradle. Taking the telephone instrument off-hook alerts the central office that a call is about to be made. |
| On-hook: | The telephone headset is resting in its cradle. The phone is not connected with a line, and only the ring-detect circuit is active. |
| ONA: | Open network architecture. The FCC has required that the telephone companies provide access to the services within the telephone network on a basis that is equal to that provided to their own internal divisions. |
| OSP: | Operator service provider. Refers to the companies that handle operator-assisted calls. |
| O – calls: | Operator-assisted calls that require the services of an operator such as third-party billing and collect calls. |
| O + calls: | Automatic credit card calls that are made with a telephone company calling card. |
| Out-of-band signaling: | Signaling on a circuit that is physically separated from the circuit carrying the voice. |

| | |
|---|---|
| Pacing algorithm: | The mathematical model that controls the dialing rate of a predictive dialing system. |
| POP: | Point of presence. The physical place within a LATA where a long-distance carrier connects with the circuits of the LEC. |
| PRI: | Primary rate interface. This is also called the *23B + D* (1.544 Mb/s) or *30B + D* (2.048 Mb/s) interface. Each B (Bearer) channel is a 64-kb/s channel and the D (Data) channel is a 16-kps. PRI is an ISDN term. |
| Ring-back signal: | The sound that the telephone caller hears when the called telephone is ringing. |
| SLDC: | Synchronous data link control. A bit-oriented synchronous communication protocol developed by IBM. With SDLC, a message may contain any sequence of bits without being mistaken for control characters. SDLC is used in IBM's *System Network Architecture* (SNA). |
| SMDI: | Station message detail interface. A digital information port available on most PBXs and COs that provides data about each call such as the time, length of the call, and the number called. |
| Space brokers: | Companies that provide all the facilities needed to start a 976 or 900 service. It includes buildings, computing equipment, telephone lines and numbers. |
| Splash: | Routing of a call to the LEC. OSPs do this when they determine that they will not be able to bill the caller for the call. |
| SS7: | Signaling system 7. This is the out-of-band signaling system used with ISDN. It provides all of the signaling associated with placing a telephone call including supervision, alerting, and addressing. It also provides fast call setup, minimization of fraud, and information that identifies the calling party. |
| Tariff: | A set of regulations and rates that a regulated utility will charge for a service. For the telephone industry, these tariffs are approved by the FCC and a state regulatory agency (known in many states as the *Public Utility Commission* (PUC)). |
| TDM: | Time-division multiplexing is a switching system in which each channel is separated by time. Bit streams from each channel are connected, one at a time into a single transmission facility. |
| Trunk holding time: | The length of time that a caller is connected with a voice-processing system. Defined from the time when the system goes off-hook to the time the port is placed back on-hook. |

# About the Author

Walt Tetschner earned his BSEE at Rutgers University in 1961. From 1981 through 1985 he served as Voice Products Group Manager at Digital Equipment Corporation. In November of 1985 he moved to Voicetek Corporation, where he was Vice President of Engineering. Currently he is president of Tern Systems, Concord, Massachusetts.

# Index

# The Artech House Telecommunications Library

Vinton G. Cerf, Series Editor